VOLUMETRIC ANALYSIS

Volume I

VOLUMETRIC ANALYSIS

I. M. KOLTHOFF
Professor and Head
Division of Analytical Chemistry
University of Minnesota
Minneapolis, Minnesota

V. A. STENGER
Analytical Research Chemist
The Dow Chemical Company
Midland, Michigan

Second Revised Edition

VOLUME I:
Theoretical Fundamentals

With 31 Illustrations

1942

INTERSCIENCE PUBLISHERS, INC.
New York, N. Y.

COPYRIGHT, 1942, BY
I. M. KOLTHOFF AND V. A. STENGER

INTERSCIENCE PUBLISHERS, INC.
250 Fifth Avenue, New York 1, N. Y.

First printing 1942
Second printing (by photo-offset) 1947
Third printing (by photo-offset) 1951
Fourth printing (by photo-offset) ... 1954
Fifth printing (by photo-offset) 1961

Printed in the United States of America

This book is dedicated to

PROFESSOR N. SCHOORL
University of Utrecht,
The Netherlands

"The theory guides,
The experiment decides."

PREFACE

This book was originally published in the German in 1927, with the cooperation of Prof. H. Menzel of Dresden. It was translated into English by Prof. N. H. Furman of Princeton University and published by John Wiley and Sons, New York, in 1928. A second German edition, somewhat revised, appeared in 1930. The present work may be regarded as a thorough revision and enlargement of its predecessors.

In general character the book remains unchanged, although some condensation and shifting in the order of presentation have been necessary to make room for considerable new material. The section on oxidation-reduction indicators has been greatly extended, with the inclusion of a selected list of indicators having oxidation potentials between 0.24 and 1.30 (against the normal hydrogen electrode). Chapters on "Catalysis and Induced Reactions" and "Adsorption and Coprecipitation Phenomena" have been rewritten. For the first time a detailed quantitative discussion has been given concerning errors caused by mixed crystal formation. The last two chapters, "Volumetric Methods of Organic Analysis" and "Methods for Determination of the Equivalence-Point," have been subjected to extensive revision and the principles of amperometric (polarimetric) titrations with polarized electrodes have been introduced. In revising the tables in the Appendix, the most reliable data have been selected after a survey of the literature. In order to keep the size of the first volume within reasonable limits, the chapter on "Stability of Solutions" has been omitted. The contents of this chapter are given at the proper places in the second volume (practical part).

The material presented in the theoretical volume is considered to be not only of didactic but also of practical worth. A thorough understanding of the theoretical fundamentals is invaluable in the development of new titration methods, in the improvement of existing methods and in the formulation of titration errors. These objects may be achieved most readily if one has available sufficient information about equilibrium constants, oxidation potentials, solubility products, etc. In many cases it is possible to predict from a theo-

vii

retical viewpoint the effect of various factors upon the accuracy of a titration. To analytical chemists it is almost superfluous to add the warning that in this respect the theory is only a guide, and that results derived from theoretical considerations should be tested experimentally. This is particularly true of cases in which such phenomena as induced reactions and coprecipitation may affect the results of a titration.

Thanks are due to A. W. Beshgetoor and Donovan Weiblen for their generous assistance in the preparation of this volume. Mr. Beshgetoor reviewed the manuscript and offered several worthwhile suggestions, while Mr. Weiblen aided in the proof-reading.

It is the authors' hope that the present volume will stimulate readers to contribute to the further scientific development of volumetric analysis. In the second volume a critical review of existing methods will be presented.

I. M. K.
V. A. S.

Minneapolis, Minnesota
Midland, Michigan
February, 1942

PREFACE TO THE FIRST GERMAN EDITION

We are indebted to Wilhelm Ostwald for placing Analytical Chemistry upon a scientific basis. When his well-known book, "The Theoretical Foundation of Analytical Chemistry," was published (1894), he said in the preface: "The development of the theoretical basis of Analytical Chemistry is in striking contrast with that which the practical side has experienced. Even in the better works, the theory is almost entirely limited to presentation of the equations which represent paths of the chemical reactions, in the ideal limiting cases."

Ostwald's book and the mighty advances of Physical Chemistry have both contributed to the fact that the methods of Analytical Chemistry have ceased to be developed in purely empirical fashion. Soon after the appearance of Ostwald's "Principles," there appeared a treatise on Qualitative Analysis by one of his pupils, Wilhelm Böttger; in this treatise the significance of the theoretical side was placed

prominently in the foreground.[1]   The theory has also been considered
thoroughly and successfully in Quantitative Analysis, and especially
in Volumetric Analysis.   We have not, at present, any comprehensive
treatise on the theory of Analytical Chemistry.   To a certain extent
this is not astonishing, since Analytical Chemistry has preeminently
a practical goal, namely, the detection and determination of substances and their constituents.   All methods that lead to this goal
are equally useful, whether or not science has at its disposal the
general ideas and laws that are necessary to explain the methods
from a theoretical standpoint.

It is perhaps possible to write a comprehensive treatise about the
modern status of Theoretical Chemistry; in considering the exact
foundations and explanations of analytical processes that differ very
extensively from each other, one is all too easily led away from the
only safe ground, experience, and is inclined to set up a theory for
every special case without being able to unite the multiplicity of such
ad hoc assumptions under a single viewpoint.

That the author still ventures to treat the scientific foundations of
Volumetric Analysis in this volume may perhaps be justified by the
fact that, with the aid of our theoretical information, we are able not
only to improve existing methods but also to devise new ones.

In this connection it is necessary to consider thoroughly both the
reactions that occur and the behavior of indicators from the standpoint of the law of mass action.   If a system is in a state of mobile
equilibrium it is relatively easy to formulate the mathematical discussion of the possibility of a titration, to find the optimum working
conditions, and to calculate the titration error.   If one knows the
equilibrium constants of the various reacting systems, one can generally decide whether a titration may be based upon a given reaction.
One can get a notion, purely theoretically, as to the accuracy of a
titration.   *A new method does not need to be developed purely empirically, it may generally be deduced theoretically.*

It must be obvious to every chemist that it is by all means necessary to make a practical test of the theoretical deductions.   It is
well known that complications often arise in practice, so that one
can not rely on theory alone.   On the other hand, one should never
be content with the practical results alone; a knowledge of the
theoretical foundations is necessary to a decision as to the general

[1] In this connection the excellent book of J. Stieglitz, "The Elements of
Qualitative Chemical Analysis," may also be mentioned.

applicability of a method. It is necessary, from a scientific stand-point, to seek out all factors that may affect the result.

Unfortunately, General Chemistry is not yet far enough advanced to enable us to explain theoretically all of the phenomena of Volumetric Analysis. As far as the methods of quantitative precipitations, complex formations, and neutralizations are concerned, we may be entirely satisfied. Theory and practice go hand in hand; not only are all of the phenomena clearly understood, but we may even draw theoretical conclusions of great practical significance. The doctrine of the accuracy of titrations may be carried through strictly scientifically.

The principles of precipitation, complex formations, and neutralization analyses will be exhaustively treated in this book. Our considerations and deductions are important not only for ordinary volumetric analyses where the end-point is perceived with the aid of an indicator, but also for physico-chemical titration methods, especially potentiometric titrations. A part of the treatment was therefore drawn from a book, "Potentiometric Titrations," by the author and N. H. Furman (John Wiley & Sons, Inc., New York, 1926). In the present volume indicator methods are put prominently in the foreground, since they enjoy very general application because of their simplicity; the physico-chemical methods will be briefly treated in a special section, where full reference to the literature will be given.

Although we may easily obtain a theoretical grasp of all the phenomena in the aforementioned branches of Volumetric Analysis, we still lack the theoretical knowledge to explain oxidation and reduction reactions completely. Only when oxidant and reductant react with the establishment of a reversible equilibrium can important conclusions be drawn from the law of mass action as to the course of the reaction. It should be remembered here that there are also indicators for oxidizing or reducing substances. They are not specific indicators for single substances, but their color change depends upon the intensity of oxidizing or reducing action. They are, therefore, indicators of a certain oxidation-reduction potential. Appreciative mention is here made of the fact that the well-known American investigator, W. Mansfield Clark, and his co-workers have published a series of splendid investigations in this field; these will be examined more closely in the chapter on indicators.

In many instances, complications occur in oxidation or reduction processes; for example, the reactions do not proceed smoothly. Frequently a catalyst must be added to aid the process. It often happens also that "induced reactions" (disturbances caused by oxygen of the air, action of hydrochloric acid in permanganate titrations) have a disturbing effect upon the results of determinations. The author has therefore thought it desirable to devote a special chapter to the theory of catalysis and induced reactions. However highly we may regard the ideas of modern chemistry concerning these questions, it must still be emphasized that we can accomplish very little in practice with the present theories. They have therefore only been treated as far as is of interest for our present purposes. It is to be hoped that the future will teach us how to extend our present deficient knowledge of oxidation and reduction processes. Wherever the status of our knowledge still forbids an explanation of the phenomena, the author has deemed it wise to call attention to these gaps, in the hope that other investigators may be stimulated to attack these problems.

Adsorption processes are additional important accompanying phenomena whose disturbing influence on our volumetric determinations should not be underestimated. Through the fruitful development of Colloid Chemistry, from the modern ideas concerning atomic structure, the lattice structure of matter and the electrical nature of chemical union, and not least from the illuminating investigations of K. Fajans and his collaborators, we have learned to interpret this whole complex of phenomena qualitatively, and in part to control it quantitatively. Indeed, adsorption reactions have even led us to a new kind of titration method, the use of "adsorption indicators" in argentometry. Hence a chapter is devoted exclusively to these extraordinarily interesting and important matters.

The volumetric methods of Organic Chemistry, especially, are frequently incapable of rigorous interpretation, since they are not based on ionic reactions. These processes have been briefly summarized, and in so doing the author has always zealously emphasized the points where a theoretical investigation might improve the practical methods of determination. At present a more exact treatment of all organic titrations is not possible.

Let it once more be strongly emphasized that the study of the theory of a titration method is always necessary if the method is to find fruitful application. Yet the practical validity of the theory must always be tested. Only then can Volumetric Analysis assume the high rôle in Analytical Chemistry that is its due.

The author has attempted in this book to present the theoretical principles of Volumetric Analysis. He is nevertheless convinced that his presentation will in part be incomplete or unsatisfactory. He therefore requests his professional colleagues to communicate to him constructive criticisms and corrections. He intends later to treat the practical side of Volumetric Analysis in a second volume of this treatise, and, as far as it seems desirable, when describing the approved procedures, to refer to the great significance of the fundamental theory.

The author wishes to express his gratitude to his friend Dr. Ing. Heinrich Menzel, of Dresden, for the care that he has taken in the critical revision and the supplementary material revision of the manuscript, and in the recasting of its language.

I. M. KOLTHOFF.

UTRECHT,
   September, 1926.

From the Translation by
  N. Howell Furman
  Princeton University,
    1928

CONTENTS

xiii

CHAPTER I

FUNDAMENTALS OF VOLUMETRIC ANALYSIS

1. Chemical Analysis.—Analytical chemistry is that branch of science which deals with the identification and quantitative determination of chemical elements or compounds. The methods of making quantitative chemical analyses[1] are broadly classified under two major headings. In *gravimetric analysis* the substance sought is precipitated by the addition of an excess of reagent, and is eventually weighed. In *volumetric analysis* the reagent is added, not in excess, but in an amount which is chemically equivalent to the substance being determined. Thus one *titrates* an acid by adding to it an alkaline solution of known concentration until the acid has been neutralized. From the volume of alkaline solution taken, one can calculate the amount of acid initially present.

2. Equivalence-point and End-point.—In making a titration, the critical step lies in recognizing the point at which just sufficient reagent has been added. When the amounts of reagent and substance being determined are chemically equivalent, the mixture is said to be at the *equivalence-point*. Any property of the mixture which changes sharply near this equivalence-point may be used for its recognition. Generally one adds an *indicator* which produces a change in the color or turbidity of the mixture. The point at which the indicator shows a pronounced change is known as the *end-point* of the titration, and in an ideal case it would correspond exactly with the equivalence-point or theoretical end-point. In practice, the end-point differs from the equivalence-point by an amount that depends upon the chemical properties of the system. This difference, called the *titration error*, is of considerable importance and will be discussed in Chapter VI.

3. Ionization; Strong and Weak Electrolytes.—Since in inorganic chemical analysis the reactions involved usually take place between

---

[1] Physical methods of analysis (spectrography, spectrophotometry, etc.) are not considered here.

ions, it is advisable to consider briefly the subject of ionization. Many compounds when dissolved in water dissociate more or less completely into positive and negative particles, called cations and anions, respectively.   Such compounds are designated as *electrolytes* and are said to be *strong* or *weak*, depending upon the extent to which dissociation takes place.   In the original theory of Arrhenius, strong electrolytes were not considered to be completely ionized, but the degree of dissociation (fraction ionized) was thought to increase in more dilute solutions.   According to modern views developed by A. A. Noyes, Debye and Hückel, Bjerrum and others, strong electrolytes are regarded as being completely dissociated in aqueous solutions.

When dealing with the equilibrium:

$$mA + nB \rightleftarrows pC + qD,$$

the equilibrium constant K of the reaction is given by the expression:

$$\frac{(C)^{p}(D)^{q}}{(A)^{m}(B)^{n}} = K.$$

The parentheses denote the *active concentrations* of the various constituents.   The active concentration is not equal to the molar concentration, but is given by the following relation:

$$(A) = a_{A} = c_{A}f_{A},$$

in which a_{A} represents the activity or active concentration of A, c_{A} is the molar concentration, and f_{A} is the so-called activity coefficient. For dilute solutions of electrolytes this activity coefficient can be calculated by means of the Debye-Hückel limiting expression, but in more concentrated solutions the individual characteristics of the ions also play a part.   In general, the activity coefficient of an electrolyte decreases with increasing concentration (ionic strength), passes through a minimum and then increases.   In any exact calculation, activities rather than molar concentrations should be used.   Nevertheless, for the sake of simplicity, calculations in this text have been given in terms of concentrations.   This is ordinarily justifiable from the analytical point of view; see, however, further discussion in the Appendix.

Most inorganic and organic salts may be considered as strong electrolytes.   The halogen acids, nitric, perchloric and sulfuric acids and inorganic bases such as the alkali and alkaline earth hydroxides also belong to this class. Weak electrolytes include most organic acids and bases, several inorganic acids and bases, and a few salts. Weak electrolytes are incompletely ionized in aqueous solution.

4. Acids and Bases.—Acids are usually regarded as compounds which when dissolved in water dissociate into hydrogen ions and anions, while bases dissociate into hydroxyl ions and cations. However, Brönsted[2] has introduced a new concept. He defines both acids and bases by the statement that an acid under suitable conditions splits off one or more protons, with the formation of a base:

$$A_{(acid)} \rightleftarrows B_{(base)} + H^+_{(proton)}. \tag{1}$$

Free protons cannot exist as such in solution, but must be combined with the solvent. Hence reaction (1) can take place only if the acid is dissolved in a solvent that is capable of uniting with protons. In other words, the solvent must have basic properties in order for dissociation to occur:

$$A \rightleftarrows B + H^+. \tag{1}$$

$$S_{(solvent)} + H^+ \rightleftarrows SH^+. \tag{2}$$

In water: $$A + H_2O \rightleftarrows B + H_3O^+. \tag{3}$$

Water, alcohols, liquid ammonia and glacial acetic acid are solvents in which strong acids can dissociate. Benzene, carbon tetrachloride, etc. are said to be *aprotic* since they do not react with protons and therefore permit no ionization of acids. Similarly, compounds dissolved in them cannot behave as bases because there are no protons available for reaction.

Although in a pure aprotic solvent reaction (1) does not proceed, it can be made to take place by addition of a compound which will react with or furnish protons. For example, trichloroacetic acid dissolved in benzene can be titrated potentiometrically under suitable conditions, with a solution of an organic base in benzene. (*Cf.* Ref. 9, page 8.)

In aqueous medium the solvated protons are hydronium ions H_3O^+, and these are what we mean in speaking of hydrogen ions in water.

2 J. N. Brönsted, *Rec. trav. chim.*, **42**, 718 (1923); *J. Phys. Chem.*, **30**, 777 (1926); *Chem. Rev.*, **5**, 232 (1928); *Ber.*, **61**, 2049 (1928).

In methanol, protons form methoxonium ions CH_3OHH^+, and in ammonia, ammonium ions NH_4^+. Although in the older concept acids and bases were considered to be electrically neutral, in the Brönsted theory they may be neutral molecules (acetic acid), cations (NH_4^+), or anions (HCO_3^-). If only aqueous solutions were to be studied, Brönsted's picture would have little value. Its true importance appears when one compares acidities and basicities in different solvents.[3]

5. Oxidation and Reduction.—Definitions of oxidizing and reducing substances have much in common with those of bases and acids. A reducing agent is capable of splitting off one or more electrons, while an oxidizing agent can react with electrons:

$$\text{Reductant} \rightleftarrows \text{Oxidant} + n \text{ Electrons.} \tag{4}$$

Since free electrons cannot exist in solution, the only way reaction (4) can proceed from left to right is by removal of electrons, as by combining them with another oxidizing agent:

$$\text{Red}_1 \rightleftarrows \text{Ox}_1 + ne, \tag{4}$$

$$\text{Ox}_2 + ne \rightleftarrows \text{Red}_2, \tag{5}$$

$$\text{Red}_1 + \text{Ox}_2 \rightleftarrows \text{Red}_2 + \text{Ox}_1. \tag{6}$$

6. Classification of Volumetric Methods.—The methods used in volumetric analysis may be grouped according to the types of reactions involved:

(a) *Neutralization or protolysis reactions.*—Hydrogen and hydroxyl ions participate in all acid-base titrations in aqueous solutions. The reaction of hydrogen ion with hydroxyl ion is called neutralization, or perhaps better from the modern point of view, protolysis:

$H_3O^+ + OH^- \rightleftarrows 2H_2O$ (strong acids and strong bases);

$HCO_3^- + H_3O^+ \rightleftarrows H_2CO_3 + H_2O$ (anion of a weak acid, i.e., an anion base, titrated by a stronger acid);

$NH_4^+ + OH^- \rightleftarrows NH_4OH$ (cation of a weak base, i.e., a cation acid, titrated by a stronger base).

[3] A more detailed discussion of the Brönsted theory is given in the monograph *Acid-Base Indicators*, I. M. Kolthoff and C. Rosenblum, The MacMillan Company, New York 1937. For a recent bibliography and discussion of nomenclature see H. N. Alyea, *J. Chem. Ed.*, **16**, 535 (1939).

(*b*) *Ion combination reactions.*—Certain cations and anions react to form compounds which have low solubility or are only slightly dissociated.[4] A special case of slight dissociation includes compounds in which several particles are held together as complexes:

$$Ba^{++} + SO_4^= \rightleftarrows BaSO_4 \text{ (slight solubility)};$$

$$Hg^{++} + 2Cl^- \rightleftarrows HgCl_2 \text{ (slight dissociation)};$$

$$Cd^{++} + 4CN^- \rightleftarrows Cd(CN)_4^= \text{ (complex formation)}.$$

(*c*) *Oxidation-reduction reactions.*—An oxidizing agent may be titrated with a suitable reductant, and vice versa. Methods involving oxidation and reduction are sometimes classified according to the reagents employed, as iodimetric, cerimetric, etc.

(*d*) *Reactions of non-electrolytes.*—In many organic analyses the substance being determined is a non-electrolyte, which may be made to react with an ion or another non-electrolyte. Such reactions usually take place slowly:

$$RC{-}H + HSO_3^- \rightleftarrows R\overset{\text{H}}{\underset{\text{SO}_3^-}{C}}{-}OH;$$

$$R_1OH + R_2\underset{O}{C}{-}Cl \rightleftarrows R_2\underset{O}{C}{-}OR_1 + HCl.$$

7. Specifications for a Satisfactory Volumetric Reaction.—In order for a reaction to serve as the basis of a volumetric method, several conditions must be met:

(*a*) *The reaction should proceed quantitatively as represented by the stoichiometric equation.*—In case side reactions take place, the principal process will be of little value for analytical purposes unless conditions can be so modified as to minimize the disturbance. Side reactions are likely to be found in organic analysis, and in oxidation-reduction titrations where several valences are possible.

(*b*) *The reaction should be rapid.*—Several factors which influence

---

[4] It will be seen that neutralization reactions proceed because of the slight dissociation of water, but they have been given a separate classification for convenience.

reaction velocity are: the nature and concentration of the reagents, the temperature, and the composition of the medium with respect to the solvent and the possible presence of catalysts or inhibitors. Slow reactions may often be made more favorable by appropriate changes in these factors; for example, molybdate may be added to catalyze the reduction of bromate by iodide, or the solution may be heated, as in the titration of oxalate with permanganate in acid medium. In other cases an excess of reagent may be added and titrated back after sufficient time, as in the saponification of esters.

(c) *There must be a satisfactory way of locating the equivalence-point.* —The use of a visual indicator is generally most convenient, although in many cases no suitable indicator is available. Several other methods are listed in Chapter X.

In general, the reactions which best fulfill the preceding specifications are those which are *reversible*. This is illustrated in quantitative neutralizations, where the reactions proceed directly, rapidly, and with the possibility of exact equivalence-point determination. Irreversible processes are more subject to side disturbances, and are hard to treat from a theoretical basis since no significant equilibrium constants are available.

8. Interfering Substances.—The above qualifications have been given without regard to the possible presence of foreign materials. Two other considerations enter when mixtures are to be titrated:

(a) *The standard solution should not be consumed by an accompanying substance.*—At least it should not be so consumed until the item being determined has reacted quantitatively and the end-point has been ascertained.

(b) *The reaction desired should not be influenced by extraneous matter.* —Some compounds which are not ordinarily affected by the reagent employed may nevertheless cause trouble when present during a titration. For instance, oxygen from the air may have little action upon a reducing solution, yet react much more rapidly when the solution is being used in a titration. This is spoken of as an "induced" reaction. In precipitation analyses, coprecipitation of foreign ions may cause errors. Induced reactions and coprecipitation are discussed in Chapters VII and VIII, respectively.

If either of these conditions is violated, the foreign material is said to interfere. If its nature is known, the possibility of interference may be tested by making titrations of known mixtures. When interference takes place, the offending compound must be removed or its effect eliminated. Thus ferric iron disturbs in the titration of iodine with thiosulfate, but may be rendered harmless by addition of fluoride, with which it forms a complex.

When the nature of the sample is uncertain, as often happens in practice, one may add to it a known amount of the substance being determined, and see whether an equivalent amount of the standard solution is required in addition to that needed by the sample. This test is not conclusive, however, as it cannot reveal constant errors caused by the foreign material. It is better to attempt a separation or to confirm the result by an independent method.

9. Solvents.—Titrations are usually carried out in aqueous solution, but solvents other than water are often of good service. Familiar examples are the solutions of bromine in carbon tetrachloride, or iodine chloride in acetic acid (Wijs solution), used for determining unsaturation in organic compounds. Fischer[5] has proposed a method for the iodimetric titration of water in methanol solution. In precipitation analysis, one may add to the aqueous solution an organic solvent. As a rule, solvents such as acetone or alcohols decrease the solubility of inorganic salts, hence the precipitation reaction goes more nearly to completion and the end-point may be determined with greater accuracy.

In neutralization or protolysis reactions, the use of organic solvents may be of great practical importance. The ionization constants of anion acids and neutral molecule acids or bases are much smaller in organic media than in water. In aqueous solution it is not possible to titrate exactly a dilute ammonium salt with a strong base, as the dissociation of ammonium hydroxide becomes too pronounced near the end-point. By working, however, in a medium containing 90% or more of ethanol, the direct titration can yield accurate results if a suitable indicator is chosen. Naturally the ionization constants of most acid-base indicators are also affected by the change of solvents.

Since reactions involving water-insoluble compounds frequently require the use of special solvents, the study of titrations in such media offers to contribute much to the development of volumetric analysis. Some liquids which have been investigated, especially with

[5] K. Fischer, *Angew. Chem.*, **48**, 394 (1935). Fischer's method and its applications will be discussed in Vol. II of this text.

regard to protolysis reactions, are acetic acid,[6] formic acid,[7] ether,[8] benzene,[9] various alcohols,[10] acetone, dioxane, etc.[11]

Solvents may be classified according to their dielectric constants.[12] Although one cannot predict solubility definitely from a given dielectric constant, a useful indication of solvent properties may be gained from it. Among other physical properties of practical interest in choosing a solvent are the vapor pressure, viscosity and density. A list of several liquids and their properties is given in the Appendix.

The stability of a solvent toward reagents to be used is an important consideration. Thus alcohols should be avoided if there is a possibility of trouble due to esterification; acetone and many other compounds interfere in bromination reactions, and esters may cause difficulty in neutralization reactions. Occasionally one must allow for the solvent effect of a liquid present in a sample to be analyzed. For example, phenolic compounds in aqueous solution are difficult to brominate completely when an immiscible substance such as carbon tetrachloride is present.

10. Expression of Concentrations.—In using the law of mass action, the exact expression of concentration is in terms of *molality*, the number of moles of solute dissolved in 1000 grams of solvent.[13] For convenience, we shall generally use the *molarity*, or number of moles

---

[6] J. B. Conant, N. F. Hall and T. H. Werner, *J. Am. Chem. Soc.*, **49**, 3047, 3062 (1927); **50**, 2367 (1928); **52**, 4436, 5115 (1930). See also N. F. Hall, *Chem. Rev.*, **8**, 191 (1931), for a summary of earlier work.

[7] L. P. Hammett and N. Dietz, Jr., *J. Am. Chem. Soc.*, **52**, 4795 (1930).

[8] G. Schwartzenbach, *Helv. Chim. Acta*, **13**, 870, 897 (1930); **14**, 1069, 1071 (1931).

[9] J. N. Brönsted, *Ber.*, **61**, 2049 (1928); V. K. LaMer and H. C. Downes, *J. Am. Chem. Soc.*, **53**, 888 (1931).

[10] L. Michaelis and M. Mizutani, *Z. physik. Chem.*, **A116**, 135 (1925); M. Mizutani, *ibid.*, **A118**, 318, 327 (1925); H. Goldschmidt and E. Mathiesen, *ibid.*, **A119**, 439 (1926); G. W. Ferner and M. G. Mellon, *Ind. Eng. Chem. Anal. Ed.*, **6**, 345 (1934); L. A. Wooten and L. P. Hammett, *J. Am. Chem. Soc.*, **57**, 2289 (1935); I. M. Kolthoff, J. J. Lingane and W. D. Larson, *ibid.*, **60**, 2512 (1938); I. M. Kolthoff and L. S. Guss, *ibid.*, **60**, 2516 (1938), **62**, 249 (1940).

[11] A. E. Ruehle, *Ind. Eng. Chem. Anal. Ed.*, **10**, 130 (1938).

[12] The dielectric constant D is the specific property of a medium which determines the force of attraction or repulsion f exerted by two charges q_1 and q_2 separated by a distance r:

$$f = \frac{1}{D} \times \frac{q_1 q_2}{r}.$$

[13] In many physico-chemical relations, concentration is expressed as the mole fraction.

of solute contained in a liter of solution. There is little difference between the molarity and the molality of a dilute aqueous solution, aside from the fact that the former varies, due to expansion or contraction of the solution, with changes in temperature.

Concentrations in volumetric analysis are usually given in terms of *normality*, for the sake of simplicity in calculations. A normal solution contains one *gram-equivalent weight* of solute per liter of solution. Since the equivalent weight of a compound is either its molecular weight or a simple fraction or multiple thereof, depending on the reaction it undergoes, the effective normality will depend upon the use to which the solution is put. The problem is therefore to find the equivalent weight in the desired reaction.

In neutralization reactions, the number of neutralizable hydrogen or hydroxyl ions per molecule is the number of equivalents per mole. Thus one mole of hydrochloric acid is one equivalent, and the equivalent weight is the same as the molecular weight. With phosphoric acid, if two hydrogens are neutralized, one mole corresponds to two equivalents and the equivalent weight is half the molecular weight. If all three hydrogens were neutralized, the equivalent weight would be one-third of the molecular weight.

This convention of defining the equivalent weight as the quantity of substance corresponding in reaction to a gram-atomic weight of hydrogen may be extended to other types of reactions. In precipitations or complex formations, the stoichiometric equation shows directly or indirectly the number of equivalents per mole. In oxidation-reduction reactions, one may consider that a certain number of oxygen atoms is given off by a molecule of oxidant or used by a molecule of reductant. This number multiplied by 2 gives the corresponding number of hydrogen atoms. When permanganate is reduced in acid solution:

$$2KMnO_4 \rightarrow K_2O + 2MnO + 5O,$$

each mole of permanganate supplies 2.5 moles of oxygen, equivalent to 5 hydrogens. While this reasoning is an aid to memory, it should not be regarded as highly scientific, for the comparison with hydrogen cannot be made directly in all cases.

Fundamentally, it is only necessary to know how much of the material in question is equal in action to a mole of a univalent substance. If one mole of it enters into reaction with x moles of univalent ion, (or $x/2$ moles of bivalent, $x/3$ moles of trivalent, etc.), the equivalent weight will be M/x, where M is the molecular weight. If a moles react with x moles of univalent substance, then:

$$Eq. \ wt. = \frac{M \times a}{x}.$$

In oxidation-reduction reactions, the number of equivalents per mole is the same as the number of electrons transferred per molecule:

$$Fe^{++} \rightarrow Fe^{+++} + e,$$

$$MnO_4^- + 8H^+ + 5e \rightarrow Mn^{++} + 4H_2O.$$

The ferrous ion has one equivalent per mole as a reductant, whereas the permanganate has five equivalents per mole as an oxidant in acid solution.[14] If x is the number of electrons involved per molecule of reagent:

$$Eq. \ wt. = \frac{M}{x}.$$

Note clearly that the *equivalent weight, in contrast with the molecular weight, is not constant for a particular material.* Where different possibilities for reaction exist, the equivalent weight may have different values. Therefore in expressing the normality of a solution it is desirable to specify the molarity also, that one may be able to recognize the type of reaction to which the normality refers.

[14] The number of equivalents per mole may also be found readily from the change in valence of the element being oxidized or reduced. Thus in the above examples, iron increases in valence from $+2$ to $+3$, a change of one, while manganese decreases in valence from $+7$ in permanganate to $+2$ in manganous ion, a change of five. In the oxidation of oxalic acid to carbon dioxide and water:

$$H_2C_2O_4 + O \rightarrow H_2O + 2CO_2,$$

the two carbon atoms are jointly increased by two positive valences, and the equivalent weight of the acid as a reductant is one-half the molecular weight. *Cf.* I. M. Kolthoff and E. B. Sandell, *Textbook of Quantitative Inorganic Analysis*, The MacMillan Company, New York 1936, p. 414; L. F. Hamilton and S. G. Simpson, *Calculations of Quantitative Chemical Analysis*, 3rd Edition, McGraw-Hill Book Company, New York 1939.

If chromic acid is titrated as a dibasic acid, the equivalent weight is half the molecular weight; but if it is titrated as an oxidant, the equivalent weight is one-third of the molecular weight:

$$\left.\begin{array}{l} H_2CrO_4 \rightarrow 2H^+ + CrO_4^=, \\ 2H^+ + 2OH^- \rightarrow 2H_2O, \end{array}\right\} \quad (x = 2);$$

$$\left.\begin{array}{l} 2H_2CrO_4 \rightarrow Cr_2O_3 + 2H_2O + 1\tfrac{1}{2}O_2, \\ CrO_4^= + 8H^+ + 3e \rightarrow Cr^{+++} + 4H_2O, \end{array}\right\} \quad (x = 3).$$

In the argentometric titration of iodide, $x = 1$, but if iodine is oxidized to iodate with standard hypochlorite solution, $x = 6$:

$$Ag^+ + I^- \rightarrow AgI;$$

$$I^- + 3OCl^- \rightarrow IO_3^- + 3Cl^-,$$

$$(I^- + 3H_2O \rightarrow IO_3^- + 6H^+ + 6e).$$

When a reaction product is titrated, the equivalent weight is determined by the reaction in the final titration. In the reaction between iodate and iodide in acid solution, the titration may be made potentiometrically so that free iodine is liberated:

$$IO_3^- + 5I^- + 6H^+ \rightarrow 3I_2 + 3H_2O,$$

$$(IO_3^- + 6H^+ + 5e \rightarrow \tfrac{1}{2}I_2 + 3H_2O).$$

In this case $x = 5$, but if the reaction product, iodine, is titrated with thiosulfate in the usual manner, $x = 6$:

$$3I_2 + 6e \rightarrow 6I^-.$$

Cyanide furnishes another example of varying equivalent weight. When it is titrated with silver nitrate to the formation of argentocyanide, the equivalent weight is twice the molecular weight:

$$2CN^- + Ag^+ \rightarrow Ag(CN)_2^- \qquad (a = 2,\ x = 1).$$

It is also possible to titrate to the point at which silver argentocyanide is completely precipitated, so that the equivalent weight is the same as the molecular weight:

$$2CN^- + 2Ag^+ \rightarrow Ag[Ag(CN)_2].$$

In another method for cyanide, it is converted to bromocyanogen, treated with iodide and acid, and the liberated iodine is titrated with thiosulfate. In this process, $x = 2$:

$$BrCN + 2I^- + H^+ \rightarrow I_2 + Br^- + HCN,$$

$$I_2 + 2e \rightarrow 2I^-.$$

11. Standardization of Solutions.—Since in volumetric analysis one determines the amount of desired substance from the volume of standard solution that is used, the preparation of the latter is an important task. The equivalent content (*titer*) of the solution must be accurately known.

The case is simplest when the materials to be contained in standard solutions are available as chemically pure products of definite formula, or when they can conveniently be brought to this state by recrystallization, drying, or other means. Solutions of exactly known concentration with respect to bichromate, bromate, silver nitrate, alkali chlorides and many other important reagents may be prepared by weighing out the equivalent weight or a known fraction of it, and diluting to a certain volume. Of course, if the solutions change their strength upon standing, there is no point in their exact preparation. Details regarding the stability of solutions will be given in Vol. II.

When substances cannot be readily obtained in a pure state, as is the case with cyanides and most acids and bases, one can prepare solutions of approximately known strength, and determine the exact content subsequently. This *standardization* is made by titration against accurately known solutions or weighed samples of pure chemical reference substances called *primary standards*. Indeed, it is desirable to control even solutions of pure chemicals by standardization against such reference materials.

The standardization of a solution, unless it is done by the rather unusual gravimetric method,[15] is generally nothing more or less than a volumetric analysis. There is the difference that in an analysis we know the strength of the solution and find that of the substance titrated, while in standardization the reverse is true, a difference which is of importance only in working out the result of the titration.

---

[15] L. Szebelledy and Z. Somogyi, *Z. anal. Chem.*, **112**, 313 (1938), standardize solutions by a coulometric method. With the aid of a silver coulometer they determine the exact amount of electricity necessary to electrolyze the standard solution quantitatively.

In order to establish the *absolute equivalent content* (true normality) of the solution, independent of the inherent errors of a particular titration method employed, the corrections corresponding to the titration error must be taken into account. Therefore titration errors are considered in detail elsewhere in this book. If corrections are made, they must also be applied when the solution is used for analytical purposes. Physico-chemical titrations, such as the potentiometric, are often to be recommended for reliable standardizations as free as possible from error.

Sometimes it is more important in practice to know the relative strength of a solution by a given analytical method with the use of a given indicator. This applies when one works under the same conditions during the standardization and subsequent use of the solution. For example, there is a small titration error in the standardization of 0.1 N hydrochloric acid using methyl orange as indicator. The relative methyl orange titer may be used in further titrations with methyl orange. Since roughly the same error is committed in both standardization and analysis, it has no great effect on the results. The same holds when alkali containing a little carbonate is standardized in the presence of phenolphthalein indicator; one may work with the "phenolphthalein titer." Likewise silver solutions standardized by Mohr's method may be used afterward for Mohr chloride determinations. *However, the errors of analysis and standardization will be exactly compensated only if the volumes and concentrations of the substance being titrated are the same in both operations.*

The practical performance of standardizations, with special instructions on experimental details, will be reserved for the second volume of this text. It is perhaps in order, however, to add here a note on the accuracy possible in volumetric analysis. Some chemists give the preference—in most cases wrongly—to gravimetric determinations. Both methods are subject in the same degree to the errors of weighing. In gravimetric analyses there are the complications of coprecipitation and adsorption, and of solubility in the wash solution. In volumetric analyses there are the systematic and titration errors. Since these can be limited and corrected in many cases, numerous volumetric procedures may even exceed gravimetric methods in accuracy.

CHAPTER II

THE PRINCIPLES OF NEUTRALIZATION AND ION COMBINATION REACTIONS

1. Ion Concentration and Ion Exponent.—In considering a 0.1 molar solution of a strong electrolyte BA, one may write:

$$[B^+] = [A^-] = 0.1 = 10^{-1}.$$

The square brackets denote molecular concentrations, $[B^+]$ being that of the cation and $[A^-]$ that of the anion. It is also practical to express ion concentrations by means of their negative Briggsian logarithms, which in accordance with a proposal by Sörensen[1] may be called ion exponents, p_I:

$$p_I = -\log [I] \quad \text{or} \quad [I] = 10^{-p_I}.$$

In the case above, if $[B^+]$ is 0.1, $p_B = -\log (0.1) = 1.0$.

One important advantage of this method of expression is its utility in covering great ranges of concentrations. When 0.1 N silver nitrate is titrated with potassium iodide, the silver-ion concentration decreases from 10^{-1} N to about 10^{-8} N at the equivalence-point, or about ten million fold from start to finish. To show this graphically, one cannot make such a change clear in ordinary coordinate units. By using ion exponents, the change is an increase in p_{Ag} from 1 to 8, or only 7 units.

At first it may seem odd that as the concentration decreases, the corresponding ion exponent increases. Furthermore, since p_I is an exponent, a small change in it represents a large difference in concentration. For example:

$$p_H = 4.0, \quad [H^+] = 1.0 \times 10^{-4};$$
$$p_H = 4.1, \quad [H^+] = 0.8 \times 10^{-4}.$$

[1] S. P. L. Sörensen, *Biochem. Zeitschr.*, **21**, 131 (1909).

A difference of 0.1 in p_H therefore corresponds to a change of 20 per cent in hydrogen-ion concentration.

2. The Dissociation of Water.—All neutralization reactions in aqueous solution are based on the union of hydrogen ions with hydroxyl ions to form water, which is very slightly ionized:

$$H^+ + OH^- \rightleftarrows H_2O. \tag{1}$$

According to the law of mass action:

$$\frac{[H^+][OH^-]}{[H_2O]} = K. \tag{2}$$

In dilute aqueous solutions the concentration of undissociated water may be regarded as a constant (about 55.5 molar), so that:

$$[H^+][OH^-] = K_w. \tag{3}$$

This quantity K_w is the *ion product* of water. Though it is often called the dissociation constant of water, this is not strictly correct, for K in equation (2) is really the dissociation constant.

The value of K_w is a function of temperature, as is shown in the following table from Kohlrausch and Heydweiller.[2] Here the negative logarithms of K_w are given under p_w, which is called the ionization exponent of water.

ION PRODUCT OF WATER AT VARIOUS TEMPERATURES

Temperature	K_w	p_w
0°C.	0.12×10^{-14}	14.93
18°	0.59×10^{-14}	14.23
25°	1.04×10^{-14}	13.98
50°	5.66×10^{-14}	13.25
100°	58.2×10^{-14}	12.24

In pure water the concentration of hydrogen ion is equal to that of hydroxyl ion. Since at room temperature the rounded value of K_w is 10^{-14}, we have:

$$[H^+] = [OH^-] = \sqrt{K_w} = \sqrt{10^{-14}} = 10^{-7}. \tag{4}$$

If $[H^+]$ exceeds $[OH^-]$, the liquid is *acid*, whereas if $[OH^-]$ is the greater, the liquid is *alkaline*. When the two are equal, the solution

[2] F. Kohlrausch and A. Heydweiller, Ann. d. Physik. (4) **28,** 512 (1909).

has a neutral reaction. These conditions may be expressed in the following statements, applying at room temperature:

$$[H^+] = [OH^-] = 10^{-7} \quad \text{(neutral reaction)}$$

$$[H^+] > 10^{-7} > [OH^-] \quad \text{(acid reaction)}$$

$$[H^+] < 10^{-7} < [OH^-] \quad \text{(alkaline reaction)}.$$

When the ionic concentrations are expressed in terms of their ion exponents, equation (3) becomes:

$$p_H + p_{OH} = p_w. \tag{5}$$

As soon as p_w is known, one may calculate for each value of the p_H a corresponding p_{OH}. At room temperature, where p_w is 14, the following relationship holds:

$$p_H = 14 - p_{OH} \tag{6}$$

$$p_{OH} = 14 - p_H. \tag{6a}$$

Friedenthal[3] proposed that, regardless of whether a fluid is acid, neutral or alkaline, its reaction should be expressed in terms of $[H^+]$ (or in p_H according to Sörensen). This has proved to be very practical. In general, at 23–25°C. the reactions of aqueous solutions are as follows:

$$p_H = 7 = p_{OH} \quad \text{(neutral)}$$

$$p_H < 7 < p_{OH} \quad \text{(acid)}$$

$$p_H > 7 > p_{OH} \quad \text{(alkaline)}.$$

Illustration: In 0.001 N hydrochloric acid, $[H^+]$ is about 10^{-3} and p_H is 3. From equation (6), $p_{OH} = 11$, hence $[OH^-] = 10^{-11}$.

In 0.002 N sodium hydroxide, $[OH^-]$ is 2.0×10^{-3} and p_{OH} is 2.7, so that p_H becomes 11.3 and $[H^+]$, 5.0×10^{-12}.

3. Ionization Constants (Protolysis Constants) of Acids and Bases.—Weak electrolytes do not dissociate completely into ions.

[3] H. Friedenthal, Z. *Elektrochem.*, **10**, 113 (1904).

The extent of dissociation of a weak acid may be expressed by the equations:

$$HA \rightleftharpoons H^+ + A^- \tag{7}$$

$$\frac{[H^+][A^-]}{[HA]} = K_a \tag{8}$$

in which K_a is the *ionization constant* of the acid and $[HA]$ is the concentration of the undissociated portion of it. In a solution containing only the acid and water, $[H^+]$ is equal to $[A^-]$, so that:

$$\frac{[H^+]^2}{[HA]} = K_a,$$

and therefore:

$$[H^+] = \sqrt{K_a[HA]}. \tag{9}$$

If the total concentration of acid is called c (this being the acid concentration that would be determined in a titration), then:

$$[HA] = c - [H^+]. \tag{10}$$

When $[H^+]$ is small compared with c, $[HA]$ may be set equal to c; then equation (9) becomes:

$$[H^+] = \sqrt{K_a \times c}, \tag{11}$$

and allowing p_a to represent the negative logarithm of K_a, that is, the *acid exponent*:

$$p_H = \tfrac{1}{2}p_a - \tfrac{1}{2} \log c. \tag{11a}$$

Illustration: Calculate $[H^+]$ and p_H for a 0.1 molar solution of acetic acid:

$$c = 0.1; \quad K_a = 1.8 \times 10^{-5}; \quad p_a = 4.74;$$

$$[H^+] = \sqrt{1.8 \times 10^{-5} \times 0.1} = 1.34 \times 10^{-3};$$

$$p_H = 2.37 + 0.5 = 2.87.$$

In this example $[H^+]$ is found to be only 1.3% of the total concentration, so that the simple equation (11) is satisfactory. When $[H^+]$

exceeds 5% of c, [HA] may not be set equal to c, but a more complicated equation, (12), may be derived from (9) and (10):

$$[H^+] = \sqrt{K_a(c - [H^+])},$$

$$[H^+]^2 + K_a[H^+] - K_a c = 0. \qquad (12)$$

Upon solving this quadratic equation for [H$^+$], the generally valid expression (13) is obtained:

$$[H^+] = -\frac{K_a}{2} \pm \sqrt{\frac{K_a^2}{4} + K_a c}. \qquad (13)$$

In this expression, as in all solutions of quadratic equations given in this text, the square root term is to be given the sign which will yield a value of real significance.

Polybasic acids.—Polybasic acids dissociate in steps; each step has a characteristic ionization constant corresponding to the splitting off of the hydrogen atom in question. The first constant is the greatest, the second next, and so on.

$$H_2A \rightleftarrows H^+ + HA^-, \qquad (14)$$

$$HA^- \rightleftarrows H^+ + A^-, \qquad (14a)$$

$$K_1 = \frac{[H^+][HA^-]}{[H_2A]}, \text{ (first ionization constant)}, \qquad (15)$$

$$K_2 = \frac{[H^+][A^-]}{[HA^-]}, \text{ (second ionization constant)}. \qquad (16)$$

Generally in calculating the hydrogen-ion concentration of a pure acid solution, one may regard the acid as monobasic. The dissociation of the second step is ordinarily so small in comparison with the first that it may be neglected. Therefore in this case the procedure is the same as for a monobasic acid. However, if neglect of the second step is not permissible, an exact equation[4] may be applied:

$$[H^+]^3 + [H^+]^2 K_1 - [H^+](K_1 c - K_1 K_2) = 2K_1 K_2 c. \qquad (17)$$

[4] For the derivation of equation (17) see Acid-Base Indicators, I. M. Kolthoff and C. Rosenblum, The MacMillan Company, New York, 1937, p. 10.

Bases.—Equations similar to those applying to acids may also be derived for bases. Instead of solving for $[H^+]$, the value of $[OH^-]$ may be found. Then from the known constant K_w it is possible to calculate $[H^+]$.

$$BOH \rightleftharpoons B^+ + OH^-,$$

$$\frac{[B^+][OH^-]}{[BOH]} = K_b \tag{18}$$

where K_b is the ionization constant of the base.

4. The Hydrolysis of Salts.

—In aqueous solution, a salt reacts with hydrogen and hydroxyl ions of water, forming free acid and base:

$$B^+ + H_2O \rightleftharpoons BOH + H^+, \tag{19}$$

$$A^- + H_2O \rightleftharpoons HA + OH^-. \tag{20}$$

If the salt is one of a strong base and an equally strong acid, its hydrolysis may be ignored because BOH and HA will be completely dissociated in dilute solution. The reaction is then neutral.

On the contrary, the salt of a strong acid and a weak base is considerably hydrolyzed in water. Here the decomposition shown in equation (20) is insignificant, since HA is a strong acid. The solution will therefore contain excess hydrogen ions and will be acid in reaction. The reverse holds true if the acid is weak and the base strong.

When both the acid and basic components of a salt are weak, equations (19) and (20) occur simultaneously. Although a solution of this kind may be practically neutral, it will contain appreciable amounts of both acid and base in undissociated form. As an example, ammonium acetate solution has the odor of acetic acid as well as of ammonia.

One may calculate the hydrogen-ion concentration of a solution containing the salt of a strong acid and weak base. Applying the mass law to equation (19):

$$\frac{[BOH][H^+]}{[B^+]} = K_{hydr.}. \tag{21}$$

$K_{hydr.}$ is the hydrolysis **constant.**

According to equations (3) and (18):

$$[H^+] = \frac{K_w}{[OH^-]}, \tag{3}$$

$$\frac{[B^+][OH^-]}{[BOH]} = K_b. \tag{18}$$

These may be combined so that:

$$K_{hydr.} = \frac{K_w}{K_b} = \frac{[BOH][H^+]}{[B^+]}. \tag{22}$$

As explained previously, the solution will be acid and equation (19) is the one applying to this hydrolysis. From it, $[H^+]$ is equal to $[BOH]$ for a solution of a pure salt. Also, since the salt is a strong electrolyte, $[B^+]$ may be considered equal to the total salt concentration c provided that $[BOH]$ is small compared to c. With these substitutions equation (22) can be solved for $[H^+]$:

$$[H^+] = \sqrt{\frac{K_w}{K_b} c}, \tag{23}$$

$$p_H = 7 - \tfrac{1}{2}p_b - \tfrac{1}{2}\log c. \tag{24}$$

In similar fashion it is found that for a solution of the salt of a weak acid and a strong base:

$$[H^+] = \sqrt{\frac{K_w K_a}{c}}, \tag{25}$$

$$p_H = 7 + \tfrac{1}{2}p_a + \tfrac{1}{2}\log c. \tag{26}$$

Illustration: Calculate $[H^+]$ for a 1.0 molar solution of ammonium chloride:

$$c = 1; \quad K_b = 1.8 \times 10^{-5}; \quad p_b = 4.74,$$

$$p_H = 7 - 2.37 = 4.63,$$

$$[H^+] = 2.35 \times 10^{-5}.$$

In cases where the hydrolysis is very slight, one has to allow for the dissociation of water. Considering the salt of a weak acid and strong base, $[HA]$ is then not equal to $[OH^-]$ in equation (20), but rather

$$[HA] = [OH^-] - [H^+].$$

From equation (22):

$$\frac{K_w}{K_a} = \frac{[HA][OH^-]}{[A^-]} = \frac{[HA][OH^-]}{c}.$$

Substituting the value of [HA] and simplifying:

$$[OH^-] = \sqrt{c\frac{K_w}{K_a} + K_w}.$$

The Effect of a Slight Excess of Acid or Base upon the Hydrogen-ion Concentration of a Salt Solution.—In the preparation of neutralization graphs, the change produced by adding small amounts of acid or base to a hydrolyzed salt is of interest. Consider the solution of a salt of a strong acid and weak base. Upon addition of acid, giving excess hydrogen-ions, the hydrolysis is repressed. Let x equal the concentration of BOH and of H^+ formed by hydrolysis, and a the concentration of acid added. Then the total hydrogen-ion concentration will be $a + x$, and [BOH] will equal x. If the salt concentration is c, the following will be found from equation 22:

$$\frac{K_w}{K_b} = \frac{(a + x)x}{c},$$

from which

$$x = -\frac{a}{2} + \sqrt{\frac{a^2}{4} + c\frac{K_w}{K_b}}. \tag{27}$$

However, if a slight excess b of base is added, [BOH] $= b + x$; and $[H^+] = x$, so that:

$$x = -\frac{b}{2} + \sqrt{\frac{b^2}{4} + c\frac{K_w}{K_b}}. \tag{28}$$

In a solution of pure salt, where a and b are zero, equation (28) becomes identical with the common hydrolysis expression (23).

Illustration: To an 0.1 molar ammonium chloride solution is added hydrochloric acid up to a concentration of 10^{-4} N. Here $a = 10^{-4}$, $c = 10^{-1}$ and $K_b = 1.8 \times 10^{-5}$, so that x is found to be 5×10^{-7}.
The total hydrogen-ion concentration is now $10^{-4} + 5 \times 10^{-7}$, or practically 10^{-4}. The hydrolysis is diminished so that the value of x is negligible

in comparison with that of a. When the original hydrolysis is great or a is small, x is significant. For example, if in the preceding illustration a were 10^{-5}, x would be 4×10^{-6}, and

$$[H^+] = 10^{-5} + 0.4 \times 10^{-5} = 1.4 \times 10^{-5}.$$

Considering a salt of the type B_2A (where A is the anion of a weak dibasic acid H_2A), or of the type BA_2 (where B is the cation of a weak diacid base), the hydrolysis equations apply unchanged. In place of the first ionization constant of the acid or base, the second constant must be used as the value of K_a or K_b.

Salts of Weak Acids and Weak Bases.—In this case both reactions (19) and (20) are to be considered. From the hydrolysis equations:

$$\frac{[BOH][H^+]}{[B^+]} = \frac{K_w}{K_b}, \tag{22}$$

$$\frac{[HA][OH^-]}{[A^-]} = \frac{K_w}{K_a}, \tag{22a}$$

and

$$[H^+][OH^-] = K_w, \tag{3}$$

one obtains:

$$\frac{[BOH][HA]}{[B^+][A^-]} = \frac{K_w}{K_a K_b}. \tag{29}$$

In the usual applications, K_a will not be less than $K_b/100$ nor more than $100 K_b$. Under these conditions the hydrogen- or hydroxyl-ion concentration of water will be so little changed that without serious error one may set [BOH] equal to [HA]. On the assumption that the salt is completely dissociated and has the concentration c, $[B^+]$ and $[A^-]$ may be considered equal to c. If hydrolysis were very pronounced, a correction would be necessary:

$$[B^+] = c - [BOH] \quad \text{and} \quad [A^-] = c - [HA].$$

From the above statements and equation (29), it follows that:

$$\frac{[BOH]^2}{c^2} = \frac{[HA]^2}{c^2} = \frac{K_w}{K_a K_b}, \tag{30}$$

$$[BOH] = [HA] = c \sqrt{\frac{K_w}{K_a K_b}}. \tag{31}$$

By substituting in (31) the value of [BOH] from (22), one can calculate the hydrogen-ion concentration in the solution of a salt of a weak acid and weak base:

$$[H^+] = \sqrt{\frac{K_w K_a}{K_b}} \tag{32}$$

$$p_H = 7 + \tfrac{1}{2}p_a - \tfrac{1}{2}p_b. \tag{33}$$

Note that here $[H^+]$ does not depend upon the salt concentration. This is not strictly true, since assumptions and simplifications have been made in the derivation, but for most practical purposes equations (32) and (33) are satisfactory. *All salts in which K_a and K_b have the same value produce neutral solutions.*

Illustration: In the case of ammonium acetate, $K_a = K_b = 10^{-4.74}$.

$$p_H = 7.0 + 2.37 - 2.37 = 7.0.$$

A solution of ammonium formate reacts acid, because K_a is larger than K_b:

$$K_a = 10^{-3.67}; \qquad K_b = 10^{-4.74};$$

$$p_H = 7.0 + 1.83 - 2.37 = 6.46.$$

The Effect of a Small Amount of Acid or Base on the Hydrogen-Ion Concentration of a Solution Containing the Salt of a Weak Acid and Weak Base.—For the preparation of titration curves and calculation of titration errors in such systems, it is necessary to know the changes in $[H^+]$ that occur near the equivalence-point.

If there is added an excess of HA corresponding to a concentration a, and there is also the amount x present due to hydrolysis, the total will be $a + x$. [BOH] is taken equal to x, so from equation (29):

$$\frac{(a + x)x}{c^2} = \frac{K_w}{K_a K_b},$$

$$x = -\frac{a}{2} + \sqrt{\frac{a^2}{4} + c^2 \frac{K_w}{K_a K_b}}. \tag{34}$$

From the value of x thus found, $[H^+]$ can be calculated:

$$[H^+] = \frac{[HA]}{[A^-]} K_a = \frac{(a + x)}{c} K_a.$$

An analogous expression for x is found in case an excess b of base has been added.

Illustration: Calculate the hydrogen-ion concentration of an 0.1 molar solution of ammonium acetate which has been made 10^{-3} molar in acetic acid:

$$c = 10^{-1}; \quad a = 10^{-3}; \quad K_a = K_b = 10^{-4.74},$$

$$x = -5 \times 10^{-4} + \sqrt{25 \times 10^{-8} + 10^{-2} \frac{10^{-14}}{10^{-9.48}}} = 2.43 \times 10^{-4};$$

$$(a + x) = 1.24 \times 10^{-3},$$

$$[H^+] = \frac{1.24 \times 10^{-3}}{10^{-1}} 10^{-4.74} = 2.26 \times 10^{-7},$$

$$p_H = 6.65.$$

If instead of acid, the same excess of ammonia had been added, the p_H would have become 7.35.

5. The Hydrogen-Ion Concentration in Mixtures of Weak Acids or Bases with Their Salts.

The dissociation of a weak acid is repressed when one of its salts is present, according to the common ion effect.

$$[H^+] = \frac{[HA]}{[A^-]} K_a. \tag{8}$$

If the repression is sufficient, one may set $[HA]$ equal to the total acid concentration a, and $[A^-]$ equal to the salt concentration b. Then it will be approximately true that:

$$[H^+] = \frac{a}{b} K_a, \tag{35}$$

or

$$p_H = -\log a + \log b + p_a. \tag{36}$$

In case a and b are equivalent, the hydrogen-ion concentration is equal to the ionization constant. For the solution of a weak base and its salt, similar expressions exist:

$$[OH^-] = \frac{[BOH]}{[B^+]} K_b = \frac{a}{b} K_b, \tag{37}$$

$$[H^+] = \frac{K_w}{K_b} \times \frac{b}{a}, \tag{38}$$

$$p_H = p_w - p_b - \log b + \log a. \tag{39}$$

Only when the dissociation is not completely repressed by the salt is it necessary to use more exact equations. During dissociation of an acid, equal numbers of hydrogen-ions and anions are formed:

$$HA \rightleftarrows H^+ + A^-.$$

Call the concentration of these ions x; then the concentration of undissociated acid will be $a - x$, and the total anion concentration will be $b + x$. Equation (35) now takes the form:

$$[H^+] = x = \frac{a - x}{b + x} K_a, \tag{40}$$

$$[H^+] = x = -\frac{b + K_a}{2} + \sqrt{\frac{(b + K_a)^2}{4} + aK_a}. \tag{41}$$

The same procedure may be followed for calculating the ionization of a weak acid in the presence of a slight excess of strong acid.

These considerations are applicable to the study of p_H changes during the titration of salts of weak bases with strong alkalies, and of weak acids with strong acids.

6. Mixtures of Two Weak Acids of Different Strengths; Hydrolysis of Acid Salts.—In a mixture of weak acids having considerably different ionization constants, it is desirable to know how the hydrogen-ion concentration changes in the vicinity of the first equivalence-point of a titration. One can decide theoretically whether the stronger acid can be titrated in the presence of the other.

If the two acids HA_I and HA_{II} have ionization constants K_1 and K_2, then in a mixture of the two with a given amount of base:

$$[H^+] = \frac{[HA_I]}{[A_I^-]} K_1 = \frac{[HA_{II}]}{[A_{II}^-]} K_2, \tag{42}$$

and

$$\frac{[HA_I]}{[A_I^-]} \cdot \frac{[HA_{II}]}{[A_{II}^-]} = K_2 : K_1. \tag{43}$$

The value $\dfrac{[HA]}{[A^-]}$ may be called the reciprocal neutralization ratio of an acid. It is evident from equation (43) that the neutralization ratios of the two acids are proportional to their ionization constants. If the ratio of K_1 to K_2 is quite large, at the beginning of a titration practically only HA_I will be neutralized while the quantity of A_{II}^- ions formed will be negligibly small.

Suppose that originally the two acids were of equivalent concentration, c_1. Then at the first equivalence-point, if a per cent of the stronger acid has been neutralized, $(100 - a)$ per cent of the second will have been changed into its salt, and one will have:

$$[A_I^-] = \frac{a}{100}\, c_1,$$

and

$$[A_{II}^-] = \frac{100 - a}{100}\, c_1,$$

so that:

$$[HA_I] = c_1 - [A_I^-] = \frac{c_1(100 - a)}{100},$$

and

$$[HA_{II}] = c_1 - [A_{II}^-] = \frac{ac_1}{100}.$$

From Equation (42) it follows that:

$$[H^+]^2 = \frac{[HA_I]}{[A_I^-]} \times \frac{[HA_{II}]}{[A_{II}^-]} K_1 K_2. \tag{44}$$

Substituting the values derived above, one finds that at the first equivalence-point:

$$[H^+]^2 = \frac{100 - a}{a} \times \frac{a}{100 - a} K_1 K_2 = K_1 K_2.$$

or

$$[H^+] = \sqrt{K_1 K_2}, \tag{45}$$

$$p_H = \tfrac{1}{2}(pK_1 + pK_2). \tag{46}$$

Similarly, for a mixture of two bases having the same initial concentration, the following equation may be derived for the first equivalence-point:

$$p_H = p_w - \tfrac{1}{2}(p_{K_1} + p_{K_2}).\tag{47}$$

The solution of an acid salt BHA may be regarded as a mixture of two acids of different ionization constants, in which the stronger acid has already been neutralized. In such a case equation (45) applies for the calculation of the hydrogen-ion concentration, K_1 and K_2 representing the first and second ionization constants, respectively. The relation is only approximate, however, and for more exact calculations[5] the following expression should be used:

$$[H^+] = \sqrt{\frac{K_1 K_2 c}{K_1 + c}},\tag{48}$$

where c represents the total salt concentration. If the magnitude of K_1 is so small that it may be neglected in comparison with c, the simpler formula (45) is obtained.

Illustration: For carbonic acid, $K_1 = 3 \times 10^{-7}$ and $K_2 = 6 \times 10^{-11}$. Therefore in a solution of sodium bicarbonate:

$$[H^+] = \sqrt{3 \times 10^{-7} \times 6 \times 10^{-11}} = 4.24 \times 10^{-9};$$

$$p_H = 8.37.$$

For tartaric acid, $K_1 = 1 \times 10^{-3}$, $K_2 = 9 \times 10^{-5}$; in an 0.1 molar solution of sodium bitartrate:

$$[H^+] = \sqrt{1 \times 10^{-3} \times 9 \times 10^{-5}} = 3 \times 10^{-4};$$

$$p_H = 3.52.$$

In more dilute solutions equation (48) should be applied. Thus in an 0.001 molar bitartrate solution:

$$[H^+] = 2.1 \times 10^{-4}; \qquad p_H = 3.68.$$

So far it has been assumed that the initial concentrations of the two acids were equal. Deviations in concentration up to about 10

[5] *Cf.* A. A. Noyes, *Z. physik. Chem.*, **A11**, 495 (1893), and also Kolthoff-Rosenblum, *loc. cit.*, p. 20, for further references to the literature.

per cent produce very little change in p_H at the equivalence-point, but with larger variations the error becomes appreciable. For example, if $[HA_I]$ is originally twice as large as $[HA_{II}]$:

$$[H^+] = \sqrt{\frac{K_1 K_2}{2}} \tag{49}$$

$$p_H = \tfrac{1}{2}(p_{K_1} + p_{K_2}) + \tfrac{1}{2}\log 2 = \tfrac{1}{2}(p_{K_1} + p_{K_2}) + 0.15. \tag{50}$$

If the two acid concentrations initially have the ratio r, the general expression for the hydrogen-ion concentration at the first equivalence-point becomes:

$$[H^+] = \sqrt{\frac{K_1 K_2}{r}}, \tag{51}$$

$$p_H = \tfrac{1}{2}(p_{K_1} + p_{K_2}) + \tfrac{1}{2}\log r. \tag{52}$$

7. The Change in Hydrogen-Ion Concentration of a Mixture of Two Acids at the First Equivalence-Point.—The accuracy possible in titrating one acid in the presence of another weaker one depends upon the sharpness of the p_H change near the equivalence-point. In the preceding paragraphs it was shown that at the first equivalence-point, a small part of HA_{II} is transformed into its salt before HA_I is completely neutralized. If now a small excess of base is added, most of it will be used in neutralizing the second acid.

Assume that the stronger acid has been a per cent neutralized, and a 1 per cent excess of base has been added. This base further neutralizes x per cent of HA, hence:

$$[A_I^-] = \frac{a + x}{100} c_1,$$

and

$$[HA_I] = \frac{100 - (a + x)}{100} c_1.$$

The remainder of the excess base neutralizes more of HA_{II} :

$$[A_{II}^-] = \frac{100 - (a + x) + 1}{100} c_1 = \frac{101 - (a + x)}{100} c_1,$$

and

$$[HA_{II}] = \frac{a + x - 1}{100} c_1.$$

Through substitution of these values in equation (43) one obtains:

$$\frac{100 - (a + x)}{a + x} \times \frac{101 - (a - x)}{a + x - 1} = \frac{K_2}{K_1}. \tag{53}$$

The value of a may be estimated from the neutralization ratios of the two acids, whereupon x is found by solving the quadratic equation (53). Then after solving for $[A_I^-]$ and $[HA_I]$, the hydrogen-ion concentration may be calculated from these and the ionization constant.

Illustrations:

I. $K_1:K_2 = 100.$

At the first equivalence-point a equals 91, hence:

$$[H^+] = \frac{9}{91} K_1 = 0.99K_1.$$

Upon the addition of 1 per cent excess base, x is calculated to be 0.4, then:

$$[H^+] = \frac{8.6}{91.4} K_1 = 0.094K_1.$$

Evidently the excess of base produces a change in $[H^+]$ of about 5 per cent, corresponding to an increase of 0.02 in p_H. This small change is not sufficient to permit the titration of one acid in the presence of the other.

II. $K_1:K_2 = 10,000.$

At the first equivalence-point a equals 99, and:

$$[H^+] = \frac{1}{99} K_1 = 0.01K_1.$$

After adding 1 per cent excess base, x becomes 0.39, while:

$$[H^+] = \frac{0.61}{99.39} K_1 = 0.0061K_1.$$

Here the value of $[H^+]$ has dropped about 39 per cent, corresponding to a p_H increase of 0.21. By the use of a reference solution in the titration, fairly good results may be obtained. As the ratio of K_1 to K_2 increases, the method becomes more exact.

For a mixture of two bases, analogous considerations apply. In this case one would first calculate $[OH^-]$ and convert over to $[H^+]$, using the ion product of water.

8. Precipitation Reactions and Solubility Products.—If two univalent ions unite reversibly to form a slightly soluble salt BA, the reaction may be expressed as an equation, and when equilibrium has been established the law of mass action may be applied:

$$B^+ + A^- \rightleftarrows BA, \tag{54}$$

$$\frac{[B^+][A^-]}{[BA]} = K. \tag{55}$$

$[BA]$, the concentration of the undissociated part of the salt, is constant at constant temperature. (The influence of dissolved electrolytes upon the activity of BA is neglected here.) Then equation (55) may be rewritten:

$$[B^+][A^-] = K \times [BA] = S_{BA}. \tag{56}$$

Here S_{BA} signifies the *solubility product*, or *ion product*. If the product of $[B^+]$ and $[A^-]$ becomes larger than S_{BA}, the solution is supersaturated with respect to BA, and a precipitate will form. In a saturated solution it may be assumed, without appreciable error, that all of the dissolved salt is dissociated into ions. Since equivalent amounts of anion and cation are present in a pure solution:

$$[B^+] = [A^-] = s, \tag{57}$$

where s is the saturation concentration of BA in water. It then follows from (56) and (57) that in the saturated solution:

$$[B^+]^2 = [A^-]^2 = s^2 = S. \tag{58}$$

In terms of ion exponents:

$$p_B + p_A = p_S \tag{59}$$

and

$$p_B = p_A = \tfrac{1}{2}p_S. \tag{60}$$

p_S, the negative logarithm of the solubility product, is called the *solubility exponent*. Equation (60) applies only to pure saturated solutions.

If solid BA is mixed with a solution containing a known excess of either B^+ or A^- ion, the concentration of the other ion may be calculated from equations (56) or (59):

$$[B^+] = \frac{S}{[A^-]}, \tag{61}$$

$$[A^-] = \frac{S}{[B^+]}, \tag{62}$$

$$\left.\begin{aligned} p_B &= p_S - p_A, \\ p_A &= p_S - p_B. \end{aligned}\right\} \tag{63}$$

Illustration: For silver chloride, $S = 10^{-10}$, or $p_S = 10$. In a saturated solution:

$$[Ag^+] = [Cl^-] = \sqrt{10^{-10}} = 10^{-5};$$

$$p_{Ag} = p_{Cl} = \tfrac{1}{2}p_S = 5.$$

The solubility of silver chloride thus corresponds to a concentration of 10^{-5} molar. If the silver-ion concentration should now be made 10^{-3}, the chloride-ion concentration would become 10^{-7}, and $p_{Cl} = 10 - 3 = 7$.

The molecular solubility of silver chloride, which is practically completely dissociated, is equal to the chloride-ion concentration if excess silver ion is present, or to the silver-ion concentration if excess chloride ion is present. Therefore the solubility is a maximum in pure saturated solution and decreases with increasing concentration of either ion. The quantity of either ion added cannot be regarded as exactly equal to the total present, for this would be neglecting the amount furnished by the dissolved salt. Actually the total concentration of the ion is somewhat greater than the quantity added.

If the added excess of B^+ ion is equivalent to a concentration a, the total concentration of B^+ will be $a + x$, where x is the solubility of BA under these conditions and is equal to $[A^-]$. Then from equation (56):

$$\left.\begin{aligned} (a + x)x &= S, \\ x^2 + ax - S &= 0. \end{aligned}\right\} \tag{64}$$

$$x = -\frac{a}{2} + \sqrt{\frac{a^2}{4} + S}. \tag{65}$$

From equation (65) it is apparent that x becomes smaller as a increases or as S decreases. In practice it is often permissible to ignore x, but this is not always the case. The following table shows values of x corresponding to the indicated values of a and S:

SOLUBILITY OF BA WITH AN EXCESS a OF [B⁺] OR [A⁻]

$S = 10^{-6}; p_S = 6$		$S = 10^{-8}; p_S = 8$		$S = 10^{-10}; p_S = 10$	
a	x	a	x	a	x
1×10^{-3}	6.2×10^{-4}	1×10^{-4}	6.2×10^{-5}	1×10^{-4}	1×10^{-6}
2×10^{-3}	4.0×10^{-4}	2×10^{-4}	4.0×10^{-5}	2×10^{-4}	5×10^{-7}
5×10^{-3}	2.0×10^{-4}	5×10^{-4}	2.0×10^{-5}	5×10^{-4}	2×10^{-7}
10×10^{-3}	1.0×10^{-4}	10×10^{-4}	1.0×10^{-5}	10×10^{-4}	1×10^{-7}

These considerations are of importance in the calculation of ion concentration changes in the vicinity of the endpoint, and therefore are needed for the determination of titration errors. As will be shown in Chapter VI, the accuracy of a titration depends not only upon the sensitivity of the indicator, but also upon the sharpness of ion concentration change near the equivalence-point. For example, if the solubility product of the compound formed is 10^{-6}, and excess B⁺ is added corresponding to 1 ml. of 0.1 N per 100 ml. of saturated BA solution, then a is equal to 10^{-3}. In this solution $[A^-] = x = 6.2 \times 10^{-4}$, whereas in the pure saturated solution $[A^-]$ would be 10^{-3} N. Thus the addition of B⁺ produced a decrease of 38 per cent in solubility. Had the solubility product been 10^{-8}, the same diminution would have been effected by 0.1 ml. of 0.1 N B⁺ solution.

If the compound involved consists of bivalent ions as well as univalent, the relations are more complicated. For a slightly soluble salt B_2A:

$$2B^+ + A^= \rightleftarrows B_2A, \tag{66}$$

$$[B^+]^2[A^=] = S_{B_2A}. \tag{67}$$

In the pure saturated solution, $[B^+]$ will be twice as large as $[A^-]$, that is, $[B^+] = 2[A^-]$, so that:

$$\tfrac{1}{2}[B^+]^3 = 4[A^=]^3 = S_{B_2A}. \tag{68}$$

Let s equal the solubility of B_2A expressed in moles per liter; then:

$$s = [A^-] = \sqrt[3]{\frac{S_{B_2A}}{4}}. \tag{69}$$

Expressed in terms of ion exponents, equation (67) becomes:

$$2p_B + p_A = p_S, \tag{70}$$

while for the saturated solution of B_2A, one obtains from equation (68):

$$p_B = p_A - \log 2 = p_A - 0.30, \tag{71}$$

and

$$3p_A - 0.60 = p_S. \tag{72}$$

When solid B_2A is in contact with a solution containing a known excess of either B^+ or A^-, the unknown ion concentration may be calculated from the following:

$$[B^+] = \sqrt{\frac{S_{B_2A}}{[A^-]}} \tag{73}$$

$$[A^-] = \frac{S_{B_2A}}{[B^+]^2} \tag{74}$$

Equation (70) may also be transposed if p_S is given.

Illustration: In round numbers, for silver chromate $S = 10^{-12}$ or $p_s = 12$. In a saturated solution:

$$[B^+] = \sqrt[3]{2S} = \sqrt[3]{2 \times 10^{-12}} = 10^{-3.9} = 1.26 \times 10^{-4},$$

and

$$[A^-] = \tfrac{1}{2}[B^+] = 0.63 \times 10^{-4}.$$

By application of equations (71) and (72) directly, it is found that:

$$p_A = \frac{p_S - 0.60}{3} = 4.2,$$

$$p_B = p_A - 0.3 = 3.9.$$

As in the case of the substance BA, the solubility of B_2A is at a maximum in the pure saturated solution. Addition of either ion in excess decreases the solubility. However, the effect of excess B^+ is not the same as the effect of an equal excess of A^-. From equation

(67) it follows that if $[B^+]$ is multiplied by 10, $[A^-]$ is divided by 100. On the other hand, if $[A^-]$ is multiplied by 10, $[B^+]$ is divided by $\sqrt{10}$, or 3.16. The solubility is, of course, divided accordingly.

When an excess of either ion is added, the total concentration of that ion will be the concentration added plus that furnished by the solubility of B_2A. If the solubility under these conditions is called x, then $2xB^+$ ions and xA^- ions will be furnished. With an excess a of B^+ added, the total concentration of B^+ will be $a + 2x$, while that of A^- will be x. Then from equation (67):

$$(a + 2x)^2 x = S_{B_2A},$$

or

$$x^3 + ax^2 + \tfrac{1}{4}a^2x - \frac{S}{4} = 0. \tag{75}$$

Although cubic equations are difficult to solve, one can plot values of x against assigned values of $[B^+]$ or $[A^-]$ for a given solubility product. By means of equation (67), values of $[A^-]$ (which are equal to x) corresponding to assigned values of $[B^+]$ may be calculated. Conversely, $[B^+]$ (equal to $2x$) can be obtained from $[A^-]$. In this way, assuming a solubility product of 10^{-12}, were found the values of x plotted against $[B^+]$ in Fig. 1, and against $[A^-]$ in Fig. 2. The ordinates in each case are in units of $x \times 10^5$, while the abcissas are $[B^+] \times 10^4$ or $[A^-] \times 10^4$.

With the aid of such curves, one can calculate what x will be if a known excess a of B^+ ions is added to a saturated solution of B_2A. As an approximation, the total concentration $[B^+]$ is set equal to $a + 2s$, where s is the molar solubility of B_2A in water. Then the corresponding value of x is located on the curve. If the approximation were correct, this would equal $[A^-]$, and the decrease in solubility caused by the addition would be known. However, since x is smaller than s, a new approximation should be made in which $[B^+] = a + 2x$. From this, a closer value of x is found; thus the correct figure may be deduced after one or two trials.

It is simpler to plot a new curve modified from Figure 1 (or Figure 2), in which are given the values of $[B^+]$ with known excess a of B^+ ions (or of $[A^-]$ with known excess). From Figure 1, for example, the value $x = 1 \times 10^{-5}$ corresponds to $[B^+] = 3.2 \times 10^{-4}$. Since the latter is $a + 2x$, it follows that a is equal to 3.0×10^{-4}. In this manner a curve of a vs. x can be obtained.

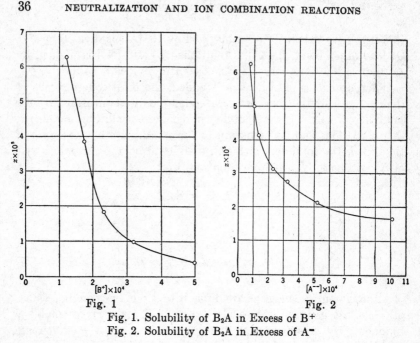

Fig. 1   Fig. 2

Fig. 1. Solubility of B_2A in Excess of B^+
Fig. 2. Solubility of B_2A in Excess of A^-

The following table lists values for x and the concentration of either ion in the presence of a known excess a of the other ion, for a compound B_2A whose solubility product is 10^{-12}:

	a	$[B^+]$	$[A^-]$	x = solubility
Excess of $[B^+]$	0	1.26×10^{-4}	6.3×10^{-5}	6.3×10^{-5}
= a:	1.0×10^{-4}	1.69×10^{-4}	3.45×10^{-5}	3.45×10^{-5}
	2.0×10^{-4}	2.36×10^{-4}	1.8×10^{-5}	1.8×10^{-5}
	3.0×10^{-4}	3.2×10^{-4}	1.0×10^{-5}	1.0×10^{-5}
	5.0×10^{-4}	5.08×10^{-4}	0.39×10^{-5}	0.39×10^{-5}
Excess of $[A^-]$	0	1.26×10^{-4}	6.3×10^{-5}	6.3×10^{-5}
= a:	0.5×10^{-4}	1.0×10^{-4}	1.0×10^{-4}	5.0×10^{-5}
	1.0×10^{-4}	8.4×10^{-5}	1.42×10^{-4}	4.2×10^{-5}
	2.0×10^{-4}	6.5×10^{-5}	2.32×10^{-4}	3.2×10^{-5}
	3.0×10^{-4}	5.5×10^{-5}	3.27×10^{-4}	2.7×10^{-5}
	5.0×10^{-4}	4.4×10^{-5}	5.22×10^{-4}	2.2×10^{-5}
	10.0×10^{-4}	3.14×10^{-5}	10.16×10^{-4}	1.6×10^{-5}

From data of this kind, one may deduce:

(a) The cases in which the solubility of B_2A is negligible, so that the concentration of the ion present in excess may be considered equal to the amount added;

(b) The solubility of B_2A in the presence of a known excess of either ion. If, for example, the solubility is too large, a direct titration will not yield good results. One might then add an excess of precipitant and titrate the excess after filtering.

The error caused by the amount of B_2A remaining in solution may also be calculated with the help of the above considerations.

For a precipitate of the composition BA_2 the same expressions apply, except that $[A^-]$ and $[B^+]$ are to be replaced by $[B^{++}]$ and $[A^-]$, respectively. If the composition is BA, where B and A are polyvalent ions of equal valence, the equations are the same as those derived for univalent ions.

With precipitates of the general composition B_xA_y, where the ions have higher and differing valences, the calculations become very complicated. The equations obtained are difficult and sometimes even impossible to solve. In such cases one may proceed by the graphical method. The precipitation is expressed by the reaction:

$$x B^{n+} + y A^{m-} \rightleftarrows B_x A_y,$$

where n is the valence of the cation and m that of the anion. According to the law of mass action:

$$[B^{n+}]^x [A^{m-}]^y = S_{B_xA_y}. \tag{76}$$

The following equations relate $[B^{n+}]$ and $[A^{m-}]$:

$$[B^{n+}] = \sqrt[x]{\frac{S_{B_xA_y}}{[A^{m-}]^y}}, \tag{77}$$

$$[A^{m-}] = \sqrt[y]{\frac{S_{B_xA_y}}{[B^{n+}]^x}}. \tag{78}$$

In terms of ion exponents these are much simpler:

$$x p_B + y p_A = p_S, \tag{79}$$

$$p_B = \frac{p_S - y p_A}{x}, \tag{80}$$

$$p_A = \frac{p_S - x p_B}{y}. \tag{81}$$

If the solubility product and one of the two ion concentrations are known, the other concentration and the corresponding solubility may be calculated. Then by subtracting from $[B^{n+}]$ the portion of it which is supplied by dissolved B_xA_y, one finds the excess a of B^{n+} ion corresponding to this solubility. When these values are plotted on a curve (*cf.* p. 36), it is possible to read off directly how the solubility and ionic concentrations change with given excess of either ion.

For a pure saturated solution of B_xA_y in water, there are x mols of B^{n+} ions per y mols of A^{m-} ions. By introducing this ratio in equations (76) and (79) there are obtained the following expressions, which of course apply only to the pure saturated solution:

$$[B^{n+}] = \sqrt[x+y]{\left(\frac{x}{y}\right)^y S_{B_xA_y}}, \tag{77a}$$

$$[A^{m-}] = \sqrt[x+y]{\left(\frac{y}{x}\right)^x S_{B_xA_y}}, \tag{78a}$$

$$p_B = \frac{1}{x+y}\left(p_S + y \log \frac{y}{x}\right), \tag{80a}$$

$$p_A = \frac{1}{x+y}\left(p_S + x \log \frac{x}{y}\right). \tag{81a}$$

9. The Presence of Two Ions which Form Slightly Soluble Compounds with a Common Ion.—If two anions A_I^- and A_{II}^- form slightly soluble salts with the same cation B^+, the result obtained by mixing a solution of B^+ ions with one containing both anions may be calculated. The compounds formed being BA_I and BA_{II}, respectively, the equilibrium expressions are:

$$[B^+][A_I^-] = S_{BA_I}$$

$$[B^+][A_{II}^-] = S_{BA_{II}}.$$

In case enough B^+ ions are added to yield a precipitate containing both compounds, it follows that:

$$[B^+] = \frac{S_{BA_I}}{[A_I^-]} = \frac{S_{BA_{II}}}{[A_{II}^-]},$$

from which

$$\frac{[A_I^-]}{[A_{II}^-]} = \frac{S_{BA_I}}{S_{BA_{II}}} . \qquad (82)$$

Consequently when both salts are present in the solid phase, the ratio of the anion concentrations at equilibrium is equal to the ratio of the corresponding solubility products.

One can titrate the least soluble ion in the presence of the other only if the first may be precipitated practically quantitatively without contamination by the second. Therefore it is of practical interest to determine under what conditions this is possible in principle. Letting BA_{II} represent the least soluble compound, one sees from equation (82) that BA_{II} alone will precipitate from the mixture until the ratio of $[A_I^-]$ to $[A_{II}^-]$ becomes equal to the ratio of the solubility products. Upon further addition of B^+ ions both compounds will precipitate in such amounts that the ratio of $[A_I^-]$ to $[A_{II}^-]$ will remain constant.

Illustration: A solution containing iodide and chloride ions is titrated with silver nitrate. Silver iodide precipitates until:

$$\frac{[Cl^-]}{[I^-]} = \frac{S_{AgCl}}{S_{AgI}} = \text{about } \frac{10^{-10}}{10^{-16}} = 10^6.$$

As soon as the iodide concentration becomes one one-millionth of the chloride concentration, silver chloride will begin to precipitate. Previous to this point, only silver iodide would have been formed. Evidently the titration gives a good separation of iodide from chloride even if the initial chloride concentration is one hundred times that of the iodide. In this case silver chloride would not begin to precipitate until all but 0.01 per cent of the iodide had been titrated, so the reaction may be called quantitative.

In titrating a mixture of bromide and chloride with silver nitrate, the ratio of the solubility products is about 500. Simultaneous precipitation of the two halides takes place when the bromide concentration decreases to one five-hundredth of the chloride concentration. The relations are thus not favorable for a quantitative separation. Moreover, the situation is complicated by the fact that coprecipitation of silver chloride with silver bromide occurs earlier during the titration as a result of mixed crystal formation, (see p. 201).

To estimate the accuracy of the titration, it is necessary to learn the ion concentration change in the vicinity of the first equivalence-point, i.e., the point at which theoretically all A_{II}^- ions have been precipitated and all the A_I^- ions remain in solution. One may set up equations similar to those in Section 8, but usually it is easier to proceed as explained below.

When a quantitative separation is possible, one can consider that $[A_{II}^-]$ just prior to the precipitation of BA_I is equal to the excess of A_{II}^- ions not yet titrated. Strictly, there should be added the concentration supplied by the solubility of BA_{II}.

As soon as the precipitation of BA_I begins, $[A_{II}^-]$ changes only very slightly, in accordance with equation (82). It may be assumed practically constant, and nearly all of the added B^+ ions will then be used for the precipitation of BA_I during which the value of $[B^+]$ also holds practically constant. In the region of the second equivalence-point, where A_I^- is completely titrated, the same considerations apply as were developed in Section 8.

To summarize, the ion concentration change at the first equivalence-point in a titration of a solution of two univalent ions is determined by the ratio of the solubility products S_{BA_I} and $S_{BA_{II}}$ and by the ratio of the ion concentrations $[A_I^-]$ and $[A_{II}^-]$.

Now, let one of the ions be univalent and the other bivalent, so that the two slightly soluble salts are BA_I and B_2A_{II}. In the presence of both solid salts:

$$[B^+] = \frac{S_{BA_I}}{[A_I^-]} = \sqrt{\frac{S_{B_2A_{II}}}{[A_{II}^-]}},$$

from which

$$\frac{[A_I^-]}{\sqrt{[A_{II}^-]}} = \frac{S_{BA_I}}{\sqrt{S_{B_2A_{II}}}}.$$

If BA_I is the less soluble of the two, addition of B^+ ions will precipitate BA_I alone until the concentration ratio of equation (83) becomes equal to the solubility product ratio as indicated.

Illustration: A solution containing chloride and oxalate ions is titrated with silver nitrate. When the mixture becomes saturated with both silver salts:

$$\frac{[Cl^-]}{\sqrt{[C_2O_4^-]}} = \frac{S_{AgCl}}{\sqrt{S_{Ag_2C_2O_4}}} = \frac{10^{-10}}{\sqrt{10^{-12}}} = 10^{-4}.$$

Silver chloride, the least soluble, will precipitate alone until $[Cl^-] = 10^{-4} \times \sqrt{[C_2O_4^-]}$. If the oxalate concentration is 5×10^{-2} molar (0.1 N), silver oxalate will not begin to precipitate until the chloride concentration decreases to 2.24×10^{-5}.

By extending this type of calculation, it is possible to arrive quite simply at the conditions under which quantitative separations are possible, even for rather complicated cases.

10. The Effect of Hydrogen-Ion Concentration on the Solubility of Slightly Soluble Salts.

—It is well known that acids have considerable influence upon the solubility of salts. While this will not be discussed in detail here, some facts of practical importance will be mentioned.

According to the Arrhenius theory, and also according to more recent views, electrolytes increase the solubility of salts. Strong acids will have this effect on the solubility of salts of strong acids, but the effect is so small compared with that which will be described below, that it may be neglected for our purpose.

The solubility of salts of weak acids is affected to the greatest extent by hydrogen ions. Regarding such a salt as completely dissociated in its saturated solution, and neglecting hydrolysis, one may write:

$$BA \rightleftarrows B^+ + A^-,$$

where A^- is the anion of the weak acid HA. These anions may combine with hydrogen ions forming the slightly dissociated acid:

$$A^- + H^+ \rightleftarrows HA.$$

Therefore if a little acid is added to a suspension of BA, A^- ions are removed and more BA will dissolve until the solubility product is reached:

$$[B^+][A^-] = S_{BA}. \tag{56}$$

If values are known for the hydrogen-ion concentration, S_{BA} and the ionization constant K_{HA} of the weak acid, one can calculate $[B^+]$ and the amount of BA that is dissolved. The latter is equal to $[B^+]$, assuming complete ionization of the strong electrolyte. For every A^- ion that is bound by a hydrogen ion or that remains as such in solution, there will be one B^+ ion, so that:

$$[B^+] = [HA] + [A^-]. \tag{84}$$

Substituting in equation (84) the value of $[B^+]$ found from equation (56), it follows that:

$$[HA] = \frac{S_{BA}}{[A^-]} - [A^-]. \tag{85}$$

From equation (8):

$$[HA] = \frac{[H^+][A^-]}{K_{HA}},$$

so

$$\frac{[H^+]}{K_{HA}} = \frac{S_{BA}}{[A^-]^2} - 1,$$

$$[A^-] = \sqrt{\frac{S_{BA}}{\frac{[H^+]}{K_{HA}} + 1}},$$

$$[B^+] = \frac{S_{BA}}{[A^-]} = \sqrt{S_{BA}\left(\frac{[H^+]}{K_{HA}} + 1\right)}. \tag{86}$$

In the special case where $[H^+] = K_{HA}$:

$$[B^+] = \sqrt{2S_{BA}} = 1.41\sqrt{S_{BA}}.$$

The solubility is therefore increased by 41 per cent in this case.

To apply the preceding equations the hydrogen-ion concentration must be known. Usually one knows rather the amount of acid that is added, from which it is difficult to derive mathematically the hydrogen-ion concentration in the presence of dissolved BA. The problem may be solved by assuming various values of $[H^+]$ and calculating the corresponding concentrations of A^- and B^+ ions for given values of K_{HA} and S_{BA}. From the principle of electroneutrality of solutions it follows that:

$$[H^+] + [B^+] = [c] + [A^-], \tag{87}$$

where $[c]$ is the concentration of anions furnished by the acid added, which is also the concentration of acid which would have been present if none of that added had reacted with BA. Substituting the corresponding values of $[H^+]$, $[B^+]$ and $[A^-]$ in equation (87), one finds the value of $[c]$ appropriate to each case.   Then for a given addition of acid one can read off directly the various concentrations.

The addition of acid to increase the solubility of a compound has important applications in analytical chemistry.   For example, both chloride and phosphate yield precipitates with silver ions in neutral solution.   In acid solution only silver chloride precipitates, so that a titration of chloride may be carried out in the presence of phosphate.

11. The Hydrolysis of Slightly Soluble Salts.—In connection with precipitation analyses it is desirable to know the concentrations of various ions in the saturated solution of a slightly soluble hydrolyzed salt.   If such a salt, BA, is composed of ions of a strong base and a weak acid, on solution in water part of the A^- ions will react:

$$A^- + H_2O \rightleftarrows HA + OH^-.$$

Then it follows that:

$$[HA] = [OH^-]$$

$$[B^+] = [A^-] + [HA] = [A^-] + [OH^-]. \tag{88}$$

From the equation for the hydrolysis constant:

$$[OH^-] = \sqrt{[A^-]\frac{K_w}{K_{HA}}}.$$

Substituting this in equation (88) and later combining with (56), one finds that:

$$[B^+] = [A^-] + \sqrt{[A^-]\frac{K_w}{K_{HA}}} = \frac{S_{BA}}{[A^-]}$$

$$[A^-]^2 + [A^-]\sqrt{[A^-]\frac{K_w}{K_{HA}}} - S_{BA} = 0.$$

Let $\sqrt{[A^-]} = x$ and $\dfrac{K_w}{K_{HA}} = K_{hydr.}$; then

$$x^4 + x^3\sqrt{K_{hydr.}} - S_{BA} = 0,$$

$$x = \sqrt[3]{\frac{S_{BA}}{x + \sqrt{K_{hydr.}}}}. \tag{89}$$

This equation is not easy to solve.   However, as a first approximation, one may neglect x or $K_{hydr.}$ in the denominator and solve for x.
If the approximate value of x thus obtained is substituted in equation
(89), a new and closer value will be found.   One cannot generally
tell at first which term of the denominator may best be neglected, but
if a trial indicates that x will be larger than $K_{hydr.}$, the latter should
be neglected, and vice versa.   Since $[A^-] = x^2$, the value of x should
be approximated rather closely in order to yield reliable ion concentrations.   From $[A^-]$ and the known constants, one can calculate
$[B^+]$, $[OH^-]$ and $[H^+]$ with the aid of the foregoing equations.

Illustration: In a saturated aqueous solution of calcium carbonate:

$$CaCO_3 \rightleftarrows Ca^{++} + CO_3^-$$

$$CO_3^- + H_2O \rightleftarrows HCO_3^- + OH^-.$$

S_{CaCO_3} is about 5×10^{-9} at 25°C.,[6] while K_w is 1×10^{-14} and K_{HA} about $5 \times$
10^{-11} (K_2 of carbonic acid).   As a first approximation one finds that x becomes
8.4×10^{-3} when $K_{hydr.}$ is neglected in the denominator of equation (89), or
7.07×10^{-3} when x is neglected.   Substituting the latter value, x becomes
6.18×10^{-3} in the second approximation, and 6.26×10^{-3} in the third, from
which $[CO_3^-]$ is found to be 3.92×10^{-5}.

$$[Ca^{++}] = \frac{S}{[CO_3^-]} = 1.27 \times 10^{-4}$$

$$[OH^-] = [HCO_3^-] = \sqrt{[A^-] \frac{K_w}{K_{HA}}} = 8.83 \times 10^{-5}.$$

The value of $[Ca^{++}]$ corresponds to 12.7 mg. of dissolved calcium carbonate
per liter, and the carbonate is about 69 per cent hydrolyzed.

It is also possible to derive expressions for the changes in solubility
and $[OH^-]$ produced by a slight excess of acid or base.   Here let it
suffice to mention that addition of a large excess of calcium represses
the carbonate-ion concentration so strongly that hydrolysis may be
neglected.   For instance, if $[Ca^{++}]$ is made 0.1 molar, $[CO_3^-]$
becomes 5×10^{-8}.   Winkler's method for the determination of
hydroxide in the presence of carbonate is based upon such a repression
of solubility and hydrolysis.   By the addition of excess barium salt,

[6] G. L. Frear and J. Johnston, *J. Am. Chem. Soc.*, **51**, 2082 (1929).

carbonate remains insoluble so that the hydroxide may be titrated with acid to a phenolphthalein endpoint.

12. The Formation of Complex Ions.—The dissociation of a complex ion takes place in several steps. In the first, simple ions and the "neutral portion" separate:

$$B_2A^+ \rightleftarrows B^+ + BA, \tag{90}$$

after which BA may dissociate as a salt:

$$BA \rightleftarrows B^+ + A^-. \tag{91}$$

If BA is a weak electrolyte, the process indicated in (90) is of analytical importance, for it governs the stability of the complex ion. According to the law of mass action:

$$\frac{[B^+][BA]}{[B_2A^+]} = K_{compl.} . \tag{92}$$

Since $K_{compl.}$ furnishes a measure of the instability of the complex ion, it is called the *complex-dissociation constant* and its reciprocal is called the *stability constant*.

In a pure solution of a complex salt, $[B^+]$ will be equal to $[BA]$ if the dissociation of the latter may be neglected. If the complex ion is quite stable, $[B_2A^+]$ may be set equal to c, the total concentration, because complex salts behave as strong electrolytes. Then:

$$[B^+] = [BA] = \sqrt{cK_{compl.}} . \tag{93}$$

This expression for $[B^+]$ is similar to that developed for $[H^+]$ in equation (11), page 18. Continuing the analogy, one can calculate the change in $[B^+]$ produced by a small addition of B^+ ions. If the excess added corresponds to a concentration a, and if a further concentration x is furnished by dissociation of the complex, it follows that:

$$[B^+] = a + x, \quad \text{and} \quad [BA] = x,$$

so from equation (92):

$$(a + x)x = cK_{compl.},$$

$$x = -\frac{a}{2} + \sqrt{\frac{a^2}{4} + cK_{compl.}} . \tag{94}$$

In the more usual case, when the "neutral portion," BA, of the complex ion is a strong electrolyte, both steps (90) and (91) must be considered. The total process may be written:

$$B_2A^+ \rightleftarrows 2\,B^+ + A^-, \tag{95}$$

$$\frac{[B^+]^2[A^-]}{[B_2A^+]} = K'_{compl.} \tag{96}$$

From equation (95) it is evident that $[B^+]$ will equal $2[A^-]$. Then, letting c represent $[B_2A^+]$:

$$4[A^-]^3 = cK'_{compl.}, \tag{97}$$

$$[A^-] = \sqrt[3]{\frac{c}{4}\,K'_{compl.}}, \tag{97a}$$

$$[B^+] = \sqrt[3]{2cK'_{compl.}} \tag{97b}$$

The change in $[A^-]$ or $[B^+]$ caused by adding a small excess of either ion can be found most readily by a graphic method, similar to that used in the case of slightly soluble salts B_2A or BA_2 (cf. p. 35). Mathematical treatment yields a cubic equation.

Illustration: Consider the complex silver cyanide ion. By averaging data in the literature,[7] $K'_{compl.}$ appears to be about 10^{-21}:

$$Ag(CN)_2^- \rightleftarrows Ag^+ + 2CN^-,$$

$$\frac{[Ag^+][CN^-]^2}{[Ag(CN)_2^-]} = K'_{compl.} = 10^{-21}.$$

Therefore, in a 0.1 molar solution of the complex silver salt:

$$[Ag^+] = \sqrt[3]{\frac{c}{4}\,K'_{compl.}} = \sqrt[3]{25 \times 10^{-24}} = 3 \times 10^{-8},$$

$$[CN^-] = 6 \times 10^{-8}.$$

In practice the neutral portion may be slightly soluble, as is silver cyanide which forms a soluble complex with potassium cyanide. If the product $[B^+][A^-]$ exceeds the solubility product S of the com-

---

[7] H. Euler, *Ber.*, **36**, 2885 (1903); G. Bodländer and W. Eberlein, *Z. anorg. allgem. Chem.*, **39**, 238 (1904).

pound BA, enough of the latter will precipitate to maintain the ion product constant, hence precipitation may take place before the equivalence-point is reached. This occurs in the case of complex mercuric iodide ion HgI_4^-, (cf. p. 154).

As soon as the solution becomes saturated with respect to BA, further changes in $[B^+]$ must take place in accordance with equation (96) and the solubility product equation:

$$[B^+] = \frac{cK'_{compl.}}{[B^+][A^-]} = \frac{cK'_{compl.}}{S_{BA}} = ck. \tag{98}$$

Therefore it follows that under these conditions $[B^+]$ varies directly with c. If precipitation of BA occurs before the equivalence-point in a titration, continued addition of reagent can produce very little change in $[B^+]$. Hence no good result can be expected if $[B^+][A^-]$ reaches S_{BA} during the titration. Since at the equivalence-point:

$$[B^+][A^-] = \frac{cK'_{compl.}}{[B^+]} = \frac{cK'_{compl.}}{\sqrt[3]{2cK'_{compl.}}} = \sqrt[3]{\frac{(cK'_{compl.})^2}{2}}, \tag{99}$$

the conditions will be unfavorable if $\sqrt[3]{\dfrac{(cK'_{compl.})^2}{2}}$ exceeds S_{BA} .

The preceding considerations apply to ions of the type B_2A^+. For more complicated types, the equations are more involved. In the case of an ion B_3A^{++}:

$$B_3A^{++} \rightleftarrows 2B^+ + BA,$$

$$\frac{[B^+]^2[BA]}{[B_3A^{++}]} = K_{compl.}. \tag{100}$$

The latter equation applies when the dissociation of BA is negligible. Then in a pure solution of the complex salt:

$$[B^+]^3 = 2cK_{compl.},$$

$$[B^+] = \sqrt[3]{2cK_{compl.}}. \tag{101}$$

If the dissociation of the complex ion takes place in steps:

$$B_3A^{++} \rightleftarrows B^+ + B_2A^+,$$

$$B_2A^+ \rightleftarrows B^+ + BA,$$

both of the corresponding constants must be considered, which further complicates the calculation.

If the "neutral portion" BA behaves as a strong electrolyte:

$$\frac{[B^+]^3[A^-]}{[B_3A^{++}]} = K'_{compl.}.$$

(102)

Then, if one may neglect the step-wise dissociation, in a pure solution of this complex salt $[B^+]$ will equal $3[A^-]$, so that:

$$[A^-] = \sqrt[4]{\frac{c}{27} K'_{compl}} \, ,$$

(103)

$$[B^+] = \sqrt[4]{3cK'_{compl.}}.$$

(103a)

The calculation of the changes in ion concentrations produced by the addition of a slight excess of either ion is most easily carried out by the graphic method.

This concludes the general discussion of principles underlying neutralization and ion-combination reactions, although a few further details will be taken up as needed in later chapters. With the aid of the considerations that have been presented, the reader will be able to derive equations covering special problems which he may meet in practice.

CHAPTER III

TITRATION CURVES FOR NEUTRALIZATION AND ION COMBINATION REACTIONS

1. The Change of Ion Concentration During a Neutralization Titration.—A discussion of titration curves is of interest both from the standpoint of ordinary volumetric analysis and from that of physico-chemical methods of analysis. The graphs for quantitative neutralizations will be considered first, and for the sake of simplicity the volume changes during titration will be assumed negligible. This, of course, is an invalid assumption, but generally the change of ion concentration at the equivalence-point is so large that the error is not significant. Furthermore, the correction for volume change can easily be made for any given point in an actual titration.

Consider first the titration of a strong acid with a strong base, for example, 0.01 N hydrochloric acid with sodium hydroxide. Originally the hydrogen-ion concentration is 0.01 N and $p_H = 2$. After 90 per cent of the acid has been neutralized, $[H^+] = 10^{-3}$ N and $p_H = 3$. Continuing until 99.9 per cent has been neutralized, $[H^+]$ becomes 10^{-5} N and $p_H = 5$. Finally, at the equivalence-point[1] the only hydrogen and hydroxyl ions present are those resulting from the dissociation of water, and their concentrations are determined by the value of the ion product K_w:

$$[H^+] = [OH^-] = \sqrt{K_w} = 10^{-7} \text{ (at 24°C.)},$$

$$p_H = p_{OH} = \tfrac{1}{2}p_w = 7 \text{ (at 24°C.)}.$$

After passing the equivalence-point, the concentration of hydroxyl ions is given directly by the concentration of sodium hydroxide added

---

[1] In practice, the equivalence-point is usually found at a p_H lower than 7 due to the presence of carbonic acid. If provision is made for complete exclusion of carbon dioxide, the practical neutralization curve corresponds very closely with that deduced theoretically.

49

in excess. In the following table are shown ion concentrations and exponents at various stages of the titration:

TITRATION OF 0.01 N HYDROCHLORIC ACID WITH SODIUM HYDROXIDE

$$K_w = 10^{-14}. \text{ Constant volume}[2]$$

Per cent of acid neutralized	$[H^+]$	p_H	p_{OH}	$\dfrac{\Delta p_H}{\Delta c}$
0	10^{-2}	2	12	
90.0	10^{-3}	3	11	0.011
99.0	10^{-4}	4	10	0.11
99.9	10^{-5}	5	9	1.1
100.0	10^{-7}	7	7	20.0

Per cent of alkali in excess				
0.1	10^{-9}	9	5	20.0
1.0	10^{-10}	10	4	1.1
10.0	10^{-11}	11	3	0.11

The sudden change or "break" in ion concentration and ion exponent near the equivalence-point is emphasized by the change in value of $\dfrac{\Delta p_H}{\Delta c}$. This difference quotient (mathematically expressed) represents the increment of the ion exponent produced by a given addition of reagent, in this case by 1 per cent of the stoichiometrically required quantity of alkali. The quotient has a maximum at the equivalence-point, and in general the titration is more exact the greater this maximum value.

In Figure 3 are shown the changes of ion exponents in the zone from 10 per cent before to 10 per cent after the equivalence-point. The ordinates on the left refer to p_H, which is plotted on the solid curve, while those on the right refer to p_{OH}, as indicated by the dotted curve. The magnitude of the ion concentration change de-

---

[2] To correct for the volume change during titration, the listed values of $[H^+]$ prior to the equivalence-point should be multiplied by $\dfrac{V_0}{V}$, where V_0 is the initial volume and V the total volume at the given stage of titration. In this example, the value of $[H^+]$ at the equivalence-point is unaffected by dilution. In the presence of excess alkali, the concentration of $[OH^-]$ should be calculated, based upon the total volume of solution, and the value of $[H^+]$ is found from $[OH^-]$ and K_w.

pends upon the value of K_w; the break becomes smaller as K_w increases. For comparison, the neutralization curves for $K_w = 10^{-12}$

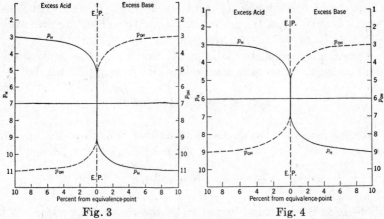

Fig. 3   Fig. 4

Fig. 3. Titration of 0.01N Hydrochloric Acid with Sodium Hydroxide at Room Temperature

Fig. 4. Titration of 0.01N Hydrochloric Acid with Sodium Hydroxide at 100°C

(at 100°C.) are given in Figure 4, and the data are listed in the table below:

TITRATION OF 0.01 N HYDROCHLORIC ACID WITH SODIUM HYDROXIDE AT 100°C.

$$K_w = 10^{-12}$$

Per cent of acid neutralized	$[H^+]$	p_H	p_{OH}	$\dfrac{\Delta p_H}{\Delta c}$
0	10^{-2}	2	10	
90.0	10^{-3}	3	9	0.011
99.0	10^{-4}	4	8	0.11
99.9	10^{-5}	5	7	1.1
100.0	10^{-6}	6	6	10.0
Percent of alkali in excess				
0.1	10^{-7}	7	5	10.0
1.0	10^{-8}	8	4	1.1
10.0	10^{-9}	9	3	0.11

As may be seen in Figures 3 and 4, the curves representing titrations of a strong acid with a strong base are symmetrical with reference to the equivalence-point, and at this point the solution is neutral provided that carbon dioxide is excluded.

Neutralization Curves in the Titration of Weak Acids with Strong .
Bases.—If a weak acid is titrated with a strong base, the equivalence-point lies on the alkaline side, while if a weak base is titrated with a strong acid, the equivalence-point lies on the acid side. If the acid or base is very weak, the neutralization curve will be unsymmetrical with respect to the equivalence-point.

According to equation (26), p. 21, the p_H at the equivalence-point in the titration of a weak acid with a strong base will be:

$$p_H = 7 + \tfrac{1}{2}p_a + \tfrac{1}{2} \log c.$$

For mixtures of a weak acid and its salt, equation (36), p. 25, applies:

$$p_H = p_a - \log a + \log c,$$

where p_a is the negative logarithm of the ionization constant, a is the total acid concentration, and c the total salt concentration.

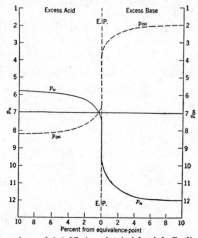

Fig. 5. Titration of 0.1 N Acetic Acid with Sodium Hydroxide

In the following table and in Figure 5 are presented data calculated for the titration of 0.1 N acetic acid with a strong base. Since the value of p_{OH} is readily obtained from the p_H, it is omitted in this and succeeding tables.

Titration of 0.1 N Acetic Acid with Sodium Hydroxide

$$K_a = 1.8 \times 10^{-5}; \; K_w = 10^{-14}$$

Per cent of acid neutralized	$[H^+]$	p_H	$\frac{\Delta p_H}{\Delta c}$
0	1.34×10^{-3}	2.87	
10.0	1.6×10^{-4}	3.79	0.092
50.0	1.8×10^{-5}	4.74	0.024
90.0	2.0×10^{-6}	5.70	0.024
99.0	1.8×10^{-7}	6.74	0.116
99.8	3.6×10^{-8}	7.44	0.88
99.9	1.8×10^{-8}	7.74	3.0
100.0	1.35×10^{-9}	8.87	**11.3**
Per cent of alkali in excess			
0.1	10^{-10}	10.0	**11.3**
0.2	5.0×10^{-11}	10.3	3.0
1.0	10^{-11}	11.0	0.7
10.0	10^{-12}	12.0	0.11

In dilute solutions and with lower values of K_a, the change in p_H at the equivalence-point is smaller. As examples, the following tables have been derived for the titration of acids whose ionization constants are 10^{-7} and 10^{-9}. The hydrolysis of the salt was considered in calculating p_H near the equivalence-point (cf. p. 21).

Titration of 0.1 N Acid with Alkali

$$K_a = 10^{-7}; \; K_w = 10^{-14}$$

Per cent of acid neutralized	$[H^+]$	p_H	$\frac{\Delta p_H}{\Delta c}$
0	10^{-4}	4.0	
9.0	10^{-6}	6.0	0.22
50.0	10^{-7}	7.0	0.024
91.0	10^{-8}	8.0	0.024
99.0	10^{-9}	9.0	0.125
99.8	2.4×10^{-10}	9.62	0.78
99.9	1.64×10^{-10}	9.785	1.65
100.0	1.0×10^{-10}	10.0	**2.15**
Per cent of alkali in excess			
0.1	6.2×10^{-11}	10.215	**2.15**
0.2	4.2×10^{-11}	10.38	1.65
1.0	1.0×10^{-11}	11.0	0.78
10.0	1.0×10^{-12}	12.0	0.11

TITRATION OF 0.1 N ACID WITH ALKALI

$$K_a = 10^{-9}; K_w = 10^{-14}$$

Per cent of acid neutralized	$[H^+]$	pH	$\frac{\Delta pH}{\Delta c}$
0	10^{-5}	5.0	
9.0	10^{-8}	8.0	0.33
50.0	10^{-9}	9.0	0.024
91.0	10^{-10}	10.0	0.024
99.0	1.62×10^{-11}	10.79	0.099
99.7	1.17×10^{-11}	10.934	0.20
99.8	1.11×10^{-11}	10.954	0.20
99.9	1.05×10^{-11}	10.978	0.24
100.0	1.00×10^{-11}	11.0	0.22
Per cent of alkali in excess			
0.1	9.5×10^{-12}	11.021	0.21
0.2	9.05×10^{-12}	11.044	0.23
1.0	6.2×10^{-12}	11.208	0.20
10.0	9.9×10^{-13}	12.004	0.089

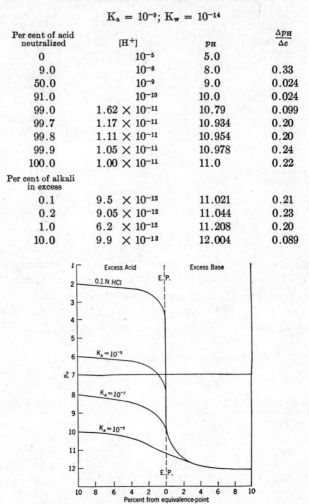

Fig. 6. Titration of 0.1N Acids of Various Ionization Constants with Sodium Hydroxide

One can see that, especially in the latter example, the p_H changes are very slight. It is therefore impossible to titrate exactly a 0.1 N solution of an acid whose $K_a = 10^{-9}$. In Figure 6 are assembled neutralization curves for acids with various constants, to illustrate the magnitude of the breaks near the equivalence-point.

Neutralization Curves for the Titration of Weak Acids with Weak Bases.—In the titration of a weak acid with a weak base, the titration curve resembles a combination of two curves, one that of a weak acid with a strong base, and the other that of a weak base with a strong acid. The two intersect at the equivalence-point, which is always close to neutrality. Because of hydrolysis, the break can never be great.

For illustration, calculations applying to the neutralization of 0.1 N acetic acid with 0.1 N ammonium hydroxide have been made. The total volume was assumed constant, and the values near the equivalence-point were found with the aid of equation (34), page 24.

TITRATION OF 0.1 N ACETIC ACID WITH 0.1 N AMMONIUM HYDROXIDE

$$K_a = K_b = 10^{-4.75}; K_w = 10^{-14}$$

Per cent of acid neutralized	$[H^+]$	p_H	$\frac{\Delta p_H}{\Delta c}$
50.0	1.8×10^{-5}	4.75	
90.0	2.0×10^{-6}	5.70	0.024
98.0	3.7×10^{-7}	6.43	0.091
99.0	2.2×10^{-7}	6.65	0.22
99.6	1.42×10^{-7}	6.85	0.33
99.8	1.20×10^{-7}	6.923	0.37
99.9	1.12×10^{-7}	6.961	0.38
100.0	1.0×10^{-7}	7.00	0.39
Per cent ammonia in excess			
0.1	9.14×10^{-8}	7.039	0.39
0.2	8.38×10^{-8}	7.077	0.38
0.4	7.08×10^{-8}	7.150	0.37
1.0	4.5×10^{-8}	7.35	0.33
2.0	2.7×10^{-8}	7.57	0.22

Part of the neutralization curve is shown in Figure 7.

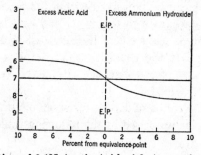

Fig. 7. Titration of 0.1N Acetic Acid with Ammonium Hydroxide

If by the use of a reference solution (*cf.* Chapter VI) the end-point can be recognized within 0.2 p_H, the titration can be made with a possible error of about 0.5 per cent. The change in p_H near the end-point, already small in this case, becomes even smaller the weaker the acid and base.

Assuming that end-points can be determined with an accuracy of 0.2 in p_H, titrations with errors not exceeding 1 per cent can be performed in the cases marked + in the following table:

Ionization constants	Concentrations			
$K_a = K_b$	1 N	0.1 N	0.01 N	0.001 N
$10^{-5.0}$	+	+	+	+
$10^{-5.5}$	+	+	+	−
$10^{-6.0}$	+	+	−	−
$10^{-6.5}$	+	−	−	−
$10^{-7.0}$	−	−	−	−

Neutralization Curves of Polybasic Acids or of Mixtures of Acids.
—With the help of deductions given in Sections 6 and 7 of Chapter II, neutralization curves for the titration of polybasic acids or acid mixtures may be constructed. It is necessary to determine the conditions at the first equivalence-point; at the second, where the weaker acid is neutralized, the situation is the same as for a single acid. Equation (46), p. 27, gives the p_H at the first equivalence-point:

$$p_H = \tfrac{1}{2}(p_{K_1} + p_{K_2})$$

p_{K_1} and p_{K_2} are the acid exponents of the two steps of the dissociation, or of the two acids, which for simplicity are assumed to be present in equal concentrations. If by the use of a comparison solution the end-point can be perceived within 0.2 p_H, and if the determination must be accurate to within 0.5 per cent, the titration will be satisfactory only in cases where K_1 is at least 10,000 times as large as K_2 (*cf.* p. 30). If the concentration of the second acid were about 100 times that of the first, the ratio $K_1 : K_2$ would have to be at least 10^6.

The approximate ratios of $K_1 : K_2$ for some of the more important dibasic organic acids are listed in the following table:

Acid	Ratio $K_1:K_2$
Oxalic...	1000
Tartaric...	10
Citric...	16
Malonic...	500
Malic...	50
Fumaric...	20
Phthalic..	200

In each of these cases the ratio is too small to permit an exact titration to the first equivalence-point. For sulfurous acid the ratio is about 10^5, and the determination as a monobasic acid is possible with methyl yellow as indicator. Phosphoric acid may be titrated either as a monobasic or dibasic acid, for $K_1:K_2$ is about 10^5 while $K_2:K_3$ is about 5×10^5.

For carbonic acid the ratio is less favorable, about 5×10^3, so that titration as a monobasic acid is not accurate to better than 1 per cent. These questions will be considered more extensively in Chapter VI, and the practical details will be discussed in Vol. II.

In the following table and in Figure 8 are shown neutralization data for a mixture of 0.1 N acetic acid and 0.1 N boric acid in the vicinity of the first end-point:

TITRATION OF A MIXTURE OF 0.1 N ACETIC ACID AND 0.1 N BORIC ACID WITH SODIUM HYDROXIDE

$$K_1 = 1.8 \times 10^{-5}, K_2 = 6 \times 10^{-10}, K_1:K_2 = 3 \times 10^{-4}$$

Per cent of acetic acid neutralized	$[H^+]$	p_H	$\frac{\Delta p_H}{\Delta c}$
90	2.0×10^{-6}	5.70	
95	9.4×10^{-7}	6.03	0.065
98	3.7×10^{-7}	6.43	0.13
99	2.3×10^{-7}	6.64	0.21
100	1.03×10^{-7}	6.99	0.35
101	4.6×10^{-8}	7.34	0.35
102	2.8×10^{-8}	7.55	0.21

The most important general cases of interest in neutralization analysis have been discussed here; special cases may be reduced to these. In the derivations, concentrations have been used in place of activities. For more exact expression of the relations existing near the equivalence-point, Kilpi[3] has considered the activities. Such

[3] S. Kilpi, Z. physik. Chem., A172, 277 (1935); A173, 223, 427 (1935); A174, 441 (1935).

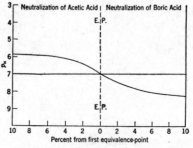

Fig. 8. Titration of a Mixture of 0.1N Acetic Acid and 0.1N Boric Acid Near the First Equivalence-Point

calculations are more complicated and from a practical standpoint are not of great importance, especially if the electrolyte content is low. One has also to consider in this connection the fact that the color equilibrium of an indicator is affected by the electrolyte content.

2. The Change of Ion Concentration During a Precipitation Reaction.—The precipitation curve for a salt of the type BA resembles the neutralization curve of a strong acid and base, the solubility product replacing the ion product of water. At the equivalence-point, equal concentrations of B^+ and A^- ions are present, and in accordance with equation (60):

$$p_B = p_A = \tfrac{1}{2}p_S .$$

In the table below and in Figure 9 are illustrated the changes occurring during the titration of 0.1 N silver nitrate solution with chloride. The abrupt change of the quotient $\dfrac{\Delta p_{Ag}}{\Delta c}$ at the equivalence-

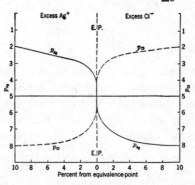

Fig. 9. Titration of 0.1N Silver Nitrate with Chloride

point reveals the accuracy possible in the titration. The sharpness of this change depends upon the magnitude of the solubility product and upon the dilution at which the titration is made. The smaller the product and the more concentrated the solution, the greater will be the break at the equivalence-point.

TITRATION OF 0.1 N SILVER NITRATE WITH CHLORIDE

$S_{AgCl} = 10^{-10}$; Constant volume

Per cent of silver precipitated	$[Ag^+]$	p_{Ag}	p_{Cl}	$\frac{\Delta p_{Ag}}{\Delta c}$
0	10^{-1}	1	9	
90.0	10^{-2}	2	8	0.011
99.0	10^{-3}	3	7	0.11
99.9	10^{-4}	4	6	1.1
100.0	10^{-5}	5	5	10.0
Per cent of chloride in excess				
0.1	10^{-6}	6	4	10.0
1.0	10^{-7}	7	3	1.1
10.0	10^{-8}	8	2	0.11

To show the effect of dilution, the foregoing data may be compared with the titration of 0.01 N silver nitrate with chloride, as shown in the next table and in Figure 10. Here equation (65) in Chapter II applies near the equivalence-point, as the solubility of silver chloride has to be taken into account.

TITRATION OF 0.01 N SILVER NITRATE WITH CHLORIDE

$S_{AgCl} = 10^{-10}$

Per cent of silver precipitated	$[Ag^+]$	p_{Ag}	p_{Cl}	$\frac{\Delta p_{Ag}}{\Delta c}$
0	10^{-2}	2.0	8.0	
90.0	10^{-3}	3.0	7.0	0.011
99.0	10^{-4}	4.0	6.0	0.11
99.9	1.6×10^{-5}	4.8	5.2	0.89
100.0	10^{-5}	5.0	5.0	2.0
Per cent of chloride in excess				
0.1	6.4×10^{-6}	5.2	4.8	2.0
1.0	10^{-6}	6.0	4.0	0.89
10.0	10^{-7}	7.0	3.0	0.11

The effect of a smaller solubility product is illustrated in the next table and in Figure 11, representing the titration of 0.01 N silver

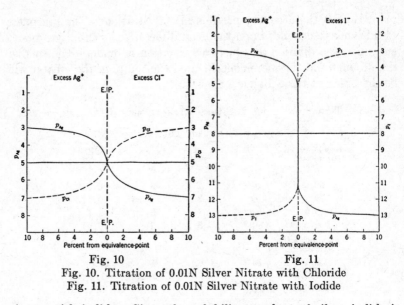

Fig. 10

Fig. 11

Fig. 10. Titration of 0.01N Silver Nitrate with Chloride

Fig. 11. Titration of 0.01N Silver Nitrate with Iodide

nitrate with iodide. Since the solubility product of silver iodide is about 10^{-16}, $[Ag^+]$ at the equivalence-point becomes 10^{-8}.

TITRATION OF 0.01 N SILVER NITRATE WITH IODIDE

$$S_{AgI} = 10^{-16}$$

Per cent of silver precipitated	$[Ag^+]$	p_{Ag}	p_I	$\dfrac{\Delta p_{Ag}}{\Delta c}$
0	10^{-2}	2	14	
90.0	10^{-3}	3	13	0.011
99.0	10^{-4}	4	12	0.11
99.9	10^{-5}	5	11	1.1
100.0	10^{-8}	8	8	**30.0**
Per cent of iodide in excess				
0.1	10^{-11}	11	5	**30.0**
1.0	10^{-12}	12	4	1.1
10.0	10^{-13}	13	3	0.11

It is to be emphasized here that these titration curves are "theoretical." In practice, the ion concentrations are influenced by adsorption phenomena. A silver halide precipitate adsorbs silver ions when these are present in excess over the halide ions, and vice versa. The order of increasing tendency toward adsorption is Cl^-, Br^-, I^-. This question will be discussed further in Chapter VIII.

Precipitation of the Compound B_2A.—In contrast with the titration curve for a compound BA, the curve for a compound B_2A is not symmetrical with respect to the equivalence-point. The value of $[B^+]$ or of $[A^=]$ is affected differently by an excess of B^+ ions than by an excess of $A^=$ ions.

As an example, the titration of 0.1 N silver nitrate with oxalate is tabulated below and plotted in Figure 12. $S_{Ag_2C_2O_4}$ is approximately 10^{-12}. The calculations of ion concentrations near the equivalence-point have been made as outlined in Chapter II, pp. 33–36, and the excess of oxalate is given in terms of normality (0.1 N = 0.05 molar).

TITRATION OF 0.1 N SILVER NITRATE WITH OXALATE

$$S_{Ag_2C_2O_4} = 10^{-12}. \quad 2p_{Ag} + p_{C_2O_4} = p_S = 12$$

Per cent of silver precipitated	$[Ag^+]$	p_{Ag}	$p_{C_2O_4}$	$\dfrac{\Delta p_{Ag}}{\Delta c}$	$\dfrac{\Delta p_{C_2O_4}}{\Delta c}$
0	10^{-1}	1.0	10.0		
90.0	10^{-2}	2.0	8.0	0.011	0.022
99.0	10^{-3}	3.0	6.0	0.11	0.22
99.7	3.2×10^{-4}	3.5	5.0	0.71	1.42
99.8	2.36×10^{-4}	3.63	4.74	1.3	2.6
99.9	1.69×10^{-4}	3.77	4.46	1.4	2.8
100.0	1.26×10^{-4}	3.90	4.20	1.3	2.6
Per cent of oxalate in excess					
0.1	1.0×10^{-4}	4.00	4.00	1.0	2.0
0.2	8.4×10^{-5}	4.08	3.84	0.8	1.6
1.0	4.4×10^{-5}	4.36	3.28	0.35	0.7

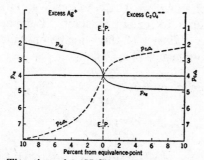

Fig. 12. Titration of 0.1N Silver Nitrate with Oxalate

The following conclusions can be drawn from the above table:

(*a*) For a given addition of reagent, the change in $p_{C_2O_4}$ is twice the change in p_{Ag}. Therefore the end-point could be recognized more sharply with an indicator for oxalate than with one for silver, assuming that the two indicators have equal sensitivities.

(*b*) The maximum values of the difference quotients occur slightly before the equivalence-point, giving rise to an error of about 0.2%. This behavior is general with precipitates of the type B_2A or BA_2, the magnitude of the error depending upon the solubility product and the dilution.

3. The Precipitation Titration of Mixtures of Ions Which Form Slightly Soluble Compounds with the Same Reagent.

—The considerations of Chapter II, pp. 38–41, apply to the titration of mixtures. If B^+ ions are added to A_I^- and A_{II}^-, both of which form slightly soluble BA salts, only the compound of lower solubility will precipitate until:

$$\frac{[A_I^-]}{[A_{II}^-]} = \frac{S_{BA_I}}{S_{BA_{II}}}. \tag{82}$$

The titration curve for A_I^- ions in the mixture will at first have the same shape as though no A_{II}^- ions were present, but differences appear as the equivalence-point is approached. The great change in $[A_I^-]$ occurs before the equivalence-point, since at this point and afterwards the values of $[A_I^-]$ are determined by equation (82). Near the second equivalence-point, the case is the same as in the titration of a pure solution of $[A_{II}^-]$ ions.

In the next table and in Figure 13 are given data for the argentometric titration of a mixture 0.01 N in iodide and 0.01 N in bromide, assuming the volume to remain constant. Comparison with Figure 11 will reveal the influence of the bromide on values for p_{Ag} and p_I after the first equivalence-point.

TITRATION OF A MIXTURE OF 0.01 N IODIDE AND 0.01 N BROMIDE WITH SILVER NITRATE

$$S_{AgI} = 10^{-16}; \quad S_{AgBr} = 5 \times 10^{-13}$$

Per cent of iodide precipitated	$[Ag^+]$	p_{Ag}	p_I	p_{Br}	$\frac{\Delta p_{Ag}}{\Delta c}$
90.0	10^{-13}	13.0	3.0	2.0	
99.0	10^{-12}	12.0	4.0	2.0	.11
99.8	5.0×10^{-12}	11.3	4.7	2.0	.88
99.9	10^{-11}	11.0	5.0	2.0	3.0
99.99	5.0×10^{-11}	10.3	5.7	2.0	**7.8**

Per cent of bromide precipitated	$[Ag^+]$	pAg	pI	pBr	$\dfrac{\Delta pAg}{\Delta c}$
1.0	5.0×10^{-11}	10.3	5.7	2.0	0.0
50.0	10^{-10}	10.0	6.0	2.3	0.006
90.0	5.0×10^{-10}	9.3	6.7	3.0	0.017
99.0	5.0×10^{-9}	8.3	7.7	4.0	0.11
99.8	2.5×10^{-8}	7.6	8.4	4.7	0.88
99.9	5.0×10^{-8}	7.3	8.7	5.0	3.0
100.0	7.1×10^{-7}	6.15	9.85	6.15	11.5

Per cent of silver in excess	$[Ag^+]$	pAg	pI	pBr	$\dfrac{\Delta pAg}{\Delta c}$
0.1	10^{-5}	5.0	11.0	7.3	11.5
0.2	2.0×10^{-5}	4.7	11.3	7.6	3.0
1.0	10^{-4}	4.0	12.0	8.3	0.88

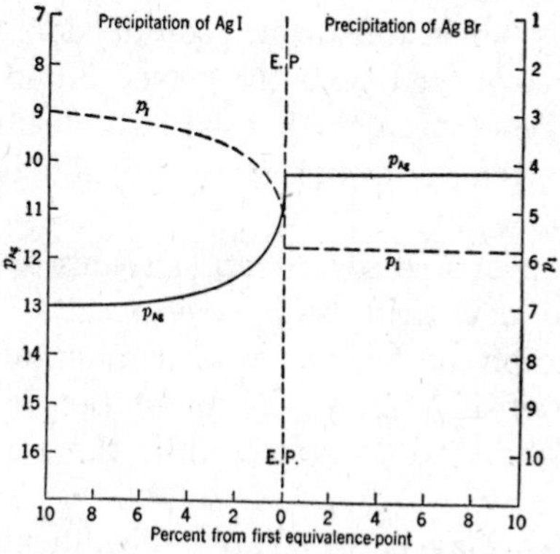

Fig. 13. Titration of a Mixture 0.01N in Iodide and 0.01N in Bromide with Silver Nitrate

If the A_{II} ions are bivalent and the A_I ions univalent, so that BA_I and B_2A_{II} are the slightly soluble salts, precipitation of the less soluble compound will not begin until:

$$\frac{[A_I^-]}{\sqrt{[A_{II}^=]}} = \frac{S_{BA_I}}{\sqrt{S_{B_2A_{II}}}} . \tag{83}$$

Titration curves for mixtures of this kind may also be deduced. In general, if BA_I has the lower solubility, the first equivalence-point will show a sharper break the smaller is $[A_{II}^=]$ and the smaller is the ratio of the solubility products.

4. Hydrolytic Precipitation Reactions.—In a hydrolytic precipitation, the cation of a strong base is titrated with the anion of a very weak acid in the form of an alkali salt, whereby a slightly soluble or slightly dissociated salt is formed and the endpoint is recognized by a decrease in hydrogen-ion concentration. As long as no excess of weak acid anion is present, $[H^+]$ changes only slightly, but as soon as excess reagent has been added, hydrolysis removes hydrogen ions.

In similar manner one can determine an anion with the cation of a weak base if the two ions form a slightly soluble or slightly dissociated compound. In either case, it is essential that the solution to be titrated contain very little free acid or base. The smaller the solubility product or dissociation constant in question, and the more strongly hydrolyzed the reagent, the more exact will be the results.

An application of hydrolytic precipitation titrations is made in determining the hardness of water. The sample after neutralization to methyl orange is boiled to expel carbon dioxide, then calcium and magnesium are precipitated from the cooled liquid with a standard soap solution. Phenolphthalein is used as indicator, soap solution being hydrolyzed strongly enough so that a slight excess causes the red color to appear.

K. Jellinek[4] has proposed several applications of hydrolytic methods, but these do not yield very exact results. For illustra⁺ consider the titration of barium with chromate as describe Jellinek and Czerwinski.[4] The barium solution is acidified to _ ,_ of about 4, and chromate is added until the p_H increases appreciably.

The change in p_H may be calculated theoretically from the solubility product for barium chromate and the second ionization cons⁺ of chromic acid:

$$[Ba^{++}][CrO_4^-] = S_{BaCrO_4} = \text{approx. } 2 \times 10^{-10}$$

$$\frac{[H^+][CrO_4^-]}{[HCrO_4^-]} = K_2 = \text{approx. } 5 \times 10^{-7}.$$

(The formation of bichromate ion:

$$2HCrO_4^- \rightleftarrows Cr_2O_7^- + H_2O,$$

may be disregarded for the present purpose.)

Assume that 100 ml. of 0.1 molar barium solution at a p_H of 4.0 is being titrated, and that the volume remains constant. After 98 per

[4] K. Jellinek and J. Czerwinski, Z. anorg. allgem. Chem., **130**, 253 (1923); cf. also K. Jellinek and H. Ens, ibid., **124**, 185 (1922), K. Jellinek and P. Krebs, ibid., **130**, 263 (1923).

cent of the barium has been precipitated, $[Ba^{++}]$ becomes 2×10^{-3}. Therefore

$$[CrO_4^-] = \frac{S}{[Ba^{++}]} = \frac{2 \times 10^{-10}}{2 \times 10^{-3}} = 10^{-7}.$$

Since the CrO_4^- ions may react with hydrogen ions to form $HCrO_4^-$, it follows that the concentration of hydrogen ions reacting is equal to the concentration of $HCrO_4^-$ ions formed. If this concentration is called x, $[H^+]$ will decrease from 10^{-4} to $10^{-4} - x$, and

$$\frac{[CrO_4^-][10^{-4} - x]}{x} = 5 \times 10^{-7}.$$

Substituting the value of $[CrO_4^-]$ which was found above to be 10^{-7}, and solving for x:

$$x = 1.67 \times 10^{-5};$$

then

$$[H^+] = 10^{-4} - 1.67 \times 10^{-5} = 8.33 \times 10^{-5}$$

$$p_H = 4.08.$$

Therefore at this stage of the titration, the p_H has increased from 4.0 to 4.08. In a similar way the calculation may be continued for further additions of chromate, with results as shown in the next table.

TITRATION OF 0.1 M BARIUM SOLUTION WITH CHROMATE

[H⁺] originally 10^{-4} N

Per cent of barium precipitated	$[H^+]$	p_H	$\frac{\Delta p_H}{\Delta c}$
98.0	8.33×10^{-5}	4.08	
99.0	7.0×10^{-5}	4.16	0.08
99.8	3.0×10^{-5}	4.52	0.45
100.0	1.7×10^{-5}	4.77	1.25
Per cent of chromate in excess			
1.0	5×10^{-8}	7.3	2.53

At the equivalence-point and just beyond, the exact calculation of $[H^+]$ is rather complicated and will not be discussed further here.

The greatest break in p_H takes place after the equivalence-point. From these theoretical considerations, it appears that the titration would give good results if an indicator changing at a p_H of about 5 were employed. If the barium solution were less concentrated, the change in p_H would be smaller.

As another example the titration of calcium with oxalate may be mentioned. The solubility product of calcium oxalate is about 2×10^{-9}, while the second ionization constant of oxalic acid is 3×10^{-5}. Assuming that the original p_H is 4.0 and the calcium concentration 0.1 molar, and that the titration is performed without volume change, the values are calculated as before.

TITRATION OF 0.1 M CALCIUM SOLUTION WITH OXALATE

$[H^+]$ originally 10^{-4} N

Per cent of calcium precipitated	$[H^+]$	p_H	$\frac{\Delta p_H}{\Delta c}$
98.0	9.7×10^{-5}	4.01	
99.0	9.4×10^{-5}	4.03	0.02
100.0	4.3×10^{-5}	4.37	0.34
Per cent of oxalate in excess			
1.0	2.9×10^{-6}	5.54	1.17

Here again the p_H change is greatest after the equivalence-point, but it is less favorable than in the titration of barium with chromate. Still this determination would appear possible with a suitable indicator, from the theoretical deductions. A preliminary study by one of the authors (K.) did not give good results. Possibly a little calcium acid oxalate, $Ca(HC_2O_4)_2$, precipitates during the titration, in which case the calculations would not be applicable. In order to ascertain the sources of error, it would be desirable to follow the p_H directly by potentiometric methods.

Experiments on the titration of barium with chromate, in which the p_H was measured by means of the quinhydrone electrode, showed that the actual titration curve was quite different from the calculated one. The deviations may be attributed to coprecipitation of hydrogen ions ($HCrO_4^-$) with the barium chromate. Much better results were obtained in the titration of lead with chromate. The lead salts of strong acids are hydrolyzed in aqueous medium; therefore it is not necessary to add a small amount of acid at the start. Moreover, the change in p_H at the equivalence-point is much more pronounced than in the titration of barium.

From a theoretical viewpoint it would be advantageous to carry out hydrolytic precipitations in the presence of considerable organic solvent, say in 50 per cent ethanol.[5] In such a medium the ionization constant of the acid corresponding to the precipitated salt is much smaller than in water. Furthermore, the solubility products of most salts are decreased by addition of alcohol. Both factors tend to make the change in p_H more pronounced at the equivalence-point. Unfortunately, in a systematic investigation it was found that the coprecipitation of hydrogen or hydroxyl ions from 50 per cent ethanol is much greater than from water. These coprecipitation phenomena are mainly responsible for the discrepancy between theoretical and experimental titration curves.

Quite generally, the presence of weak acid anions or weak base cations interferes with titrations by the hydrolytic precipitation method. Thus the determination of barium with chromate would be impossible in a solution containing acetate. The hydrolysis of acetate would minimize the change in p_H produced by an excess of chromate.

5. Titrations Involving Complex Formation.—For the formation of a complex cation from the ions B^+ and A^-, one may write:

$$2B^+ + A^- \rightleftarrows B_2A^+, \tag{95}$$

$$\frac{[B^+]^2[A^-]}{[B_2A^+]} = K'_{compl.} \tag{96}$$

Suppose that the initial concentration of a solution of B^+ ions is $2c$, and to this is added an amount of A^- ions corresponding to a concentration b (both expressed in molarity). Then, since each A^- ion reacts with two B^+ ions, one finds that:

$$[B^+] = 2(c - b),$$

$$[B_2A^+] = b,$$

$$[A^-] = \frac{[B_2A^+]}{[B^+]^2} K'_{compl.} = \frac{b}{4(c - b)^2} K'_{compl..}$$

[5] Recently we found in cooperation with E. F. Orlemann that barium can be titrated accurately with sodium carbonate in a medium of about 50 per cent ethanol, with phenolphthalein or thymol blue as indicator. These studies are being continued more systematically.

Strictly speaking, $[B^+]$ is slightly greater than $2(c - b)$ and $[B_2A^+]$ is slightly smaller than b, on account of dissociation of the complex ion. These small corrections have been neglected for the sake of simplicity.

At the equivalence-point (that is, in a pure solution of the complex), $[B_2A^+]$ becomes equal to c, and the following equations which were developed in Chapter II may be applied:

$$[B^+] = \sqrt[3]{2cK'_{compl.}}, \tag{97a}$$

$$[A^-] = \sqrt[3]{\frac{c}{4} K'_{compl.}} \tag{97b}$$

In the presence of an excess of A^- ions equivalent to a concentration a (in terms of molarity):

$$[A^-] = a,$$

$$[B_2A^+] = c \text{ (approximately)},$$

$$[B^+] = \sqrt{\frac{[B_2A^+]}{[A^-]} K'_{compl.}} = \sqrt{\frac{c}{a} K'_{compl.}}$$

The above equations may be employed for calculating titration curves for the reaction:

$$2B^+ + A^- \rightleftarrows B_2A^+,$$

or with suitable changes, for:

$$B^+ + 2A^- \rightleftarrows BA_2^-.$$

In practice, the neutral portion of the complex ion may often be a salt of low solubility. From the point at which BA begins to precipitate, the equations have to be modified by taking into account the solubility product.

To illustrate the method of calculation, consider the titration of cyanide with silver solution, which is of practical importance.

$$2CN^- + Ag^+ \rightleftarrows Ag(CN)_2^-,$$

$$\frac{[Ag^+][CN^-]^2}{Ag(CN)_2^-} = K'_{compl.} = 10^{-21}.$$

The silver salt of argentocyanide ion, $Ag[Ag(CN)_2]$ (often erroneously called silver cyanide), is only slightly soluble, so that its solubility product must be considered:[6]

$$[Ag^+][Ag(CN)_2^-] = S_{Ag[Ag(CN)_2]} = 4 \times 10^{-12}.$$

During the titration, complex argentocyanide ion will be formed until:

$$[Ag^+] = \frac{S}{[Ag(CN)_2^-]}.$$

After the silver-ion concentration reaches this value, precipitation takes place and further addition of silver solution produces very little change in $[Ag^+]$.

If the cyanide solution originally has a concentration $2c = 0.1$ molar, and if the total volume remains constant, then at the equivalence-point the concentration of argentocyanide ion (c) will be 5×10^{-2} molar. From equation (97b) one finds that:

$$[Ag^+] = \sqrt[3]{\frac{c}{4} K'_{compl.}} = 2.3 \times 10^{-8}; \qquad p_{Ag} = 7.64.$$

However, this concentration is not reached because precipitation takes place as soon as:

$$|Ag^+] = \frac{S}{[Ag(CN)_2^-]} = \frac{4 \times 10^{-12}}{5 \times 10^{-2}} = 8.0 \times 10^{-11}; \qquad p_{Ag} = 10.1.$$

In other words, precipitation occurs before the equivalence-point, but as can be seen in the accompanying table, the two points practically coincide. This table was calculated for the titration of 0.1 molar cyanide with silver solution, using the equation:

$$[Ag^+] = \frac{[Ag(CN)_2^-]}{[CN^-]^2} \times 10^{-21}.$$

[6] In a saturated solution, the silver-ion concentration is 2.2×10^{-6} at 25°C. according to R. Lucas, Z. anorg. allgem. Chem., **41**, 196 (1904), or 1.5×10^{-6} at 20°, according to W. Böttger, Z. physik. Chem. **A46**, 602 (1903).

TITRATION OF 0.1 M CYANIDE SOLUTION WITH SILVER NITRATE

$$K'_{compl.} = 10^{-21}; \ S_{Ag[Ag(CN)_2]} = 4 \times 10^{-12}.$$

Per cent of cyanide titrated	$[Ag^+]$	p_{Ag}	$\frac{\Delta p_{Ag}}{\Delta c}$
10	6.2×10^{-22}	21.21	
50	10^{-20}	20.00	0.030
80	10^{-19}	19.00	0.033
90	4.5×10^{-19}	18.35	0.065
95	1.9×10^{-18}	17.72	0.126
98	1.2×10^{-17}	16.92	0.27
99	4.95×10^{-17}	16.31	0.61
99.7	5.5×10^{-16}	15.26	1.5
99.8	1.25×10^{-15}	14.90	3.6
99.9	5.0×10^{-15}	14.30	6.0
100.0	8.0×10^{-11}	10.10	**42.0**
Per cent of silver in excess (in terms of cyanide)			
0.1	8.0×10^{-11}	10.10	0
0.2	8.0×10^{-11}	10.10	0
1.0	8.0×10^{-11}	10.10	0

When 10 per cent of the cyanide has been titrated, its concentration is 9×10^{-2} while that of the argento-cyanide ion is 5×10^{-3}; hence Ag^+ becomes 6.2×10^{-22} and $p_{Ag} = 21.21$.

The other values were calculated in the same manner. After 99.9 per cent of the cyanide has been converted into complex, $[Ag^+]$ is still only 5×10^{-15}, too low to cause precipitation. During addition of the last tenth of one per cent, $[Ag^+]$ increases until precipitation begins at 8×10^{-11}. After this there is practically no increase

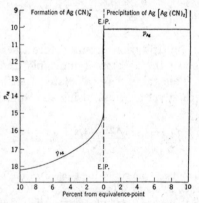

Fig. 14. Titration of 0.1N Cyanide with Silver Nitrate

in the silver-ion concentration until nearly all the argento-cyanide ion has been precipitated as its silver salt.   Concentrations at this second equivalence-point could be calculated, if desired, the same as in ordinary precipitation titrations.

In Figure 14 is shown the curve of p_{Ag} in the region around the first equivalence-point.

The calculations would be more complicated if several complex ions could be formed, as in the case of mercury cyanides:

$$Hg^{++} + 3\ CN^- \rightleftarrows Hg(CN)_3^-,$$

$$Hg^{++} + 4\ CN^- \rightleftarrows Hg(CN)_4^=.$$

One would then have to consider the various constants.   These involved cases will not be discussed further, since their practical importance is rather limited.

CHAPTER IV

THE PRINCIPLES OF OXIDATION-REDUCTION REACTIONS. TITRATION CURVES

1. Oxidation-Reduction Reactions.—Reactions involving oxidation and reduction are the basis for a great number of volumetric methods. If such reactions are reversible, they may be considered from the standpoint of the mass-action law and the changes in ion concentrations during a titration may be calculated. However, a complete mathematical treatment will be omitted here for two reasons: first, since many oxidation and reduction reactions are not strictly reversible, the mass law does not apply in all cases; second, on the practical side of volumetric analysis the exact calculations are of limited importance.

A substance is an *oxidant* when it can combine with one or more electrons, the reaction product being the *reductant* of the conjugate system:

$$\text{Ox} + ne \rightleftarrows \text{Red.}$$

Thus a substance is oxidized when it gives off electrons and is reduced when it combines with electrons.

$$2I^- - 2e \rightarrow I_2 \text{ (oxidation)}$$

$$Ag^+ + e \rightarrow Ag \text{ (reduction)}$$

$$Sn^{++} - 2e \rightarrow Sn^{++++} \text{ (oxidation)}$$

$$Fe^{+++} + e \rightarrow Fe^{++} \text{ (reduction)}$$

In such a process, the electrons must be transferred to or from another substance, since very few free electrons, if any, can exist in solution. Thus every oxidation involves reduction of another substance, and vice versa. In titrations and most chemical reactions the two substances are mixed together. In electrolytic oxidation and reduction it is possible for the reacting substances to be kept in separate containers which are electrically connected.

If the process approaches an equilibrium state, it may be expressed in an equation to which the law of mass action applies:

$$Fe^{+++} + e \rightleftarrows Fe^{++},$$

$$\frac{[Fe^{+++}][e]}{[Fe^{++}]} = K;$$

and for a generalized reaction involving n electrons:

$$\frac{[Ox][e]^n}{[Red]} = K. \tag{104}$$

Here [Ox] represents the concentration of the oxidant, while [Red] is that of the reductant. The term [e] is the "electron concentration," if indeed one can speak of such a quantity and include it as an active mass in equation (104).

In various oxidation reactions hydrogen ions participate:

$$MnO_4^- + 8\ H^+ + 5e \rightleftarrows Mn^{++} + 4\ H_2O,$$

$$Cr_2O_7^= + 14\ H^+ + 6e \rightleftarrows 2\ Cr^{+++} + 7\ H_2O.$$

In such cases the hydrogen ion concentration strongly affects the conditions of equilibrium, as shown in the equation:

$$\frac{[MnO_4^-][H^+]^8[e]^5}{[Mn^{++}]} = K.$$

For exact calculations, activities rather than concentrations should be written in this and succeeding expressions. Concentrations have been used in this book for the sake of simplicity.

2. Oxidation Potential.—A strip of noble metal (electrode of platinum, palladium or gold) dipped in a solution of an oxidant or reductant assumes a definite potential. The more strongly oxidizing is the solution, the more positive is the electrode. The potential to which the electrode becomes charged relative to the solution is called the *oxidation potential.*[1]

[1] For a physico-chemical discussion of oxidation potentials, see W. M. Latimer, *The Oxidation States of the Elements and Their Potentials in Aqueous Solutions*, Prentice-Hall, Inc., New York 1938.

A noble metal is essentially an indicator for [e], since its potential depends on the hypothetical electron concentration:

$$\pi = \frac{RT}{F} \, ln \, \frac{A}{[e]}. \tag{105}$$

Here π represents the potential of the electrode in volts, R is the gas constant, T the absolute temperature, and F the Faraday or number of coulombs necessary for changing the charge of one gram-equivalent of ions. A is an individual constant for each system, [e] is the electron concentration, and ln indicates the natural logarithm.

Substituting the numerical values of the various constants, converting natural logarithms to common logarithms (base 10), and considering the temperature to be 25°C. (T = 298°), one has

$$\pi = A' - 0.0591 \log [e]. \tag{106}$$

From equation 104:

$$[e] = \sqrt[n]{\frac{[Red]}{[Ox]} K}, \tag{107}$$

so that:

$$\pi = A' - \frac{0.0591}{n} \log K - \frac{0.0591}{n} \log \frac{[Red]}{[Ox]}. \tag{108}$$

The quantity $A' - \dfrac{0.0591}{n} \log K$ is again a constant for each system. In the special case where [Red] and [Ox] are both unity, one obtains:

$$\pi = A' - \frac{0.0591}{n} \log K = \pi_0. \tag{109}$$

This value π_0 is called the *normal potential* of the system, and it is ordinarily expressed with reference to the potential of the normal hydrogen electrode.

For general cases where [Red] and [Ox] may have any values, equations (108) and (109) may be combined:

$$\pi = \pi_0 - \frac{0.0591}{n} \log \frac{[Red]}{[Ox]}. \tag{110}$$

If, furthermore, hydrogen ions are involved in the reaction, as in the case of permanganate and dichromate oxidations, the equation becomes:

$$\pi = \pi_0 - \frac{0.0591}{n} \log \frac{[\text{Red}]}{[\text{Ox}][\text{H}^+]^m}, \tag{111}$$

where n is the number of electrons and m the number of hydrogen ions as indicated in the stoichiometric equation. For the reduction of permanganate in acid solution, n equals 5 and m equals 8. It should be mentioned, however, that complicated reactions such as these are not strictly reversible. Calculations based upon normal potentials are exact only for strictly reversible reactions and when activities instead of concentrations are written. Especially when dealing with ions of high valence, as in the ceric-cerous or ferro-ferri-cyanide systems, the ionic strength has a marked effect upon the oxidation potential.

3. The Relation Between Normal Potentials and Equilibrium Constants.—If a strip of zinc is dipped into a copper solution, the folowing reaction occurs:

$$\text{Zn} + \text{Cu}^{++} \rightleftarrows \text{Cu} + \text{Zn}^{++}. \tag{112}$$

The metallic zinc is oxidized and cupric ions are reduced. This equation may be regarded as the sum of two "half-reactions"

$$\text{Zn} \rightleftarrows \text{Zn}^{++} + 2\ e,$$

$$\text{Cu}^{++} + 2\ e \rightleftarrows \text{Cu}.$$

With the aid of equation (110), the potential of the zinc or copper can be calculated. In such cases, [Red] is considered to be the concentration of the metal in question. Assuming that the solution is saturated with metal atoms, [Red] may be regarded as constant, so that:

$$\pi_{\text{Zn}} = \pi_{0_{\text{Zn}}} + \frac{0.0591}{2} \log [\text{Zn}^{++}],$$

$$\pi_{\text{Cu}} = \pi_{0_{\text{Cu}}} + \frac{0.0591}{2} \log [\text{Cu}^{++}].$$

Reaction (112) will proceed until the potential of the zinc has become equal to that of the copper, i.e., until $\pi_{Zn} = \pi_{Cu}$. At this point the system is in equilibrium, and:

$$\pi_{0_{Zn}} + \frac{0.0591}{2} \log [Zn^{++}] = \pi_{0_{Cu}} + \frac{0.0591}{2} \log [Cu^{++}]. \quad (113)$$

Referred to the normal hydrogen electrode, the π_0 values are:

$$\pi_{0_{Zn}} = -0.76 \text{ volt},$$

$$\pi_{0_{Cu}} = +0.34 \text{ volt.}^2$$

Upon substituting these in equation (113), one finds:

$$0.76 + 0.34 = 0.0295 \log \frac{[Zn^{++}]}{[Cu^{++}]}.$$

Therefore at equilibrium:

$$\log \frac{[Zn^{++}]}{[Cu^{++}]} = \frac{1.10}{0.0295} = 37.3$$

$$\frac{[Zn^{++}]}{[Cu^{++}]} = 2 \times 10^{37}.$$

The equilibrium constant $\left(K = \dfrac{[Zn^{++}]}{[Cu^{++}]} \right)$ thus has a value of 2×10^{37}. Zinc will dissolve and copper precipitate out until the zinc-ion concentration becomes 2×10^{37} times as large as the copper-ion concentration.

It is apparent that the value of the equilibrium constant comes directly from the values of the normal potentials. By the same procedure one can obtain the constant for the reaction:

$$2\,I^- + Br_2 \rightleftarrows I_2 + 2\,Br^-,$$

assuming the solution to be saturated with both halogens so that [Ox] is constant in each case. The two half-reactions are:

$$2\,I^- \rightleftarrows I_2 + 2\,e,$$

$$Br_2 + 2\,e \rightleftarrows 2\,Br^-.$$

---

[2] All succeeding potentials are expressed in volts, as is customary. Whenever the word "volt" is omitted, it is to be understood.

At equilibrium:

$$\pi_{I_2} = \pi_{Br_2} = \pi_{0_{I_2}} - \frac{0.0591}{2} \log [I^-]^2 = \pi_{0_{Br_2}} - \frac{0.0591}{2} \log [Br^-]^2,$$

$$\pi_{0_{I_2}} = +0.54,$$

$$\pi_{0_{Br_2}} = +1.08,$$

$$\log \frac{[Br^-]^2}{[I^-]^2} = \log K = \frac{2(1.08 - 0.54)}{0.0591} = 18.3,$$

$$\log \frac{[Br^-]}{[I^-]} = \tfrac{1}{2} \log K = 9.15,$$

$$\frac{]Br^-]}{[I^-]} = 1.4 \times 10^9.$$

Therefore at equilibrium the concentration of bromide ions is a little more than 10^9 times that of iodide ions, when the solution is saturated with both halogens at 25°C.

Consider now the general reaction:

$$a \ Ox_1 + b \ Red_2 \rightleftarrows a' \ Red_1 + b' \ Ox_2. \tag{114}$$

In most practical cases, $a = a'$ and $b = b'$, so that with this simplification the expression for the equilibrium constant may be written:

$$\left\{ \frac{[Ox_1]}{[Red_1]} \right\}^a \left\{ \frac{[Red_2]}{[Ox_2]} \right\}^b = K, \tag{115}$$

assuming that the reaction is reversible.

The half-reactions involved in (114) are:

$$a \ Ox_1 + ne \rightleftarrows a \ Red_1,$$

$$b \ Red_2 \rightleftarrows b \ Ox_2 + ne.$$

For each system there is a definite oxidation potential whose value is represented by an equation similar to (110). When equilibrium has been established the two oxidation potentials are equal:

$$\pi_1 = \pi_2 = \pi_{0_1} + \frac{0.0591}{n} \log \left\{ \frac{[Ox_1]}{[Red_1]} \right\}^a$$

$$= \pi_{0_2} + \frac{0.0591}{n} \log \left\{ \frac{[Ox_2]}{[Red_2]} \right\}^b, \quad (116)$$

from which:

$$\frac{n(\pi_{0_2} - \pi_{0_1})}{0.0591} = \log \left\{ \frac{[Ox_1]}{[Red_1]} \right\}^a \left\{ \frac{[Red_2]}{[Ox_2]} \right\}^b = \log K. \quad (117)$$

Illustrations:

I. $Ce^{++++} + Fe^{++} \rightleftarrows Ce^{+++} + Fe^{+++}$

$a = 1, b = 1, n = 1.$

$$K = \frac{[Ce^{++++}][Fe^{++}]}{[Ce^{+++}][Fe^{+++}]}$$

$\pi_{0 \, Ce^{+++} \to Ce^{++++}} = +1.60$

$\pi_{0 \, Fe^{++} \to Fe^{+++}} = +0.76$

$$\log K = \frac{0.76 - 1.60}{0.0591} = -14.2$$

$K = 6.3 \times 10^{-15}$

II. $2Fe^{+++} + Sn^{++} \rightleftarrows 2Fe^{++} + Sn^{++++}$

$a = 2, b = 1, n = 2.$

$$K = \left\{ \frac{[Fe^{+++}]}{[Fe^{++}]} \right\}^2 \left\{ \frac{[Sn^{++}]}{[Sn^{++++}]} \right\}$$

$\pi_{0 \, Fe^{++} \to Fe^{+++}} = +0.76$

$\pi_{0 \, Sn^{++} \to Sn^{++++}} = +0.138$ (in normal HCl)

$$\log K = \frac{2(0.138 - 0.76)}{0.0591} = -21.0$$

$K = 1.0 \times 10^{-21}.$

III. $MnO_4^- + 8H^+ + 5Fe^{++} \rightleftarrows Mn^{++} + 5Fe^{+++} + 4H_2O$

$a = 1, b = 5, n = 5$

$$K = \frac{[MnO_4^-][H^+]^8[Fe^{++}]^5}{[Mn^{++}][Fe^{+++}]^5}$$

$\pi^0_{Mn^{++} \rightarrow MnO_4^-} = +1.52$, when $[H^+] = 1$

$\pi^0_{Fe^{++} \rightarrow Fe^{+++}} = +0.76$

$$\log K = \frac{5(0.76 - 1.52)}{0.0591} = -64.3$$

$K = 5 \times 10^{-65}$.

In this last example, the result has only qualitative significance, since the reaction is not strictly reversible.

4. Relationships Applying at the Equivalence-Point.—If an oxidant is titrated with a reductant according to the reaction:

$$Ox_1 + Red_2 \rightleftarrows Red_1 + Ox_2, \tag{118}$$

the concentrations of Red_1 and Ox_2 will be equal at the equivalence-point. Furthermore, any concentration of Ox_1 remaining unreduced will be accompanied by an equal concentration of Red_2. Therefore:

$$[Red_1] = [Ox_2], \tag{119}$$

$$[Ox_1] = [Red_2]. \tag{120}$$

The equilibrium constant for the reaction is:

$$K = \frac{[Ox_1][Red_2]}{[Red_1][Ox_2]}, \tag{121}$$

so that, by combining (119), (120) and (121), one obtains:

$$K = \frac{[Ox_1]^2}{[Red_1]^2} = \frac{[Red_2]^2}{[Ox_2]^2},$$

or

$$\frac{[Ox_1]}{[Red_1]} = \frac{[Red_2]}{[Ox_2]} = \sqrt{K}. \tag{122}$$

Illustration:

$$Ce^{++++} + Fe^{++} \rightleftarrows Ce^{+++} + Fe^{+++}$$

$$K = 6.3 \times 10^{-15}.$$

At the equivalence-point:

$$\frac{[Ce^{++++}]}{[Ce^{+++}]} = \frac{[Fe^{++}]}{[Fe^{+++}]} = \sqrt{K} = 7.9 \times 10^{-8}.$$

A more general case of oxidation-reduction titration is represented by the reaction:

$$a\ Ox_1 + b\ Red_2 \rightleftarrows a\ Red_1 + b\ Ox_2. \tag{114}$$

Since the ions react in the ratio $a:b$, one finds at the equivalence-point that:

$$\frac{[Red_1]}{[Ox_2]} = \frac{[Ox_1]}{[Red_2]} = \frac{a}{b},$$

from which:

$$\frac{[Ox_1]}{[Red_1]} = \frac{[Red_2]}{[Ox_2]}. \tag{123}$$

The expression for the equilibrium constant is:

$$K = \left\{\frac{[Ox_1]}{[Red_1]}\right\}^a \left\{\frac{[Red_2]}{[Ox_2]}\right\}^b. \tag{115}$$

It follows from equations (115) and (123) that:

$$\left\{\frac{[Ox_1]}{[Red_1]}\right\}^{a+b} = \left\{\frac{[Red_2]}{[Ox_2]}\right\}^{a+b} = K,$$

$$\frac{[Ox_1]}{[Red_1]} = \frac{[Red_2]}{[Ox_2]} = \sqrt[a+b]{K}. \tag{124}$$

Illustration: In the reaction between permanganate and ferrous ions, for which K was calculated on page 80, $a + b = 6$. If the solution has a hydrogen-ion concentration of 1 N, then at the equivalence-point:

$$\frac{[MnO_4^-]}{[Mn^{++}]} = \frac{[Fe^{++}]}{[Fe^{+++}]} = \sqrt[6]{K},$$

$$\log K = -64.3; \quad \tfrac{1}{6} \log K = -10.7, \quad \sqrt[6]{K} = 2 \times 10^{-11}.$$

From this value of the ratio, it is evident that the reaction proceeds quantitatively.

5. Titration Curves.—In the preceding sections it was shown that relationships at the equivalence-point may be found from the equilibrium constant, which in turn may be derived from normal potentials. With the equations that have been developed, one can calculate the changes taking place in the ratio $\dfrac{[Ox_1]}{[Red_1]}$ or $\dfrac{[Red_2]}{[Ox_1]}$ before and after the equivalence-point. Thus from the normal potentials of the half-reactions one can establish theoretically the changes in oxidation potential during a titration. It is necessary to know the total quantity of oxidant or reductant titrated, and to calculate the single concentrations of the various ions.

For example, in the titration of ferrous ion with ceric:

$$Ce^{++++} + Fe^{++} \rightleftarrows Ce^{+++} + Fe^{+++}$$

the equilibrium constant was found on page 79 to be:

$$K = \frac{[Ce^{++++}][Fe^{++}]}{[Ce^{+++}][Fe^{+++}]} = 6.3 \times 10^{-15},$$

while at the equivalence-point:

$$\frac{[Ce^{++++}]}{[Ce^{+++}]} = \frac{[Fe^{++}]}{[Fe^{+++}]} = 7.9 \times 10^{-8}.$$

If the initial ferrous solution was 0.1 molar and the volume change is negligible, then at the equivalence-point both $[Fe^{+++}]$ and $[Ce^{+++}]$

become approximately 0.1 molar. It follows that $[Fe^{++}]$ and $[Ce^{++++}]$ must be 7.9×10^{-9}. Upon the addition of a 1 per cent excess of ceric ion, $[Ce^{++++}]$ increases to 10^{-3} while $[Fe^{++}]$ drops to 6.3×10^{-14}.

From these considerations it will also be apparent that, between corresponding stages of titration, the changes in the ratios

$$\frac{[Fe^{+++}]}{[Fe^{++}]} \quad \text{and} \quad \frac{[Ce^{++++}]}{[Ce^{+++}]}$$

are independent of the initial concentration of the substance titrated.

A few examples will serve to demonstrate the changes in oxidation potential that occur during titration. If Ox_1 is titrated with Red_2 according to the reaction:

$$Ox_1 + Red_2 \rightleftarrows Red_1 + Ox_2,$$

then when 9 per cent of Ox_1 has been reduced:

$$\pi = \pi_{0_1} + 0.059 \log \frac{[Ox_1]}{[Red_1]} = \pi_{0_1} + 0.059 \log \frac{91}{9} = \pi_{0_1} + 0.059.$$

After reduction of 50 per cent, $[Ox_1] = [Red_1]$, and since log 1 is zero, π becomes equal to π_{0_1}. When 91 per cent has been reduced:

$$\pi = \pi_{0_1} - 0.059,$$

and at the equivalence-point:

$$\pi = \pi_{0_1} + 0.059 \log \frac{[Ox_1]}{[Red_1]} = \pi_{0_2} + 0.059 \log \frac{[Ox_2]}{[Red_2]} = \frac{\pi_{0_1} + \pi_{0_2}}{2}.$$

If an excess of Red_2 is added, π may be calculated from the expression:

$$\pi = \pi_{0_2} + 0.059 \log \frac{[Ox_2]}{[Red_2]}.$$

In this way were obtained the values shown in the following table:

TITRATION OF CERIC ION WITH FERROUS ION

$$\pi_{0_1} = +1.60; \quad \pi_{0_2} = +0.76$$

Per cent of ceric ion reduced	$\dfrac{[Ce^{++++}]}{[Ce^{+++}]}$	π
9.0	10.	$1.60 + 0.059 = 1.659$
50.0	1.0	$1.60 = 1.60$
91.0	0.1	$1.60 - 0.059 = 1.541$
99.0	0.01	$1.60 - 2.0 \times 0.059 = 1.482$
99.8	0.002	$1.60 - 2.7 \times 0.059 = 1.44$
99.9	0.001	$1.60 - 3.0 \times 0.059 = 1.423$
100.0	7.9×10^{-8}	$1.60 - 7.1 \times 0.059 = 1.18$

Per cent of ferrous ion in excess	$\dfrac{[Fe^{+++}]}{[Fe^{++}]}$	
0.1	1000.	$0.76 + 3.0 \times 0.059 = 0.937$
0.2	500.	$0.76 + 2.7 \times 0.059 = 0.920$
1.0	100.	$0.76 + 2.0 \times 0.059 = 0.878$

At the equivalence-point there is a pronounced drop in oxidation potential, which shows plainly in Figure 15. Here π in volts, referred to the normal hydrogen electrode as zero, is plotted in the region 10 per cent on either side of the equivalence-point.

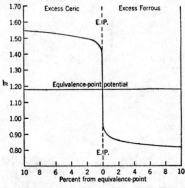

Fig. 15. Titration of Ceric Ion with Ferrous Ion

If the titration involves a reaction of the type:

$$2\,Ox_1 + Red_2 \rightleftarrows 2\,Red_1 + Ox_2,$$

one can deduce that the equivalence-point potential is:

$$\pi = \frac{\pi_{0_1} + 2\pi_{0_2}}{3}.$$

So long as Ox_1 is present in excess, the potentials may be calculated in the same manner as for the previous example. When an excess of Red_2 is added, one has to take into account the reaction:

$$Red_2 \rightleftharpoons Ox_2 + 2\,e,$$

$$\pi = \pi_{0_2} + \frac{0.059}{2} \log \frac{[Ox_2]}{[Red_2]}.$$

For the titration of ferric ion with stannous tin according to the reaction:

$$2Fe^{+++} + Sn^{++} \rightleftharpoons 2Fe^{++} + Sn^{++++},$$

the half-reactions and expressions for π are:

$$2Fe^{+++} + 2e \rightleftharpoons 2Fe^{++}, \qquad \pi = \pi_{0_{Fe}} + \frac{0.059}{2} \log \left\{ \frac{[Fe^{+++}]}{[Fe^{++}]} \right\}^2;$$

$$Sn^{++} \rightleftharpoons Sn^{++++} + 2e, \qquad \pi = \pi_{0_{Sn}} + \frac{0.059}{2} \log \frac{[Sn^{++++}]}{[Sn^{++}]};$$

$$\pi_{0_{Fe^{++} \rightarrow Fe^{+++}}} = +0.76; \qquad \pi_{0_{Sn^{++} \rightarrow Sn^{+++}}} = +0.138 \text{ (in 1 N HCl)}.$$

TITRATION OF FERRIC ION WITH STANNOUS ION

Per cent of ferric ion reduced	$\dfrac{[Fe^{+++}]}{[Fe^{++}]}$		π
50.0	1.0	0.76	= 0.76
91.0	0.1	0.76 $-$ 1.0 $\times$ 0.059	= 0.701
99.0	0.01	0.76 $-$ 2.0 $\times$ 0.059	= 0.642
99.8	0.002	0.76 $-$ 2.7 $\times$ 0.059	= 0.600
99.9	0.001	0.76 $-$ 3.0 $\times$ 0.059	= 0.583
100.0	1.0 $\times 10^{-7}$	0.76 $-$ 7.0 $\times$ 0.059	= 0.346

Per cent of stannous ion in excess	$\dfrac{[Sn^{+++}]}{[Sn^{++}]}$		
0.1	1000.	0.138 $+$ 1.5 $\times$ 0.059	= 0.227
0.2	500.	0.138 $+$ 1.35 $\times$ 0.059	= 0.218
1.0	100.	0.138 $+$ 1.0 $\times$ 0.059	= 0.197

This brief summary of the theory of oxidation-reduction titrations will suffice for this text. For further details the reader is referred to the more comprehensive works which are available.[3] The point to be emphasized is that one can, in general, calculate equilibrium

[3] Cf. E. Müller, *Die Elektrometrische Massanalyse*, 5th Edition, Th. Steinkopf, Dresden 1932; I. M. Kolthoff and N. H. Furman, *Potentiometric Titrations*, 2nd Edition, John Wiley and Sons, Inc., New York 1931.

conditions for a complete system from the normal potentials of its simultaneous partial reactions.

In volumetric analysis the case often arises in which an ion is reduced in acid solution with a metal, and the reduction product is titrated with an oxidant. Thus ferric ion may be reduced to the ferrous state by zinc, cadmium, lead, or even mercury or silver. Amalgams of the base metals are also useful; the over-voltage required for liberation of gaseous hydrogen on mercury is greater than on the base metals, hence the amalgam reduction is more efficient. The completeness of such reduction processes will be discussed in Vol. II, along with practical details of the determinations.

CHAPTER V

INDICATORS

1. General Considerations.—An indicator may be defined as a substance whose presence during a titration renders the endpoint visible.

The indicator effect may consist of: (1) the color change of a solution at or near the equivalence-point; (2) the formation of a precipitate in a clear solution or the clearing up of a turbidity; (3) the formation or disappearance of a colored precipitate, (for example, silver chromate in the Mohr titration of chloride); or (4) the color change of a precipitate formed during titration (as when an adsorption indicator is used). In general, then, near or at the equivalence-point the indicator produces in the system a change which is easily perceptible to the eye.

Occasionally the reagent or the substance being determined acts as an indicator, so that no added material is necessary. For example, in the titration of oxalate with permanganate the reagent is highly colored, but prior to the endpoint it is decolored by oxalate. A persisting permanganate color indicates the endpoint. The reverse behavior is met when one titrates iodine with thiosulfate: the endpoint is revealed by disappearance of the yellow color.

However, in most cases a special indicator must be added. Indicators may be classified according to the type of reaction in which they are to be used. The grouping below is made partly from theoretical and partly from practical considerations:

    (*a*) Indicators for acid-base reactions;
    (*b*) Indicators for precipitation reactions;
    (*c*) Indicators for oxidation-reduction reactions.

In this chapter, the action of indicators will be considered largely from the theoretical standpoint.

2. Indicators for Acid-Base Reactions.—Indicators for neutralization titrations may readily be discussed as a group because all of them, regardless of chemical nature, react specifically to hydrogen or hydroxyl ions.   In view of their practical importance and amenability to theoretical treatment, they are worthy of study.

In this section will be discussed the properties of the indicators which are commonly used.   Those that are seldom employed in volumetric analysis (such as ammoniacal copper solution which is decolored by acid, or salts of heavy metals, which are precipitated by an excess of base) will be left out of consideration.

All color indicators of practical value are organic compounds: they behave as weak acids or bases having a different color in the undissociated condition from that which they have in the form of their ions.   An indicator, regarded as an acid, exists in a state of equilibrium with a certain concentration of its ions in solution, according to the reaction:

$$HIn \rightleftarrows H^+ + In^-.$$

In this equation, HIn represents the acid form, which has the "acid color," while In^- denotes the alkaline form, which has the "alkaline color."   Applying the mass law:

$$\frac{[H^+][In^-]}{[HIn]} = K_{HIn},$$

$$\frac{[In^-]}{[HIn]} = \frac{K_{HIn}}{[H^+]}.$$

The color of an indicator in a given solution depends on the ratio $[In^-]:[HIn]$.   In a solution whose hydrogen-ion concentration is equal to K_{HIn}, $[In^-]$ will equal $[HIn]$.   The concentrations of acid form and basic form being equal, the indicator is said to be half "changed."   From the equation it also follows that the color change occurs, not abruptly, but gradually, as $[H^+]$ changes.   For each value of $[H^+]$ there will be a definite ratio between the concentrations of the two forms.   Since there is a lower limit to the amount of either form which the eye can perceive in the presence of the other, the change of the indicator is practically confined to a definite range of hydrogen-ion concentration.   The limits are not of theoretical significance, but are merely statements of the values of $[H^+]$ or of p_H between which a visible color change occurs.   The region between the two limiting values is called the *transition interval*, or *color change interval*, of the indicator.   For some indicators the color of the acid or alkaline form can be seen more readily than for others, so the magnitude of the interval may vary with different compounds.

If one assumes that about 10 per cent of the indicator must be present in alkaline form to show a difference from the pure acid color, then:

$$\frac{[In^-]}{[HIn]} = \frac{K_{HIn}}{[H^+]} = \frac{1}{10},$$

$$[H^+] = 10K_{HIn},$$

and

$$p_H = p_{HIn} - 1,$$

where p_{HIn} represents the negative logarithm of K_{HIn} and may be called the *indicator exponent*. Its value is numerically equivalent to the p_H at which the indicator is half changed.

In similar manner one may assume that when 10 per cent of the indicator is in the acid form it will show only a faint difference from the alkaline color:

$$\frac{[In^-]}{[HIn]} = \frac{K_{HIn}}{[H^+]} = 10,$$

$$[H^+] = \tfrac{1}{10}K_{HIn},$$

$$p_H = p_{HIn} + 1.$$

The transition interval of this indicator lies, therefore, between p_H values of $p_{HIn} - 1$ and $p_{HIn} + 1$; it covers a range of two p_H units. In fact, the range is about two units for most indicators. It should be clearly understood that the transition interval is set arbitrarily by limitations of the eye, and is not based on theoretical principles. The ratio of $[In^-]:[HIn]$ continues to change with changing p_H far beyond the apparent color change interval, as has been shown by measurements of absorption spectra.

If the indicator is a base, the same considerations apply as for an indicator acid:

$$InOH \rightleftarrows In^+ + OH^-,$$

$$\frac{[In^+]}{[InOH]} = \frac{[acid\ form]}{[alkaline\ form]} = \frac{K_{InOH}}{K_w}[H^+] = K'[H^+].$$

Here K' is an indicator constant whose value depends upon the ionization constant of the indicator base and the ion product of water, K_w.

In the table on page 91 are listed the transition intervals and colors of the more important indicators.[1] Under the heading p_T are given the p_H regions for which the corresponding indicators are most suitable. The table continues with a list of appropriate concentrations for the indicator solutions, and the amounts that should be used in titrations. The letters (A) or (B) following the name signify, respectively, that the compound is an indicator acid or base.

The selection of an indicator to be used in a titration is based upon the neutralization curve of the substance being determined. In principle it is advisable to choose an indicator whose transition interval will include the p_H at the equivalence-point. If the p_H change at this point is very large, several indicators will have transition intervals within the proper range. Thus in the titration of a strong acid with a strong base, the equivalence-point p_H is 7, so that any indicator changing near this value may be used. By considering the neutralization curve, one finds (p. 50) that in the titration of 0.01 N solutions, the p_H change is from 5 at a state 0.1 per cent before the equivalence-point to 9 at a state 0.1 per cent after it. Then any indicator between chlorophenol red and cresol red could give a result accurate in principle to 0.1 per cent. If 0.1 N solutions were being titrated, the corresponding p_H range would extend from 4 to 10. Even methyl yellow could be used if the titration were carried to the pure yellow color, and phenolphthalein or even thymolphthalein would be satisfactory if just enough base were added to make the alkaline color barely visible. Obviously the latter indicators should not be used unless the solutions are free from carbonate.

In titrating weak acids, the situation is different. For example, in the neutralization of 0.1 N acetic acid (p. 53), the p_H is 8.87 at the equivalence-point and changes from 7.74 to 10 over the region 0.1 per cent on either side of it. Therefore, to titrate with an error of less than 0.1 per cent, one should use an indicator like phenolphthalein or thymol blue (alkaline range), which would be half-changed at a p_H of 9. Phenol red and cresol red could also be used if the titration were carried to the alkaline color, but indicators changing in the acid region would be useless as they would show an endpoint much too soon. *In general, weak acids should be titrated in the presence of indicators which change in slightly alkaline solutions.*

---

[1] For further details and the properties of other indicators see I. M. Kolthoff, *Acid-Base Indicators*, translated by C. Rosenblum, The MacMillan Company, New York 1937.

TRANSITION INTERVALS AND COLOR CHANGES OF ACID-BASE INDICATORS

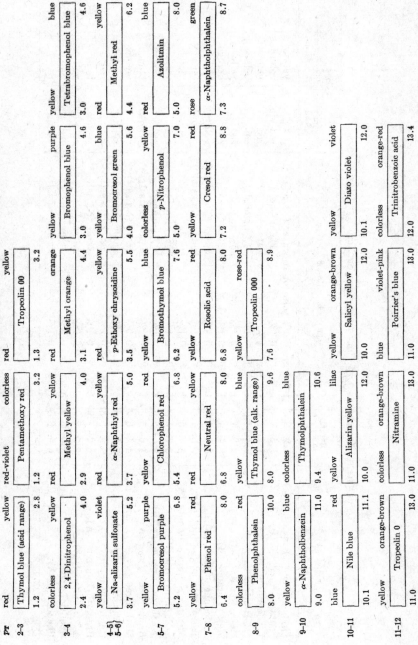

pₜ	Indicator	Acid color	Low	High	Alkaline color
2–3	Thymol blue (acid range)	red	1.2	2.8	yellow
2–3	Pentamethoxy red	red-violet	1.2	3.2	colorless
2–3	Tropeolin 00	red	1.3	3.2	yellow
3–4	2,4-Dinitrophenol	colorless	2.4	4.0	yellow
3–4	Methyl yellow	red	2.9	4.0	yellow
3–4	Methyl orange	red	3.1	4.4	yellow
3–4	Tetrabromophenol blue	yellow	3.0	4.6	blue
3–4	Bromophenol blue	yellow	3.0	4.6	purple
4–5 / 5–6	Na-alizarin sulfonate	yellow	3.7	5.2	violet
4–5 / 5–6	α-Naphthyl red	red	3.7	5.0	yellow
4–5 / 5–6	p-Ethoxy chrysoidine	red	3.5	5.5	yellow
4–5 / 5–6	Methyl red	red	4.4	6.2	yellow
4–5 / 5–6	Bromcresol green	yellow	4.0	5.6	blue
5–7	Bromcresol purple	yellow	5.2	6.8	purple
5–7	Chlorophenol red	yellow	5.4	6.8	red
5–7	p-Nitrophenol	colorless	5.0	7.0	yellow
5–7	Azolitmin	red	5.0	8.0	blue
7–8	Phenol red	yellow	6.4	8.0	red
7–8	Neutral red	red	6.8	8.0	yellow
7–8	Bromothymol blue	yellow	6.2	7.6	blue
7–8	Rosolic acid	yellow	6.8	8.0	red
7–8	Cresol red	yellow	7.2	8.8	red
7–8	α-Naphtholphthalein	rose	7.3	8.7	green
8–9	Phenolphthalein	colorless	8.0	10.0	red
8–9	Thymol blue (alk. range)	yellow	8.0	9.6	blue
8–9	Tropeolin 000	yellow	7.6	8.9	rose-red
9–10	α-Naphtholbenzein	yellow	9.0	11.0	blue
9–10	Thymolphthalein	colorless	9.4	10.6	blue
10–11	Nile blue	blue	10.1	11.1	red
10–11	Alizarin yellow	yellow	10.0	12.0	lilac
10–11	Salicyl yellow	yellow	10.0	12.0	orange-brown
10–11	Diazo violet	yellow	10.1	12.0	violet
11–12	Tropeolin 0	yellow	11.0	13.0	orange-brown
11–12	Nitramine	colorless	11.0	13.0	orange-brown
11–12	Poirrier's blue	blue	11.0	13.0	violet-pink
11–12	Trinitrobenzoic acid	colorless	12.0	13.4	orange-red

Transition Intervals and Color Changes of Acid-Base Indicators

Indicator	Interval in pH	Quality of indicator per 10 cc.	Color	
			Acid	Alkaline
Thymol blue (A) (acid range)	1.2– 2.8	1–2 drops 0.1% solution in water (Na salt)[a]	red	yellow
Pentamethoxy red (B)	1.2– 3.2	1 " " 0.1% " 70% alcohol	red-violet	colorless
Tropeolin 00 (B)	1.3– 3.2	1 " " 1% " water	red	yellow
2,4-Dinitrophenol (A)	2.4– 4.0	1–2 " " 0.1% " 50% alcohol	colorless	yellow
Methyl yellow (B)	2.9– 4.0	1 " " 0.1% " 90% alcohol	red	yellow
Methyl orange (B)	3.1– 4.4	1 " " 0.1% " water	red	orange
Bromophenol blue (A)	3.0– 4.6	1 " " 0.1% " water (Na salt)[a]	yellow	blue-violet
Tetrabromophenol blue (A)	3.0– 4.6	1 " " 0.1% " water (Na salt)[a]	yellow	blue
Alizarin sodium sulfonate (A)	3.7– 5.2	1 " " 0.1% " water	yellow	violet
α-Naphthyl red (B)	3.7– 5.0	1 " " 0.1% " 70% alcohol	red	yellow
p-Ethoxy chrysoidine (B)	3.5– 5.5	1 " " 0.1% " 90% alcohol	red	yellow
Bromocresol green (A)	4.0– 5.6	1 " " 0.1% " water (Na salt)[a]	yellow	blue
Methyl red (A)	4.4– 6.2	1 " " 0.1% " water (Na salt)[a]	red	yellow
Bromocresol purple (A)	5.2– 6.8	1 " " 0.1% " water (Na salt)[a]	yellow	purple
Chlorophenol red (A)	5.4– 6.8	1 " " 0.1% " water (Na salt)[a]	yellow	red
Bromothymol blue (A)	6.2– 7.6	1 " " 0.1% " water (Na salt)[a]	yellow	blue
p-Nitrophenol (A)	5.0– 7.0	1–5 " " 0.1% " water	colorless	yellow
Azolitmin (A)	5.0– 8.0	5 " " 0.5% " water	red	blue
Phenol red (A)	6.4– 8.0	1 " " 0.1% " water (Na salt)[a]	yellow	red

	pH range					acid	base
Neutral red (B)	6.8– 8.0	1	"	0.1%	" 70% alcohol	red	yellow
Rosolic acid (A)	6.8– 8.0	1	"	0.1%	" 90% alcohol	yellow	red
Cresol red (A)	7.2– 8.8	1	"	0.1%	" water (Na salt)(a)	yellow	red
α-Naphtholphthalein (A)	7.3– 8.7	1–5	"	0.1%	" 70% alcohol	rose	green
Tropeolin 000 (B)	7.6– 8.9	1	"	0.1%	" water	yellow	rose-red
Thymol blue (A) (alk. range)	8.0– 9.6	1–5	"	0.1%	" water (Na salt)(a)	yellow	blue
Phenolphthalein (A)	8.0–10.0	1–5	"	0.1%	" 70% alcohol	colorless	red
α-Naphtholbenzein (A)	9.0–11.0	1–5	"	0.1%	" 90% alcohol	yellow	blue
Thymolphthalein (A)	9.4–10.6	1	"	0.1%	" 90% alcohol	colorless	blue
Nile blue	10.1–11.1	1	"	0.1%	" water	blue	red
Alizarin yellow (A)	10.0–12.0	1	"	0.1%	" water	yellow	lilac
Salicyl yellow (A)	10.0–12.0	1–5	"	0.1%	" 90% alcohol	yellow	orange-brown
Diazo violet	10.1–12.0	1	"	0.1%	" water	yellow	violet
Tropeolin 0 (B)	11.0–13.0	1	"	0.1%	" water	yellow	orange-brown
Nitramine (B)	11.0–13.0	1–2	"	0.1%	" 70% alcohol	colorless	orange-brown
Poirrier's blue	11.0–13.0	1	"	0.1%	" water	blue	violet-pink
Trinitrobenzoic acid (indicator salt)	12.0–13.4	1	"	0.1%	" water	colorless	orange-red

(a) For the preparation of sodium salt solutions see Volume II.

The reverse is true in the titration of a weak base with a strong acid. When 0.1 N ammonium hydroxide is titrated with hydrochloric acid, the p_H is 6.26 after 99.9 per cent has been neutralized, 5.13 at the equivalence-point, and 4.0 in the presence of a 0.1 per cent excess of acid. An indicator with transition interval between 4 and 6 should be employed. Methyl red or bromocresol green will serve the purpose. If phenolphthalein were used, the red color would begin to fade early in the titration and the change to colorless would be very gradual, but it would be complete long before the equivalence-point. *Weak bases should be titrated in the presence of indicators which change in slightly acid solution.* In any case, a suitable indicator for the purpose can be chosen from that part of the neutralization (or displacement) curve which lies in the region of the equivalence-point.

Assume that a weak acid like acetic has to be titrated with a weak base like ammonium hydroxide. From the neutralization data on page 55, one can see that the p_H change over the region 0.1 per cent on either side of the equivalence-point amounts to only 0.08 units. Here there are only a few useful indicators, and the titration has to be completed at a definite p_H of 7.00. The change in p_H is so small that it cannot be shown by a sharp difference in the color of any indicator. The transition interval is crossed slowly, and to secure results accurate to within 0.5 per cent one would have to titrate to a definite color. In this case, the color to be matched would be that of a reference solution of $p_H = 7.00$. A solution of pure ammonium acetate would be appropriate for comparison. This procedure, of titrating to a definite p_H, is frequently useful in the determination of substances that otherwise are difficult to titrate precisely. N. Bjerrum proposed that the hydrogen exponent which has to be equalled in such a titration should be called the *titration exponent,* p_T (*cf.* page 91). The endpoint may often be observed more sharply with the aid of a mixture of indicators. Mixed indicators and specific applications of the method are described in Volume II.

In case a one-color indicator is to be used in titrating to a certain p_H, the indicator concentration must be controlled closely. For a one-color indicator HIn, of which the In^- ion is the colored form, the color will be determined by the value of $[In^-]$:

$$[In]^- = \frac{K_{HIn}}{[H^+]} [HIn].$$

If the hydrogen-ion concentration is held constant (as in a *buffer solution*), at a value within the transition interval of the indicator, then the color intensity of the solution must increase with increasing indicator concentration up to the saturation point. Therefore, to attain a certain p_H with a one-color indicator like phenolphthalein, one must have the same concentration of indicator in the reference solution as in the titrated solution at the endpoint. Also one must look through equal depths in making the color comparison.

Transition intervals listed on page 91 refer to 18C°. and apply for practical purposes at average room temperatures. With pronounced change in temperature the intervals are displaced, especially those of basic indicators. The latter follow the equation:

$$\frac{[In^+]}{[InOH]} = \frac{K_{InOH}}{]K_w]} [H^+].$$

Since K_w increases with temperature more rapidly than does K_{InOH}, the equilibrium shifts toward the formation of more InOH. In other words, the indicator becomes less sensitive[2] toward hydrogen ions at higher temperature. In the following table are compared the transition ranges of several indicators at 18° and 100°:

TRANSITION INTERVALS AT 18° AND 100°C.

$p_w = 14.2$ at 18°; 12.2 at 100°.

Indicator	Interval at 18°	Interval at 100°
Thymol blue (A) (acid range)	1.2– 2.8	1.2– 2.6
Tropeolin 00 (B)	1.3– 3.2	0.8– 2.2
Methyl yellow (B)	2.9– 4.0	2.3– 3.5
Methyl orange (B)	3.1– 4.4	2.5– 3.7
Bromophenol blue (A)	3.0– 4.6	3.0– 4.5
Bromocresol green (A)	4.0– 5.6	4.0– 5.6
Methyl red (A)	4.4– 6.2	4.0– 6.0
p-Nitrophenol (A)	5.0– 7.0	5.0– 6.5
Bromocresol purple (A)	5.2– 6.8	5.4– 6.8
Bromothymol blue (A)	6.0– 7.6	6.2– 7.8
Phenol red (A)	6.4– 8.0	6.6– 8.2
Cresol red (A)	7.2– 8.8	7.6– 8.8
Thymol blue (A) (Alk. range)	8.0– 9.6	8.2– 9.4
Phenolphthalein (A)	8.0–10.0	8.0– 9.2
Thymolphthalein (A)	9.4–10.6	8.9– 9.6
Nitramine (B)	11.0–13.0	9.0–10.5

[2] The sensitivity of an indicator for a given kind of ion is measured by the smallest concentration of the latter which will cause the indicator to change color.

From these data it appears that for indicators of acid character the sensitivity toward hydrogen ions remains almost constant, while for indicators of basic nature, it decreases appreciably. Hence methyl orange is not entirely suitable for the titration of 0.1 N hydrochloric acid at boiling, while bromophenol blue is, although the two have practically the same range at room temperature.

One must realize that if an indicator retains its sensitivity for hydrogen-ions at higher temperatures, it will be considerably less sensitive for hydroxyl ions. Since K_w is 100 times as great at 100° as at 18°, the hydroxyl-ion concentration corresponding to a given $[H^+]$ will also be 100 times as great. This increased concentration produces the same effect on the indicator as did the original $[OH^-]$ at 18°. The indicators for which this is of most interest are those which change in alkaline solution. Thus thymolphthalein is sensitive to a p_{OH} of 4.8 at 18°, but only to 3.3 at 100°. In considerations of this kind, one has to remember that at 100° the p_H (and p_{OH}) of a neutral solution is 6.1. Also, the ionization constants of weak acids and bases are increased at higher temperatures.

The effect of the solvent on an indicator's transition range should be mentioned. Titrations are frequently carried out in media containing organic solvents such as alcohol, which affect the ionization constant of an indicator. The constant decreases with increasing concentration of alcohol. Therefore, acidic indicators become more sensitive to hydrogen ions, while basic indicators become less sensitive. Organic solvents also decrease the ionization constants of weak acids and bases. For a given concentration of alcohol, if the transition intervals of indicators and the ionization constants of acids or bases are known, then the various relationships can be predicted and proper conditions established just as in the case of aqueous solutions. Further information about the behavior of indicators in the presence of alcohol is to be found in "Acid-Base Indicators" (*loc. cit.*, ref. 1), in which the properties of fluorescent indicators are also discussed.

3. Indicators for Precipitation and Complex-Formation Reactions.

—Indicators for these ion-combination reactions may be classified according to their effect, as mentioned in the first section of this chapter. In this section, the first three types will be discussed briefly, while the fourth type, covering adsorption indicators, will be treated separately later.

(a) *The indicator produces a color change in the solution.*—This case is comparable with the action of indicators in quantitative neutralizations. Indeed, the acid-base indicators may be employed in certain ion-combination reactions, for example, the hydrolytic precipitations noted on page 64. A similar application may be made to complex-formation titrations if the complex that is formed is only slightly dissociated, as is mercuric cyanide. One can titrate a neutral solution of mercuric salt with potassium cyanide to the red color of phenolphthalein. For such titrations one can select a suitable indicator if the titration curve can be derived. Changes in p_H during titration may be calculated from the ionization constant of the weak acid (or base) whose salt is used as reagent, and from the solubility product of the precipitate or ionization constant of the slightly dissociated compound that is formed.

A more general case involves the titration of one ion with another, in which one of the ions can react with the indicator to produce a colored substance. A prerequisite for success is that just at the equivalence-point, or very close to it, the concentration of the ion that is disappearing shall become so small that it no longer gives a color with the indicator, or the concentration of reagent ion shall become large enough so that it reacts with the indicator. The use of a ferric salt as indicator in the titration of thiocyanate with silver ion in acid solution is well known. Silver thiocyanate is not sufficiently soluble to react with ferric ion, but in the presence of a small excess of thiocyanate the solution becomes reddish-brown.

If one knows the sensitivity of an indicator and the solubility product of the precipitate, one can predict whether the indicator will be suitable. Whether or not the indicator change is reversible has to be determined experimentally. Thus it is found that the titration of thiocyanate, using ferric ion as indicator, is difficult to perform with a silver salt as reagent, because some ferric thiocyanate is occluded by the precipitate. By titrating with a highly dissociated mercuric salt in place of the silver, this difficulty can be avoided.

(b) *A precipitate forms or dissolves at the endpoint.*—Two cases may be distinguished. In one the reactants themselves furnish the indicator action, while in the other an indicator has to be added. A very old method of the former type consists in titrating until a portion of the filtrate does not yield a precipitate upon the addition of more reagent. The method is troublesome and the endpoint difficult to locate exactly. In 1828, Gay-Lussac[3] described this means of

[3] J. L. Gay-Lussac, *Ann. chim. phys.*, **39**, 352 (1828).

determining sulfate with barium solution. Wildenstein[4] simplified the practical procedure. The method has often been proposed since, without finding general application. In some cases the use of a centrifuge is of assistance, as in the determination of barium with chromate or vice versa.[5]

For the determination of silver with sodium chloride, Gay-Lussac[6] succeeded by careful investigation in formulating a procedure which is still serviceable. It is of practical advantage here that silver chloride, which during titration remains partly in colloidal solution, coagulates and flocculates out near the endpoint. Violent shaking hastens the separation. After the precipitate settles, a portion of the supernatant liquid is tested with a reagent solution that has been diluted tenfold, to see whether turbidity develops. The titration and testing are continued until finally no further turbidity occurs. By withdrawing two portions and adding to one a trace of silver nitrate and to the other an equivalent amount of sodium chloride, and observing (under suitable illumination) whether the turbidities are the same, it is possible to perceive the endpoint still more sharply. Exactly at the equivalence-point the supernatant liquid is a pure saturated solution of silver chloride, so the precipitation produced by addition of a little silver ion should be the same as that produced by an equivalent amount of chloride ion. On either side of the equivalence-point, a difference in the two turbidities would be perceptible. This method of Gay-Lussac ranks among the most exact titrations if it is carried out under proper conditions. It has enduring significance in the fundamental atomic weight determinations of silver and the halogens (cf. the classical studies of Richards).

Continued investigations on titrations to the equivalence-point without the use of indicators have been made by Bucherer and Meyer.[7] They recommend the method for determinations of calcium with oxalate, sulfate with barium, copper and zinc with sulfide, manganese with phosphate, and magnesium, zinc, iron and aluminum with 8-hydroxyquinoline. By all means, one should be careful in applications of the method, since the presence of neutral salts considerably increases the solubility, especially in the presence

---

[4] R. Wildenstein, Z. anal. Chem., 1, 432 (1862); see also G. Brügelmann, ibid., 16, 19 (1877), R. F. LeGuyon, Compt. rend., 184, 945 (1927).

[5] J. Vogel, Monatsh., 46, 266 (1925).

[6] J. L. Gay-Lussac, Instruction sur l'essai des matières d'argent par la voie humide, Paris, 1832. See also H. Beckurts, Die Methoden der Massanalyse, Braunschweig 1913.

[7] H. Th. Bucherer and F. W. Meyer, Z. anal. Chem., 82, 1 (1930).

of excess precipitant. Nevertheless the procedure can be of service under good conditions.

In some complex-formation titrations the reagents also furnish the indicator action. For example, if iodide is titrated with a mercuric salt, complex $HgI_4^=$ ions form at first. These can react with more mercuric ions, precipitating red mercuric iodide:

$$Hg^{++} + 4I^- \rightleftarrows HgI_4^=,$$

$$HgI_4^= + Hg^{++} \rightleftarrows 2HgI_2.$$

The accuracy of such a determination depends upon the dilution and upon the values of the complex-dissociation constant and solubility product. In the example mentioned, the turbidity ordinarily appears too early; in Liebig's titration of cyanide in alkaline solution with silver nitrate, it comes a little too late.

If the reactants have no indicator action, an indicator may be added. Thus chloride ions may be titrated with mercuric nitrate, forming slightly dissociated mercuric chloride. If a little sodium nitroprusside is added as indicator, at the end-point a slight excess of mercuric ions will cause a turbidity. Since the same considerations apply in this case as in those above and in the next paragraph, they will not be repeated here. Practical details for all these titration methods will be given in Volume II. It should, however, be mentioned that precipitates are often slow to form or dissolve, so that one should approach the end-point slowly, keeping the solution or suspension well stirred.

(c) *The indicator forms a colored precipitate.*—If in a precipitation titration the precipitate is white or has only a light color, there exists the possibility of finding an indicator which will form a more darkly colored precipitate with the reagent or the ion being titrated. The best known instance is the behavior of chromate as indicator in halogen titrations according to Mohr's method. After the precipitation of silver halide, a small excess of silver ion produces slightly soluble, red silver chromate. The indicator's sensitivity depends upon the solubility product of the indicating precipitate, the concentration of indicator added, and occasionally also (as in this case) upon the hydrogen-ion concentration.

Taking silver chromate as an illustration:

$$Ag_2CrO_4 \rightleftarrows 2Ag^+ + CrO_4^=.$$

Silver chromate will precipitate when:

$$[Ag^+]^2[CrO_4^-] > S_{Ag_2CrO_4}, \text{ (about } 2 \times 10^{-12});$$

$$[Ag^+] > \sqrt{\frac{2 \times 10^{-12}}{[CrO_4^-]}}.$$

If enough chromate is added to make its concentration 10^{-4} molar, the theoretical sensitivity for silver ion is:

$$[Ag^+] \lessgtr \sqrt{\frac{2 \times 10^{-12}}{10^{-4}}} = 1.4 \times 10^{-4},$$

while if the chromate is increased to 10^{-2} molar, the sensitivity becomes:

$$[Ag^+] \lessgtr \sqrt{\frac{2 \times 10^{-12}}{10^{-2}}} = 1.4 \times 10^{-5}.$$

Therefore it is possible to vary the sensitivity toward silver ion through appropriate changes in chromate concentration. Such theoretical deductions should always be tested experimentally. The rate of formation of the precipitate may be altered under different conditions, or the sensitivity of one's eye for the same amount of silver chromate may change. At higher chromate concentrations the color of chromate ion obscures the endpoint. The influence of temperature should also be considered; if the solubility increases with temperature, the sensitivity decreases accordingly.

Hydrogen-ion concentration affects the sensitivity if the indicator anion is that of a weak acid. In the case of silver chromate, chromate ions react with hydrogen ions:

$$CrO_4^- + H^+ \rightleftarrows HCrO_4^-$$

so that increasing the acidity results in decreased sensitivity. For good results in a Mohr titration, the p_H should be equal to or slightly greater than 7. Finally, it should be noted that the change in this method is not strictly reversible. If an excess of silver is added, it is precipitated as silver chromate. Upon addition of chloride, this silver chromate reacts rather slowly, especially if it becomes covered with a layer of silver chloride.

The selection of an indicator for a titration such as Mohr's is based in principle on the general case in which two anions form slightly soluble salts (of different solubility) with the same cation, as discussed on page 38. The extent to which the least soluble will be precipitated before the other is determined by the solubility products and the relative concentrations.

In the reactions:

$$Ag^+ + Cl^- \rightleftarrows AgCl,$$

$$2Ag^+ + CrO_4^{--} \rightleftarrows Ag_2CrO_4,$$

silver chloride is precipitated alone until:

$$\frac{[Cl^-]}{\sqrt{[CrO_4^{--}]}} = \frac{S_{AgCl}}{\sqrt{S_{Ag_2CrO_4}}} = \frac{1.1 \times 10^{-10}}{1.4 \times 10^{-6}} = 7.9 \times 10^{-5}.$$

As soon as the chloride concentration drops to $7.9 \times 10^{-5} \times \sqrt{[CrO_4^{--}]}$, the precipitation of silver chromate begins. If the chromate concentration is made 10^{-2} molar, silver chromate will precipitate when the chloride becomes 7.9×10^{-6} molar. This will take place just after the equivalence-point, at which $[Cl^-] = \sqrt{S_{AgCl}} = 10.5 \times 10^{-6}$. Had the chromate originally been 4×10^{-2} molar, the change would have occurred immediately before the equivalence-point, at $[Cl^-] = 15.8 \times 10^{-6}$. Either concentration is useful in principle. Considerations of this type are of greatest significance in the titration of dilute solutions.

If the ion to be titrated forms a silver salt more soluble than silver chloride, the conditions are less favorable for the use of chromate as indicator. For example, if the ion A^- is being determined, and the solubility product, S_{AgA}, is 10^{-8}, then silver chromate begins to precipitate when:

$$[A^-] = 7.1 \times 10^{-3} \times \sqrt{[CrO_4^{--}]}.$$

Taking $[CrO_4^{--}]$ as 10^{-2} molar, the silver chromate starts to form when $[A^-] = 7.1 \times 10^{-4}$, nearly 0.001 N. Such a titration could not give a good result. One might pursue either of the following courses:

(a) Add silver nitrate in excess and back-titrate silver ion in the filtrate, thus calculating the amount precipitated.

(b) Resort to a spotting method, as in the determination of phosphate with uranyl solution or of zinc with sulfide. In making spot tests it is necessary to guard against the presence of any precipitate in the test drop, otherwise the solid might react with indicator and show the change prematurely.

4. Adsorption Indicators.—Fajans and his co-workers introduced a special class of indicators which produce a color change on a precipitate formed during titration. These are generally referred to as *adsorption indicators*. The following experiments of Fajans and Hassel[8] are quoted by way of description; they were repeated by Kolthoff with identical results.

"If one takes 20 ml. of a solution of eosin (sodium salt) whose concentration is 1.25×10^{-5} molar, one can add as much as 1 cc. of 0.1 N silver nitrate solution without obtaining a color change. Therefore at this concentration the silver salt of eosin is soluble and dissociated. If now a drop of 0.1 N alkali bromide solution is added to the mixture containing silver, the color changes to a red-violet shade which is deepened by further addition of bromide. The fluorescence of the clear liquid is strongly repressed at this stage; *upon adding a very small excess of bromide past the equivalence-point, the color changes sharply to the original shade of the eosin solution. From this point the color change is reversible* and may be repeated indefinitely by addition of $AgNO_3$ (change to red-violet) or KBr (change to rose).

"*The presence of colloidally dispersed silver bromide particles is a necessary condition for the color change.*

"The mechanism of the titration is as follows: When silver ions are present in slight excess, they are adsorbed by silver bromide particles. In turn, anions of the dye add on, and *become deformed,*[9] *with change in color.* Upon addition of excess bromide ions, the eosin ions are displaced from the surface and return to the solution with their normal color."

In order for a adsorption anion indicator to work well, the precipitate must strongly adsorb its own cations when they are present in slight excess. Conditions are then favorable for the adsorption of indicator anions, whereby the surface of the precipitate becomes highly colored through deformation effects on the compound of cation

---

[8] K. Fajans and O. Hassel, *Z. Elektrochem.*, **29**, 495 (1923).

[9] Concerning the interesting phenomenon of deformation, see especially K. Fajans, *Naturwissenschaften*, **11**, 165 (1923).

and indicator anion. *The dye anion, therefore, is an indicator for silver ions adsorbed on a silver halide surface.*[10] Besides being able to withdraw silver ions from solution by adsorption, silver halides can adsorb halide ions if the latter are present in excess. Thus silver bromide adsorbs bromide ions, and it might be expected that a basic dyestuff could serve as an indicator for adsorbed bromide in the same way that eosin (an acid dye) does for adsorbed silver. In fact, Fajans and Wolff[11] demonstrated that the basic dye "Rhodamine 6G" is suitable as an indicator for the titration of silver with bromide. As long as silver ions are in excess, they cover the surface of the precipitate, and the dye adsorption is so slight that most of the indicator remains in solution. Only very close to the equivalence-point, and especially just after it is passed, do bromide ions cover the precipitate and adsorb the dye cations with resulting change in color.

Sufficiently sharp color changes can be obtained only if part of the silver halide remains in the form of a *sol*. If coagulation is practically complete, the adsorbing surface becomes too small; the color change is confined to the silver halide surface and does not occur throughout the entire liquid.

An essential condition for useful indicator action is that the precipitate shall not become colored before the equivalence-point; that is, until the reagent is added in very small excess. Assume that chloride is being titrated with silver nitrate, with fluorescein or eosin as indicator. At first silver chloride is precipitated, adsorbing chloride ions. The anions of some indicators may be more strongly adsorbed than chloride, in which case the precipitate would become colored long before the equivalence-point, and the indicator would be worthless. This actually happens if eosin is used in a chloride titration. On the other hand, fluorescein is less strongly adsorbed than eosin, and with it excellent results can be obtained.[12]

Therefore one has to consider the adsorbability of an indicator anion as compared with that of the halide ion. The tendency for

[10] Further details and literature references on adsorption by silver halides are given by K. Fajans and v. Beckerath, *Z. physik. Chem.*, **A97**, 478 (1921), and by Fajans and W. Frankenburger, *ibid.*, **105**, 255 (1923).

[11] K. Fajans and H. Wolff, *Z. anorg. allgem. Chem.*, **137**, 221 (1924).

[12] For a more complete theoretical discussion, see I. M. Kolthoff, *Chem. Rev.*, **16**, 87 (1935). A detailed account of the properties of adsorption indicators is given by K. Fajans in *Newer Methods of Volumetric Chemical Analysis*, W. Böttger, editor; translation by R. E. Oesper, D. Van Nostrand Company, New York 1938.

halides to be adsorbed increases in the order Cl^-—Br^-—I^-, and for this reason eosin is a suitable indicator for bromide or iodide, but not for chloride titrations. In contrast, erythrosin (tetraiodofluorescein) is so strongly adsorbed that it will not show a sharp change even in the titration of iodide. Similar considerations apply to indicator cations; to be useful they must not be adsorbed more strongly than silver ions.

The adsorption of erythrosin on negatively charged silver bromide sols has been studied thoroughly by Weir.[13] With increasing bromide concentration, the adsorption of erythrosin decreases. Thiocyanate also has a strong displacing action on the dye, while chloride has very little effect and iodate, carbonate, phosphate, sulfate and nitrate have no influence at all. Likewise, the action of various anions on adsorption by negative silver chloride suspensions was studied.

Conversely, the adsorption of the basic dyes phenosafranine and Rhodamine 6G by positive silver bromide suspensions was investigated. Here increasing the silver content decreases adsorption of indicator cations. With Rhodamine 6G the adsorption rises sharply at the equivalence-point, this compound therefore serving as an excellent indicator for titrations of silver with bromide. With phenosafranine the change of adsorption at the equivalence-point is small, yet the dye is a satisfactory indicator since the color changes from blue with excess silver to red with excess bromide. The mechanism of this color shift is not yet clear.

The effect of hydrogen-ion concentration upon the color change of an adsorption indicator may be explained as follows: Dyes such as fluorescein and eosin are weak acids. In titrating strongly acid solutions, the dissocation of the indicator acid may be so far repressed by hydrogen ions that not enough dye anions will remain to form a colored adsorption layer. The utility of an indicator depends essentially upon its ionization constant, the solubility product of its colored salt, and the tendency of its anions to be adsorbed by the precipitate. For example, the titration of chloride with fluorescein as adsorption indicator cannot be carried out in acid medium. If fluorescein is replaced by dichlorofluorescein, a stronger acid whose anions are adsorbed more tenaciously than those of fluorescein, the titration gives good results at a p_H of 4 or even lower. Bromide can be titrated at a p_H of 1 with eosin as indicator. Basic indicators are also likely to be useful in acid solution, but there is a possibility that hydrogen ions

[13] H. McColloch Weir, *Dissertation*, Munich 1926.

may displace indicator cations from the adsorption layer, and thus diminish the active surface. Fajans and Wolff[11] showed experimentally that Rhodamine 6G is suitable as an indicator for bromide titrations in acid concentrations up to 0.5 N.

Silver ions are not alone in their tendency to deform dye anions, producing colored compounds. Mercuric, lead, copper and some other ions show this behavior. Adsorption indicators thus are not specific for silver halides, but may be used for other titrations involving precipitation reactions. In general, a precipitate is capable of adsorbing or taking into its crystal lattice the kinds of ions of which it is composed. Consequently a silver halide absorbs either silver ions or halogen ions, whichever are available. Lead sulfate fixes lead ions or sulfate ions. Titrations with adsorption indicators, however, are limited mainly to those with silver or mercurous ions as reagents.[14] The more important applications are reviewed in Volume II.

5. Indicators for Oxidation-Reduction Reactions.—Oxidation-reduction indicators may be considered under two distinct headings, according to their action:

(a) *The indicator reacts specifically with the oxidant or reductant.*— Examples of such indicators are starch, which gives the well-known dark blue color with iodine (or tri-iodide ion, I_3^-), and thiocyanate, which indicates the appearance or disappearance of ferric ions in the oxidation or reduction of iron solutions. It is not feasible to discuss specific reactions of this sort in a general way. They will instead be considered separately, with respect to their proper applications, in Volume II.

(b) *The indicator may be oxidized or reduced with a resultant change in color* (*redox indicator*).—In this case the indicator itself acts as an oxidizing or reducing agent, of which the oxidized form, I_{ox}, has a different color than the reduced form, I_{red}.

One may, for example, regard a dilute solution of iodine or iodide as an indicator for oxidation-reduction reactions. Iodide will be oxidized to iodine by substances of higher oxidation potential than iodine, while the reverse change will be brought about by reagents of lower oxidation potential than iodide. If a solution of a strong reductant is titrated with a strong oxidant in the presence of iodide as indicator, iodine will be liberated only after the reductant has been

---

[14] In this connection see O. Hassel, *Kolloid-Z.*, **34**, 305 (1924).

oxidized.   Conversely, iodine can serve as indicator for the titration of a strong oxidant with a strong reductant.   The indicator action of the iodide-iodine system *is not based upon the specific character of the oxidant or reductant involved, but upon the relative oxidation potentials of the system being titrated and the indicator.   The iodide or iodine thus behaves as indicator for a definite oxidation potential.*   This kind of indicator is of great importance in analytical chemistry, and will be considered in detail.

For the sake of clarity, the function of oxidation-reduction indicators will be illustrated by the behavior of benzidine toward oxidants.   Benzidine, $NH_2C_6H_4C_6H_4NH_2$, like several other diphenyl compounds is colored intensely by oxidizing agents.   In neutral or faintly alkaline solution there is formed a dark blue substance;[15] in strongly acid solutions, most oxidants transform benzidine into a yellow compound rather than to the blue.   This fact must be considered when benzidine is used as a reagent for detecting chlorine in water; the sensitivity and the color stability depend upon the hydrogen-ion concentration.   Besides chlorine, other oxidants such as chromate, ferricyanide, and bromine produce the blue to violet color. A pure aqueous solution of iodine gives the blue, but iodine solutions containing iodide do not react with benzidine.   *The addition of iodide lowers the oxidation potential enough so that no oxidation of benzidine occurs.*

That benzidine is indeed converted to the colored form only at a definite oxidation potential is clearly shown by the effect of ferric-ferrous solutions on it.   A solution containing only 10 mg. of ferric iron per liter gives a violet color after standing with benzidine for some time.   If the solution contains an excess of ferrous iron, no reaction takes place.   The following table presents the details:

REACTION OF BENZIDINE WITH FERRIC-FERROUS MIXTURES

Ratio of Ferric:Ferrous	Total Iron, mg. per liter	Reaction with Benzidine Acetate
9:1	1000	All blue-violet after
	100	one hour.
	10	
5:5	1000	
	100	Gradually become green
	10	
1:9	10	
	1	No reaction
	0.1	

[15] W. Schlenk, *Ann.*, **363**, 313 (1908).

It is evident that the occurrence of the reaction depends not on the total quantity of iron present, but rather on *the ratio of ferric to ferrous*. It follows that benzidine is an indicator for a definite oxidation potential. Whether or not the blue color forms is determined by the intensity of the oxidizing action and not by the total quantity of oxidant present.

Actually the situation is somewhat more complicated. From the thorough investigations of Clark, Cohen and Gibbs,[16] it appears that the oxidation products of benzidine and tolidine are not stable and soon decompose. Furthermore, the color change of benzidine is not reversible, so it is not a satisfactory indicator for oxidimetry.

Since the oxidation potential of a system is, within reasonable limits, unaffected by dilution, the sensitivity of an indicator for a certain oxidation potential is not defined by the total quantity of oxidant and reductant, but only by their ratio. Compounds that respond in this way may be termed oxidation-reduction indicators, or according to a proposal by Michaelis,[17] *redox* indicators.

If the conversion of an indicator's oxidized form into its differently colored reduced form is expressed by the equation:

$$I_{ox} + e \rightleftarrows I_{red},$$

then from equation (110), Chapter IV:

$$\pi = \pi_0 + 0.059 \log \frac{[I_{ox}]}{[I_{red}]}, \qquad (\text{at } 25°\text{C.}).$$

Here π is the oxidation potential of the liquid and π_0 the normal potential of the indicator system. The color shown by the indicator depends upon the ratio of $[I_{ox}]$ to $[I_{red}]$:

$$\log \frac{[I_{ox}]}{[I_{red}]} = \frac{\pi - \pi_0}{0.059}.$$

In the same way that the transition interval of an acid-base indicator was estimated, the interval of an oxidation-reduction indicator may be approximated. If the eye perceives the color change over

[16] W. M. Clark, B. Cohen and H. D. Gibbs, Studies on Oxidation-Reduction. *Pub. Health Repts.*, No. IX, Suppl. 54 (1926).

[17] L. Michaelis, *Oxydations-Reductionspotentiale*, 2nd Ed., Julius Springer, Berlin 1933.

a range of from $\dfrac{[I_{ox}]}{[I_{red}]} = 10$ to $\dfrac{[I_{ox}]}{[I_{red}]} = \dfrac{1}{10}$, the two limiting potentials of the transition interval will be:

$$\pi = \pi_0 \pm 0.059.$$

For this simple case, then, the transition interval of the indicator lies between two oxidation potentials, one of which is about 59 millivolts larger, the other 59 millivolts smaller, than the indicator's normal potential.

In case the indicator reaction is:

$$I_{ox} + ne \rightleftarrows I_{red},$$

the transition interval becomes smaller, and is limited arbitrarily by the values

$$\pi = \pi_0 \pm \dfrac{0.059}{n} \qquad \text{(at 25°C.)}.$$

From a knowledge of the transition interval or normal potential of a given indicator, one can predict its color in a medium of definite oxidation potential.   Now, from the considerations given in Chapter IV, the changes in potential during a titration, especially near the equivalence-point, may be calculated (or the same values may be determined experimentally by potentiometric titration).   Consequently if there is available a series of indicators having different normal potentials, one can select the appropriate indicator for any given titration.

Suppose that ferrous ions are to be titrated with ceric:

$$Fe^{++} + Ce^{++++} \rightleftarrows Fe^{+++} + Ce^{+++}.$$

At the equivalence-point, the oxidation potential (see page 83) becomes:

$$\pi = \dfrac{\pi_{0_{Fe}} + \pi_{0_{Ce}}}{2},$$

while at 0.1 per cent before and after the equivalence-point,

$$\pi = \pi_{0_{Fe}} + 3 \times 0.059 \quad \text{(excess of ferrous)},$$

$$\pi = \pi_{0_{Ce}} - 3 \times 0.059 \quad \text{(excess of ceric)}.$$

Therefore if the titration is to be accurate to 0.1 per cent, an indicator whose transition interval is between these limits should be chosen. Since the value of $\pi_{0_{Fe}}$ is $+0.76$ volt, and of $\pi_{0_{Ce}}$ about $+1.60$ (referred to the normal hydrogen electrode), the transition interval should lie between $+0.94$ and $+1.42$ volt. The conditions for other titrations may be established in the same way (cf. page 82). It now remains to consider the indicators themselves.

Since the normal potential of the ferric-ferrous system is equal to $+0.76$ volt, it is convenient from a practical standpoint to classify redox indicators in two groups: those whose oxidation potentials are greater than $+0.76$, and those whose potentials are smaller. Representatives of the former group, which will be discussed in section 7 of this chapter, are in common use in analytical laboratories. Those with smaller potentials find less application in volumetric analysis; a number of them are described in the following section.

6. Redox Indicators with Normal Oxidation Potentials Smaller than $+0.76$ Volt.—Although these indicators are rarely used in analytical work, they may be of practical importance in titrations with strong reductants such as titanous, chromous and stannous chlorides. In considering applications of the indicators, it should be kept in mind that their oxidation potentials vary with the p_H of the solution, while also the effect of the ionic strength should be taken into account. Moreover, it should be remembered that the oxidation potentials of the substance being titrated and of the reagent vary always with the ionic strength and usually with the p_H. A systematic investigation of the applications of redox indicators having low oxidation potentials is much to be desired.

The characteristic properties of these indicators have been studied mainly by Clark,[18] Michaelis[17, 36] and their coworkers. These authors

[18] *Studies on Oxidation-Reduction:*
  I. W. M. Clark, Introduction. *Pub. Health Repts.*, **38**, 443 (1923).
  II. W. M. Clark and B. Cohen, Analysis of the Theoretical Relations between Reduction Potentials and p_H. *ibid.*, **38**, 666 (1923).
  III. M. X. Sullivan, B. Cohen and W. M. Clark, Electrode Potentials of Mixtures of 1-Naphthol-2-Sulfonic Acid Indophenol and the Reduction Product. *ibid.*, **38**, 993 (1923).
  IV. M. X. Sullivan, B. Cohen and W. M. Clark, Electrode Potentials of Indigo Sulfonates, Each in Equilibrium with its Reduction Product. *ibid.*, **38**, 1669 (1923).
  V. B. Cohen, H. D. Gibbs and W. M. Clark, Electrode Potentials of Simple

have also derived mathematical expressions for the relationships between p_H and the ionization constants of the various forms of these indicators on one hand, and the oxidation potentials on the other.

Indigo Sulfonic Acids.—The potassium salts of indigo mono-, di-, tri-, and tetra-sulfonic acids have been investigated by Sullivan, Cohen and Clark,[18,IV] who also described methods of preparation. The solubilities of the salts increase with increasing sulfonation. In water, the mono-sulfonated salt gives a deep blue solution; with further sulfonation the color shifts toward a reddish blue. The absorption spectra have been recorded by Holmes.[19] The reduced forms (leuco compounds) are colorless.

In these excellent researches it was found that the potentials of the indigo sulfonic acids in equilibrium with their leuco forms can be expressed by an equation:

$$\pi = \pi_0 + \frac{0.06}{2} \log \frac{[I_{ox}]}{[I_{red}]} + \frac{0.06}{2} \log (K_1[H^+] + [H^+]^2) \quad (30°).$$

Indophenols, Each in Equilibrium with its Reduction Product. *ibid.*, **39**, 381 (1924).

VI. B. Cohen, H. D. Gibbs and W. M. Clark, A Preliminary Study of Indophenols. *ibid.*, **39**, 804 (1924).

VII. H. D. Gibbs, B. Cohen and B. K. Cannan, A Study of Dichloro-Substitution Products of Phenol Indophenol. *ibid.*, **40**, 649 (1925).

VIII. W. M. Clark, B. Cohen and H. D. Gibbs, Methylene Blue. *ibid.*, **40**, 1131 (1925).

IX. W. M. Clark, B. Cohen and H. D. Gibbs, A Potentiometric and Spectrophotometric Study of Meriquinones of the *p*-Phenylene Diamine and the Benzidine Series. *Pub. Health Repts.*, Supplement No. 54 (1926).

X. B. K. Cannan, B. Cohen and W. M. Clark, Reduction Potentials in Cell Suspensions. *ibid.*, Supplement No. 55 (1926).

XI. Max Phillips, W. M. Clark and B. Cohen, Potentiometric and Spectrophotometric Studies of Bindschedler's Green and Toluylene Blue. *ibid.*, Supplement No. 61 (1927).

XII. W. M. Clark, B. Cohen and M. X. Sullivan, A Note on the Schardinger Reaction (in reply to Kodama). *ibid.*, Supplement No. 66 (1927).

XIII. H. D. Gibbs, W. L. Hall and W. M. Clark, Preparation of Indophenols Which May be Used as Oxidation-Reduction Indicators. *ibid.*, Supplement No. 69 (1928).

XIV. W. L. Hall, P. W. Preisler and B. Cohen, Equilibrium Potentials of Various Benzenone Indophenol Derivatives. *ibid.*, Supplement No. 71 (1928).

W. M. Clark, Recent Studies on Reversible Oxidation-Reduction in Organic Systems. *Chem. Rev.*, **2**, 127 (1925).

[19] W. C. Holmes, *J. Am. Chem. Soc.*, **46**, 208 (1924).

Values for K_1, the ionization constant of the leuco form, are assembled in the following table, along with those for π_0.

System	π_0 at 30°C.	K_1 at 30°C.
Indigo monosulfonic acid $\rightleftarrows$ leuco form	+0.262	1.6×10^{-8}
Indigo disulfonic acid $\rightleftarrows$ " "	+0.291	4.9×10^{-8}
Indigo trisulfonic acid $\rightleftarrows$ " "	+0.332	7.7×10^{-8}
Indigo tetrasulfonic acid $\rightleftarrows$ " "	+0.365	11.2×10^{-8}

The values for π_0 (referred to the normal hydrogen electrode) are valid for a solution normal in hydrogen ions. As the table shows, the oxidation potential rises with increasing sulfonation. Still it is always so small that only strong reductants, such as titanous chloride, convert these compounds into their colorless forms.

For practical use the above equation may be simplified to give approximate results. Thus for $[H^+] > 10^{-8}$, $(p_H < 8)$, one has:

$$\pi = \pi_0 + 0.03 \log \frac{[I_{ox}]}{[I_{red}]} + 0.06 \log [H^+]$$

$$\pi = \pi_0 + 0.03 \log \frac{[I_{ox}]}{[I_{red}]} - 0.06 \, p_H$$

while for $[H^+] < 10^{-8}$, $(p_H > 8)$:

$$\pi = \pi_0 + 0.03 \log \frac{[I_{ox}]}{[I_{red}]} + 0.03 \log K_1 + 0.03 \log [H^+]$$

$$\pi = \pi_0 + 0.03 \log \frac{[I_{ox}]}{[I_{red}]} + 0.03 \log K_1 - 0.03 \, p_H.$$

The tetrasulfonic acid of thioindigo has been studied by Preisler and Hempelmann,[20] who followed the reduction process over a p_H range from 0.0 to 11.5. The oxidation potential π_0 is 0.409 volt at 25°, K_1 for the reduced form is 3×10^{-5}, and two equivalents of reductant are required per mole. Between p_H values of from 8.5 to 11.5 a deep red semiquinone forms. The system is suitable as an oxidation-reduction indicator only at a p_H lower than 2.5. The oxidized form is orange-red, the reduction product yellow.

Indophenols.—In the third paper of the series on oxidation-reduction, Sullivan, Cohen and Clark[18] described properties of the disodium

[20] P. W. Preisler and L. H. Hempelmann, *J. Am. Chem. Soc.*, **58**, 2305 (1936).

salt of 1-naphthol-2-sulfonic acid-indophenol:

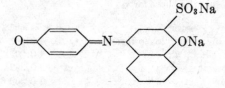

of which the reduction product is:

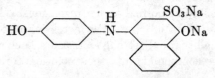

The dark red disodium salt of the oxidized form is soluble in water, methyl and ethyl alcohols, and acetone. In acid solution the color is red; in alkaline, blue. The compound behaves as an acid-base indicator and its first ionization constant in this sense is $10^{-8.7}$.

The reduced form is colorless. The effect of hydrogen-ion concentration upon the electrode potential is much more complicated in this case than with the indigo sulfonic acids, because there are three dissociation steps and hence three ionization constants. The potential at 30° is:

$$\pi = +0.544 + 0.03 \log \frac{[I_{ox}]}{[I_{red}]}$$

$$+0.03 \log (K_2 K_r [H^+] + K_r [H^+]^2 + [H^+]^3)$$

$$-0.03 \log (K_0 + [H^+]);$$

where

$$K_0 = 2.1 \times 10^{-9} \qquad K_r = 9.0 \times 10^{-10} \qquad K_2 = 2.0 \times 10^{-11}.$$

K_0 is the phenolic ionization constant of the oxidized form, K_r the corresponding constant of the reduced form, and K_2 that of the phenol group formed on reduction. Provided that the value of $[H^+]$ is larger than 10^{-9}, (p_H less than 9), the equation may be simplified to the following:

$$\pi = +0.544 + 0.03 \log \frac{[I_{ox}]}{[I_{red}]} -0.06 \; p_H.$$

In their fifth and sixth papers, Clark and his coworkers[18] studied various other indophenols; they found that the introduction of two halogen atoms, as in 2,6-dibromophenol indophenol, increases the ionization constant of the acid enough so that the compound remains blue in quite strongly acid solution.

Values for the normal oxidation potentials are assembled below, as obtained at 30° by Clark *et al*:

Substance	π_0
Phenol indophenol	+0.649
o-Bromophenol indophenol	+0.659
o-Chlorophenol indophenol	+0.663
2,6-Dibromophenol indophenol	+0.668
o-Cresol indophenol	+0.616
Thymol indophenol	+0.592

The approximate equation applying when the p_H is lower than 8 is:

$$\pi = \pi_0 + 0.03 \log \frac{[I_{ox}]}{[I_{red}]} - 0.06 \; p_H.$$

Upon comparison of indigo sulfonic acids with the phenol indophenols it becomes apparent that at $[H^+] = 1$, the normal potentials of the former are about +0.3, and of the latter about +0.6. This means that the indophenols are easier to reduce than the indigo sulfonic acids. Thus, 2,6-dibromophenol indophenol should be a suitable indicator for the titration of cuprous salts with ferric in weakly acid solution, while an indigo sulfonic acid would be oxidized to the blue form long before the equivalence-point. From the normal potentials of the partial reactions it may be calculated that in this titration the transition interval required is between +0.58 and +0.35 volt. At a p_H of 4, the normal potential of an indigo sulfonic acid is $+0.3 - (4 \times 0.06) = +0.06$ volt; that of phenol indophenol is $+0.65 - (4 \times 0.06) = +0.41$ volt. Since the hydrogen-ion concentration has such a marked effect on the transition intervals of these indicators, one can establish the most suitable conditions for a given titration by finding the optimum acidity.

Oxazines and Thiazines.—These compounds comprise a group of dyes whose oxidation-reduction equilibria may be represented by the following simple examples:

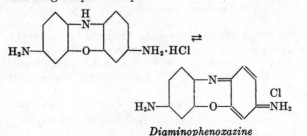

Diaminophenoxazine

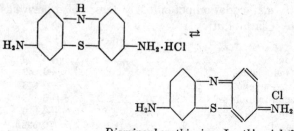

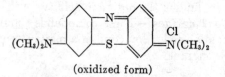

+2H^+ + 2e

Diaminophenothiazine, Lauth's violet[21]

In general, the oxazines and thiazines have normal potentials between those of the indigo sulfonic acids and the indophenols. The effect of p_H is very large, especially below 5. For example, the redox potential of methylene blue is $+0.53$ volt at a p_H of 0, and $+0.04$ volt at a p_H of 6. Of the thiazines, methylene blue and Lauth's violet have been studied by Clark, Cohen and Gibbs.[18,VIII] The relation between the potential and the hydrogen-ion concentration of the solution is quite complex, involving ionization constants for the various basic groups. However, the expression may be simplified into two equations, which are also applicable to the oxazines:

$$p_H < 5, \pi = \pi_0 + 0.03 \log \frac{[I_{ox}]}{[I_{red}]} - 0.09\, p_H;$$

$$p_H > 5, \pi = \pi_0' + 0.03 \log \frac{[I_{ox}]}{[I_{red}]} - 0.03\, p_H.$$

Values of π_0 and π_0' for the various compounds are tabulated on page 116.
  Methylene Blue:[22]

(oxidized form)

Methylene blue is a strong polyacid base whose constants are too large to be determined exactly. The reduced form (methylene white) is white in the solid state and colorless in solution. Its solubility is about 5×10^{-4} molar in acid medium and 2×10^{-5} molar in alkaline. Light causes methylene white to turn blue.

[21] F. Kehrmann, E. Havas and E. Grandmougin, *Ber.*, **47**, 1881 (1914).
[22] See also P. Hirsch and P. Rüter, *Z. anal. Chem.*, **69**, 193 (1926).

It was found experimentally that salts have a fairly large influence on the potential. Therefore redox indicators are subject to a salt error, as are acid-base indicators.

Lauth's Violet (see formula on page 114):
This simple thiazine was prepared by Clark and his collaborators through oxidation, with ferric chloride, of a solution of *p*-phenylene diamine in ten per cent hydrochloric acid saturated with hydrogen sulfide. The oxidized form has a basic ionization constant of 1.9×10^{-3}.

Nile Blue (Ethyl Nile blue; aminonaphthodiethylaminophenoxazine sulfate):[23,24]

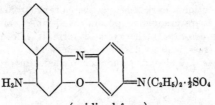

(oxidized form)

This compound is the chief constituent of Handel's Nile Blue A. It is slightly soluble in cold water, somewhat more so in hot water, and behaves as an acid-base indicator. At p_H values between 1 and 8.4 it is blue; a red-violet fluorescence is evident at 9.4. At higher alkalinities the red color becomes more pronounced and the insoluble free base precipitates. The reduced form is colorless (yellow in high concentration) over the p_H range from 1 to 8.4 and reddish above 9.4. Between 6.4 and 10 the solution is readily oxidized by air; below 5.4 air oxidation is very slow or does not take place at all. Oxidation with ferricyanide proceeds almost instantaneously. The reduced form of Nile blue can be crystallized in white needles, easily soluble in water.

Brilliant Cresyl Blue (brilliant blue C, cresyl blue BBS, 3-amino-9-dimethyl amino-10-methyl phenoxazine chloride):[23,24]

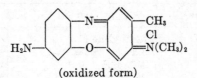

(oxidized form)

The oxidized form is blue at p_H between 1 and 10, and red above 10. The reduced form is colorless below 10; above, it goes from blue through red to colorless. Aqueous solutions of the blue reduced form are not stable.

---

[23] B. Cohen and P. W. Preisler, Studies on Oxidation-Reduction, XVI. *U. S. Pub. Health Repts.*, Suppl. No. 92 (1931). See also L. Rapkine, A. P. Struyk and R. Wurmser, *J. chim. phys.*, **26**, 340 (1929).

[24] M. Letort, *Compt. rend.*, **194**, 711 (1932).

Methyl Capri Blue (zinc chloride double salt of 3,9-bisdimethylaminophenoxazine chloride):[23]

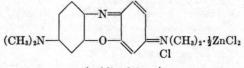

(oxidized form)

The aqueous solution is dark blue over the p_H range from 1 to 10. In strong alkaline solution there gradually appears a red-violet color and finally the solution becomes colorless. The reduced form is colorless, but is light-sensitive and becomes blue as does methylene white.

Ethyl Capri Blue (3,9-bisdiethylaminophenoxazine nitrate):[23]

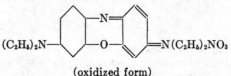

(oxidized form)

Ethyl Capri blue is similar to the methyl compound, but the aqueous solution is more green in color.

Values of π_0 and π_0' at 30°C. for the above indicators, from which may be calculated their potentials according to the appropriate equation (page 114), are given in the following table:

π_0	p_H Range	Indicator	π_0'	p_H Range
+0.532	0–5.5	Methylene blue	+0.22	5.5–12
+0.563	0–5	Lauth's violet	+0.26	5 –10
+0.406	0–4	Nile blue	+0.08	7 –10
+0.583	0–5	Brilliant cresyl blue	+0.26	6 –10
+0.477	0–5	Methyl Capri blue	+0.15	6 –12
+0.540	0–7	Ethyl Capri blue	+0.12	8 –10

Below are listed the redox potentials of various indicators[23] for the p_H region between 5 and 9; these apply at 30°C. and represent the potentials at which $[I_{ox}] = [I_{red}]$:

Indicator	Redox Potential at the p_H Listed				
	5.0	6.0	7.0	8.0	9.0
Methylene blue..................	+0.101	+0.047	+0.011	−0.020	−0.050
Lauth's violet..................	+0.135	+0.093	+0.060	+0.030	0.000
Nile blue.......................	−0.011	−0.071	−0.122	−0.159	−0.192
Brilliant cresyl blue.............	+0.149	+0.089	+0.047	+0.015	−0.016
Methyl Capri blue..............	+0.038	−0.021	−0.061	−0.093	−0.123
Ethyl Capri blue................	+0.089	+0.001	−0.072	−0.115	−0.146
Indigo tetrasulfonate............	+0.065	+0.006	−0.046	−0.083	−0.114
Phenol indophenol..............	+0.349	+0.288	+0.227	+0.158	+0.084

Among the indicators studied by Letort[24] are two other oxazines, *fast cotton blue* and *muscarin.* Letort's measurements, made at 20° ± 2°, were expressed only in the form of curves, from which the redox potentials given below have been interpolated.

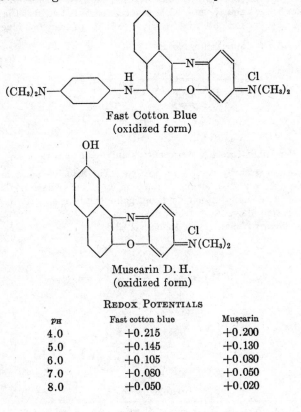

Fast Cotton Blue
(oxidized form)

Muscarin D. H.
(oxidized form)

REDOX POTENTIALS

p_H	Fast cotton blue	Muscarin
4.0	+0.215	+0.200
5.0	+0.145	+0.130
6.0	+0.105	+0.080
7.0	+0.080	+0.050
8.0	+0.050	+0.020

The following redox indicators were investigated and recommended by Michaelis and Eagle,[25] who found the oxidation-reduction processes to be reversible:

Gallocyanine (Colour Index No. 883):

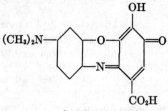

(oxidized form)

This compound is amphoteric in nature, being easily soluble in alkaline or strongly acid media, but almost quantitatively precipitated at p_H 3.5 to 5.5 (isoelectric point). Between p_H 5.5 and 8 the oxidized form is blue, while it is red-violet below 4 and above 8. The reduced form has two phenolic hydroxyl groups. The oxidation potential lies close to that of methylene blue.

Gallophenine (Colour Index No. 879):

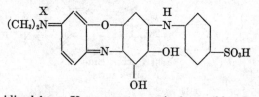

(oxidized form; X represents a univalent acid radical)

Gallophenine is easily soluble at any p_H. The color in water is blue, in strong acid green, and in strong alkali purple. The oxidation potential is near that of indigomonosulfonic acid, but gallophenine is superior on account of its greater solubility.

Brilliant alizarin blue (Colour Index No. 931):

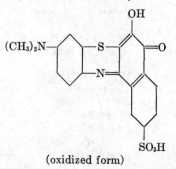

(oxidized form)

[25] L. Michaelis and H. Eagle, *J. Biol. Chem.*, **87**, 713 (1930).

This fairly soluble dye can be extracted from the crude product with cold water; the filtrate is stable indefinitely. The color is violet in water and blue in strong acid (p_H about 1). Of interest is the low oxidation potential.

Below are listed Michaelis and Eagle's values for the normal oxidation potentials at 25°, together with the acid exponents of oxidized and reduced forms:

p_H	Gallocyanine	Gallophenine	Brilliant alizarin blue
5.0	....	−0.003	−0.040
6.0	+0.080	−0.077	−0.112
7.0	+0.021	−0.142	−0.173
8.0	−0.037	−0.202	−0.226
9.0	−0.095	−0.262	−0.279
10.0	−0.140	......	−0.337
$p_{K_{ox}}$	10.1	....	8.2
$p_{K_{red}}$	9.1	....	7.8

Azines.—Among dyes of the azine group, the safranines are distinguished by their low oxidation potentials. The potentials for several systems have been studied at 30° by Stiehler, Chen and Clark.[26] On standing, the reduced forms undergo changes as shown by potential drifts and alterations of absorption spectra; otherwise the redox process is reversible. The following safranines were investigated:

Phenosafranine ($C_{18}H_{15}N_4Cl$):

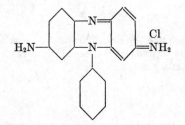

Maximum absorption at 520 mμ. (in 10^{-5} molar solution).

---

[26] R. D. Stiehler, T.-T. Chen and W. M. Clark, *J. Am. Chem. Soc.*, **55**, 891 (1933).

Dimethylphenosafranine ($C_{20}H_{19}N_4Cl$, Fuchsia):

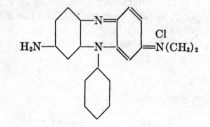

Maximum absorption at 550 mμ.

Tetramethylphenosafranine (iodide) ($C_{22}H_{23}N_4I$):

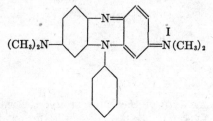

Maximum absorption at 578 mμ.

Tetraethylphenosafranine (Amethyst Violet):

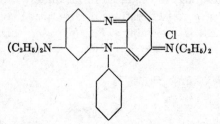

The material studied was the zinc chloride double salt, with maximum absorption at 558 mμ. In neutral or alkaline solutions the free base precipitates, even when as dilute as 10^{-5} molar.

Safranine T (Safranine O):

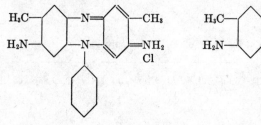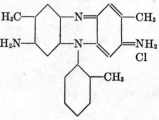

Apparently a mixture of two very similar dyes having maximum absorption at 518 mμ.

The oxidation potentials of all the above safranines change with hydrogen ion concentration according to the equation:

$$\pi = \pi_0 + 0.030 \log \frac{[I_{ox}]}{[I_{red}]} + 0.030 \log ([H^+]^3 + K_{r_1}[H^+]^2 + K_{r_2}[H^+]).$$

The potentials vary slightly with the dye concentration. In 10^{-4} molar solutions at 30°, the following values apply:

Indicator	π_0	Potential at $p_H = 7.0$	K_{r_1}	K_{r_2}
Phenosafranine	+0.280	−0.252	1.1×10^{-5}	1.7×10^{-6}
Dimethylphenosafranine	+0.286	−0.260	1.3×10^{-5}	4.7×10^{-7}
Tetramethylphenosafranine	+0.288	−0.273	4.8×10^{-6}	3.6×10^{-7}
Tetraethylphenosafranine	+0.355	−0.254	4×10^{-7}	2×10^{-8}
Safranine T	+0.235	−0.289	2×10^{-5}	2×10^{-6}

Several more complicated azine dyes (aposafranines) have been investigated by Stiehler and Clark.[27] Neutral blue and the isorosindulines have the general structure:

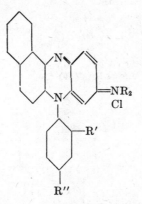

Neutral blue has its maximum absorption at 560 mμ and the isorosindulines are quite similar. The potentials of systems involving these dyes can be measured only at p_H values smaller than 4.2, since the reduced forms are so slightly soluble. In each case the potentials at 30° follow the equation:

$$\pi = \pi_0 + 0.030 \log \frac{[I_{ox}]}{[I_{red}]} - 0.060 \ p_H.$$

[27] R. D. Stiehler and W. M. Clark, *J. Am. Chem. Soc.*, **55**, 4097 (1933).

Indicator	π_0	Substituent Groups		
		R	R'	R''
Neutral blue..........................	+0.170	CH_3	H	H
Isorosinduline No. 1...................	+0.199	C_2H_5	H	H
Isorosinduline No. 2...................	+0.195	C_2H_5	H	CH_3
Isorosinduline No. 3...................	+0.202	C_2H_5	CH_3	H

Induline scarlet:

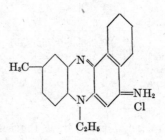

Maximum absorption at 500 mμ.

$$\pi = 0.047 + 0.030 \log \frac{[I_{ox}]}{[I_{red}]} + 0.03 \log (K_{r_1}[H^+] + [H^+]^2).$$

In this equation (applying at 30°), K_{r_1}, the first ionization constant of the reduced cation, has a value of 3.1×10^{-5}.

Sulfonated rosindone:

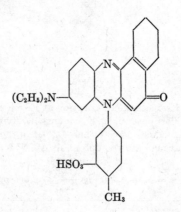

Stiehler and Clark[27] found the expression for the oxidation potential to be very complicated, on account of association phenomena and a specific salt effect of the buffers employed. For practical purposes the following equation may be used at p_H below 8:

$$\pi = 0.24 + 0.03 \log \frac{[I_{ox}]}{[I_{red}]} - 0.09 \, p_H \, .$$

Rosinduline 2G (Colour Index No. 830): This indicator is the sodium salt of a monosulfonated rosindone dye, in which the sulfonic acid group is on one of the benzene rings. Its indicator properties were studied by Michaelis.[28] The free acid is precipitated by mineral acids and may be crystallized easily. A great advantage in the use of rosinduline 2G is that the oxidized and reduced forms are sufficiently soluble at all p_H values. The oxidized dye is scarlet-red while the leuco form is colorless in dilute solution, light yellow-brown in concentrated solution.

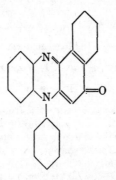

The reduction product has an acid ionization constant of about 3×10^{-10} at 30° ($p_K = 9.5$), due to a phenolic group which is not present in the oxidized form. Michaelis reported the normal potentials for various p_H values (see table on page 124); they lie in a very low range.

Pyocyanine: Various pigments, of which pyocyanine is the best known, are produced by *Bacillus pyocyaneus.* Pyocyanine can easily be isolated because of its solubility in chloroform, and it may be obtained in crystalline condition. The dye, wine-red in acid solution and indigo-blue in alkaline, can be reduced to a leuco form.[29] Wrede and Strack[30] consider it to be a methylated oxy-

---

[28] L. Michaelis, *J. Biol. Chem.*, **91**, 369 (1931); **92**, 211 (1931).

[29] E. Ledderhose, *Deut. Z. Chir.*, **28**, 201 (1888). (Quoted by Michaelis[32]); see also H. McCombie and H. A. Scarborough, *J. Chem. Soc.*, **123**, 3279 (1923); B. Elema and A. C. Sanders, *Rec. trav. chim.*, **50**, 796 (1931).

[30] F. Wrede and E. Strack, *Z. physiol. Chem.*, **140**, 1 (1924); **142**, 103 (1925).

phenazine, while according to Wrede[31] the reversible redox process may be represented by the equilibrium:

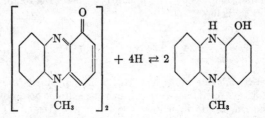

The studies of Michaelis[32] show that pyocyanine as an acid-base indicator is "half-changed" at p_H 4.9. On reduction in alkaline solution the blue changes to colorless, while in acid solution the reduction takes place in two steps, first from the red to a green form and then to colorless. Michaelis regards the alkaline reduction (p_H 6 to 12) as analogous to the quinone-hydroquinone system:

$$X + 2H^+ + 2e \rightleftarrows XH_2, \tag{1}$$

and the acid reduction as involving intermediate formation of a semiquinone:

$$X + H^+ + e \rightleftarrows XH \text{ (semiquinone)} \tag{2a}$$

$$XH + H^+ + e \rightleftarrows XH_2. \tag{2b}$$

A p_H change of one unit would be expected from equation (1) to produce a potential shift of 0.06 volt, and Michaelis observed practically this effect from p_H 6 to 11. Above p_H 12 the blue dye is slowly and irreversibly oxidized. In acid solution the behavior is somewhat complicated, but has been interpreted by Michaelis and independently by Elema.[33] The reduced form has an ionization constant of 6.4×10^{-11} ($p_K = 10.2$); Elema calculated a value of 3×10^{-10} ($p_K = 9.5$).

In the following table are given Michaelis' values for the normal potentials of rosinduline 2G and pyocyanine at 30°:

p_H	Rosinduline 2G	Pyocyanine 1st step	Pyocyanine 2nd step
3	....	+0.207	+0.097
4	....	+0.146	+0.068
5	−0.161	+0.086	+0.078
6	−0.221	+0.026	
7	−0.281	−0.034	
8	−0.340	−0.093	
9	−0.395	−0.149	
10	−0.438	−0.198	
11	−0.480	−0.246	

[31] F. Wrede, *ibid.*, **177**, 177 (1928); **181**, 58 (1929).

[32] E. Friedheim and L. Michaelis, *J. Biol. Chem.*, **91**, 355 (1931).

[33] B. Elema, *Rec. trav. chim.*, **50**, 807 (1931).

Chlororaphine: Chlororaphine is the green pigment produced by *Bacillus chlororaphis* (Guignard and Sauvageau). Kögl and Postowsky[34] found that oxychlororaphine is identical with phenazine-α-carbonamide, and that it can be reduced with zinc and water to chlororaphine. Elema[35] showed that the latter is a semiquinone rather than a meriquinone (in other words, that it is a single molecule or free radical, not a double molecule like quinhydrone). Further reduction in the presence of colloidal palladium produces dihydrophenazine-α-carbonamide, which at a p_H of 1 is orange-yellow:

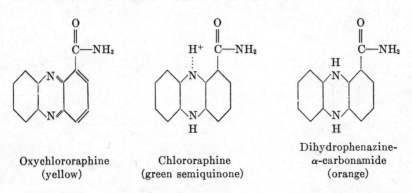

Oxychlororaphine	Chlororaphine	Dihydrophenazine-
(yellow)	(green semiquinone)	α-carbonamide
		(orange)

The semiquinone does not form at p_H above 4 (*cf.* pyocyanine). According to Elema, the normal potential π_0' (the potential of the system when half reduced) varies with p_H between 2 and 10 as follows:

$$\pi_0' = 0.305 - 0.060 \, p_H.$$

α-Oxyphenazine: Michaelis[36] has studied in detail the formation of a semiquinone from α-oxyphenazine. The completely reduced compound is represented by formula I (or by Ia as a cation in strong acid solution); II is the semiquinone which exists only in acid solution and which contains divalent nitrogen, so to speak. The completely oxidized holoquinoid form present in acid solution ($p_H < 2$) is given by III, while that present in weakly acid or neutral solution (p_H 2 to 8) is shown in IV. Finally, V represents the substance formed in alkaline solution ($p_H > 10.5$).

---

[34] F. Kögl and J. J. Postowsky, *Ann.*, **480**, 280 (1930); F. Kögl, B. Tönnis and H. J. Groenewegen, *ibid.*, **497**, 265 (1932).

[35] B. Elema, *Rec. trav. chim.*, **52**, 569 (1933); see also L. Michaelis, *Naturwissenschaften*, **19**, 461 (1931), and page 127 of this text.

[36] L. Michaelis, *J. Biol. Chem.*, **92**, 211 (1931); for a review of this subject see Michaelis, *Chem. Rev.*, **16**, 243 (1935).

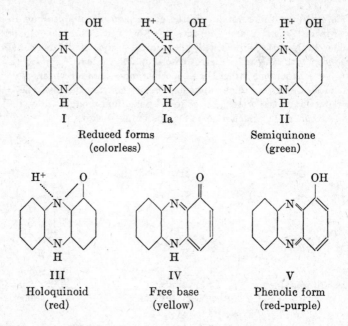

I
Reduced forms
(colorless)

Ia

II
Semiquinone
(green)

III
Holoquinoid
(red)

IV
Free base
(yellow)

V
Phenolic form
(red-purple)

The change of oxidation potential with p_H is shown in Fig. 16, together with the regions of existence of the various forms.

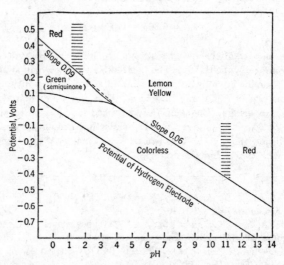

Fig. 16. Effect of pH on the Oxidation Potential of α-Oxyphenazine (according to Michaelis)

Continuing the investigations, Michaelis and Hill[37] obtained further evidence for their views concerning the structure of the so-called semiquinones. They studied, for example, phenazine and its reduction products, which without regard to ionization may be written

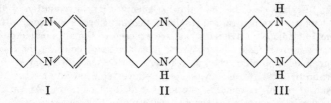

I   II   III

I is the oxidized form of phenazine, II the intermediary form apparently containing bivalent nitrogen, and III the completely reduced form. II is found only in acid solutions, so it is evidently a cation. Considering all the forms as cations, they become:

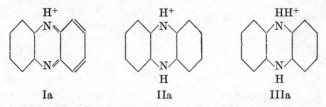

Ia   IIa   IIIa

To explain the existence of a molecule such as IIa, it is rewritten as shown in IIb; here e represents an electron that is shared by both nitrogens, oscillating between the two.

IIb

Neutral Red: Neutral red, called *toluylenroth* by Witt,[38] is an azine of a series whose simplest member, according to Bernthsen and Schweitzer,[39] has the formula I. The neutral red employed as an acid-base indicator is shown

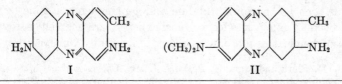

I   II

[37] L. Michaelis and E. S. Hill, *J. Am. Chem. Soc.*, **55**, 1481 (1933).

[38] O. N. Witt, *Ber.*, **12**, 931 (1879).

[39] A. Bernthsen and H. Schweitzer, *Ann.*, **236**, 332 (1886).

in II; its oxidation-reduction properties were studied by Clark and Perkins.[40] The system is only partly reversible, since the reduced form can be converted into a yellow, strongly fluorescent substance; the amount of this formed depends upon the p_H at which the reduction takes place and the time allowed. Clark and Perkins describe the following effects: "Rapid reduction of dilute, buffered solutions of neutral red results in almost colorless solutions. If such solutions immediately after reduction are exposed to the air, complete oxidation occurs and the solutions obtained have the same color as the original. However, a solution reduced at p_H 5.3 has a noticeable yellow tint after slow reoxidation by air. In case one keeps a reduced solution in an inert atmosphere and at p_H 8.2, it remains colorless for at least an hour. At p_H 2.7 the solution slowly acquires a yellow color with a green fluorescence, while at p_H 5.3 the yellow-green fluorescence develops rapidly."

The oxidation potentials of the simple *Toluylenroth* (I) and neutral red (II) systems at 30° follow the equation

$$\pi = \pi_0 + 0.030 \log \frac{[I_{ox}]}{[I_{red}]} - 0.030 \log \frac{K_0 + [H^+]}{K_{r_1} K_{r_2} + K_{r_2}[H^+] + [H^+]^2}$$

$$+ 0.030 \log [H^+]^2.$$

	π_0	K_0	p_{K_0}	K_{r_1}	$p_{K_{r_1}}$	K_{r_2}	$p_{K_{r_2}}$
I	+0.237	4.79×10^{-7}	6.32	1.10×10^{-6}	5.96	1.12×10^{-5}	4.95
II	+0.240	1.59×10^{-7}	6.80	6.92×10^{-7}	6.16	5.01×10^{-6}	5.30

In acid solution the potential decreases by 0.09 volt for an increase of one p_H unit, while in alkaline solution the change is only 0.06 volt. The two curves of π vs. p_H come together in the p_H region between 4.5 and 6.5.

Diamines.—The stepwise oxidation of diamines leads to strongly colored substances, which according to Willstatter and Piccard[41] are comparable with quinhydrones and which they designated as *meri-quinones* in contrast with the completely oxidized compounds or *holoquinones*. Clark, Cohen and Gibbs,[18,IX] made a thorough potentiometric and spectrophotometric study of the oxidation of diamines. The behavior of these is so complicated by side reactions that compounds such as benzidine, tolidine and *p*-phenylene diamine, which have been of much service in biochemistry, are scarcely suited to physico-chemical evaluation as redox indicators. On oxidation the

[40] W. M. Clark and Marie E. Perkins, *J. Am. Chem. Soc.*, **54**, 1228 (1931); *cf.* E. Vellinger, *Arch. phys. biol.*, **7**, 113 (1929); L. Rapkine, A. P. Struyk and R. Wurmser, *J. chim. phys.*, **26**, 340 (1929).

[41] R. Willstätter and J. Piccard, *Ber.*, **41**, 1458 (1908); see also Willstätter and E. Mayer, *ibid.*, **37**, 1494, (1904), Willstätter and A. Pfannenstiehl, *ibid.*, **38**, 4605 (1905).

potentials do not remain constant, but shift more or less rapidly toward negative values. One of the interfering reactions was explained as a condensation of the primary oxidation product with some of the original compound, the hydrogens reducing more of the oxidized form as in the following reaction scheme for p-phenylene diamine:

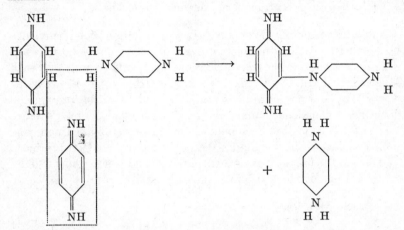

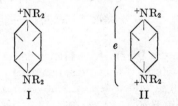

The entire mechanism is made still more involved by the fact that actually semiquinone analogues rather than meriquinones are formed in a great number of cases, according to Michaelis.[42] These monomolecular imino-amino compounds, comparable with free radicals, can be represented according to Weitz by formula I below, or better dynamically according to Michaelis by formula II. R may be hydrogen or an organic group while e represents an electron.

Benzidine (4,4'-diaminobiphenyl): Between p_H values of 0 and 3, the oxidation potential[43] at 30° is:

$$\pi = 0.921 + 0.03 \log \frac{[I_{ox}]}{[I_{red}]} - 0.060 \ p_H.$$

---

[42] L. Michaelis, *J. Am. Chem. Soc.*, **53**, 2953 (1931); *cf.* also L. Weitz, *Z. Elektrochem.*, **34**, 538 (1928).

[43] These indicators have normal potentials greater than 0.76, but are considered here because of their similarity to diamines of lower potential.

During oxidation the system is less stable than tolidine.

o-Tolidine (3,3'-dimethyl-4,4'-diaminobiphenyl): From $p_H = 0$ to $p_H = 3$, the oxidation potential at 30° is:

$$\pi = 0.873 + 0.03 \log \frac{[I_{ox}]}{[I_{red}]} - 0.060 \; p_H.$$

A blue or green color is produced by oxidation of *o*-tolidine.

Alkylated Aromatic Diamines.—In the oxidation of *p*-phenylene-diamine with bromine the color changes successively to yellow, green, red and colorless. The first oxidation product is so unstable that Michaelis and Hill[44] were unable to make reliable potential measurements. In contrast, Wurster's red,[45] the first oxidation product of dimethyl-*p*-phenylene diamine, is more stable, and Wurster's blue, that of the tetramethyl compound, is completely stable. Upon continued oxidation the very labile di-imonium compounds are formed. Thus while the first step is reversible, the second is not, and the indicators are not of much use in volumetric analysis.

Dimethyl-p-phenylenediamine:

$$\text{At } p_H = 4.6, \quad \pi = 0.447 + 0.06 \log \frac{[I_{ox}]}{[I_{red}]}, \quad (30°);$$

Tetramethyl-p-phenylene diamine:

$$\text{At } p_H = 3.66, \quad \pi = 0.420 + 0.06 \log \frac{[I_{ox}]}{[I_{red}]}, \quad (30°);$$

$$\text{At } p_H = 4.63, \quad \pi = 0.365 + 0.06 \log \frac{[I_{ox}]}{[I_{red}]}, \quad (30°).$$

Phenylated Aromatic Diamines.—Michaelis and Hill[44] found that the oxidation products of diphenyl-*p*-phenylene diamine are stable. Symmetrical diphenyl-*p*-phenylenediimine (azophenylene) was described by von Bandrowski[46] as a red dye. From their potentiometric investigation, Michaelis and Hill concluded that the oxidation takes place in two steps and that the intermediate product is a semi-quinone. On account of the diamine's slight solubility, they used a

[44] L. Michaelis and E. S. Hill, *J. Am. Chem. Soc.*, **55**, 1481 (1933).
[45] E. Wurster and R. Sendtner, *Ber.*, **12**, 1803 (1879).
[46] E. von Bandrowski, *Monatsh.*, **8**, 475 (1887).

solvent consisting of 90% acetic acid and 10% water. In this medium:

$$\pi = 0.592 + 0.06 \log \frac{[I_{ox}]}{[I_{red}]} \quad \text{(first step)};$$

$$\pi = 0.795 + 0.06 \log \frac{[I_{ox}]}{[I_{red}]} \quad \text{(second step)}.$$

Dipyridyls.—If a solution of γ,γ'-dipyridyl in dilute acetic acid is reduced with chromous chloride, a deep violet color develops. According to Michaelis and Hill[47] the colored product is a semiquinone which exists only as a cation in acid solution. More stable at varying acidities is the semiquinone of *N,N'-dimethyl-γ,γ'-dipyridylium chloride*, which has a dark blue color with maximum absorption at 602 mμ. This quaternary ammonium base yields its semiquinone in alkaline as well as in acid solutions. The oxidation potential is independent of p_H, which is explained by the great basic strength of both forms and the fact that they differ only by an electron, not by a hydrogen ion:

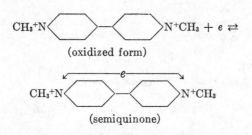

(oxidized form)

(semiquinone)

The normal potential is strongly negative, -0.446 volt between p_H 8 and 13.

Ferrous Dimethylglyoxime.—Charlot[48] found that in alkaline medium ferrous dimethylglyoxime acts as a reversible oxidation-reduction indicator. The ferrous compound, like that of nickel, has an intense red color while the ferric form is practically colorless. The maximum sensitivity is obtained in an ammonia-ammonium chloride buffer at a p_H of 9.4, the indicator being useful at this p_H in the titration of sulfide and hyposulfite with ferricyanide. The change to colorless occurs at a potential of $+0.25$ volt.

[47] L. Michaelis and E. S. Hill, *J. Am. Chem. Soc.*, **55**, 1489 (1933).
[48] G. Charlot, *Bull. soc. chim.*, [5], **6**, 970, 978, 1447 (1939).

Preparation of the indicator solution: To 4 or 5 ml. of a saturated solution of dimethylglyoxime in alcohol add one ml. of 0.02 M ferrous sulfate and 0.5 ml. of concentrated ammonium hydroxide. The solution is slowly oxidized by air.

Porphyrexide and Porphyrindine.—These compounds were suggested as redox indicators by Kuhn and Franke,[49] who found that the oxidized forms behave as free radicals. Red porphyrexide is water-soluble and upon reduction yields colorless porphyrexine:

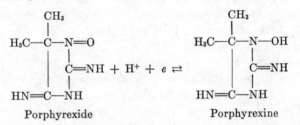

Porphyrexide   Porphyrexine

At 18°C. and at a p_H of 7.0, the normal potential against the normal hydrogen electrode is +0.725 volt, and it increases by about 0.053 volt for each unit that the p_H decreases. One has to use considerable indicator since porphyrexide is only weakly colored.

The redox potentials of the porphyrindine system are not consistently reproducible. Apparently reduction proceeds according to the equation:

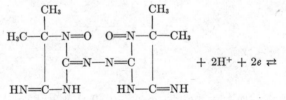

Porphyrindine

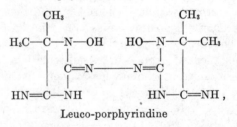

Leuco-porphyrindine

yet the system behaves as though only one electron participates in the reaction. Kuhn and Franke were unable to explain the potential curve of the double radical in neutral solution. The normal potential is +0.565 volt at a

---

[49] R. Kuhn and W. Franke, *Ber.*, **68**, 1528 (1935).

p_H of 7.0 and varies with p_H in somewhat the same way as that of porphyrexide. The water-soluble porphyrindine has a very intense blue color, comparable to indigo. One would expect it to be a good redox indicator.

7. Redox Indicators with Normal Oxidation Potentials Equal to or Greater than +0.76 Volt.

—These indicators have come to be widely used in analytical chemistry, largely because of their applicability to titrations involving the ferrous-ferric system. In some methods strong oxidants are employed in excess, and the excess back-titrated with ferrous solution, while in other cases ferrous ion is used as a reductant and the excess is titrated with an oxidant. One is not restricted to iron titrations, however; many other applications may be made if the oxidation potentials of the systems are known.

Diphenylamine, Diphenylbenzidine and Derivatives.—In 1924, J. Knop[50] found diphenylamine to be an excellent indicator for the titration of ferrous iron with dichromate; the transition of the indicator from colorless to violet is a reversible process. It was later established that diphenylbenzidine is suited for the same purpose. Studies on the behavior of these compounds were conducted by Kolthoff and Sarver.[51] They showed that upon treatment of diphenylamine in acid solution with a strong oxidant such as chromate or permanganate, the first action is an irreversible oxidation to diphenylbenzidine:

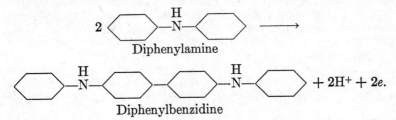

Diphenylamine

Diphenylbenzidine

The latter is further reversibly oxidized to a violet holoquinoid (blue in strong acids):

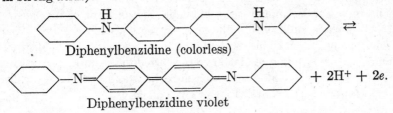

Diphenylbenzidine (colorless)

Diphenylbenzidine violet

[50] J. Knop, *J. Am. Chem. Soc.*, **46**, 263 (1924).

[51] I. M. Kolthoff and L. A. Sarver, *Z. Elektrochem.*, **36**, 139 (1930), *J. Am. Chem. Soc.*, **52**, 4179 (1930).

The color change takes place at an oxidation potential of 0.76 ± 0.1 volt (against the normal hydrogen electrode); this value is practically independent of the hydrogen-ion concentration.

In the application of diphenylamine or -benzidine one meets several difficulties:

1. The oxidation of diphenylamine to diphenylbenzidine is irreversible. After addition of a small amount of the oxidant, a part of the benzidine can be further oxidized before all the amine is converted, especially in strong acid solution.

2. The holoquinoid reacts with diphenylbenzidine to form a slightly soluble, green meriquinoid. The precipitation of this compound may under certain conditions interfere with recognition of the endpoint.

3. Diphenylbenzidine has a low solubility in water, about 0.06 mg. per liter. Since the ionization constant of the base is very small (about 2×10^{-14}), the solubility does not increase greatly in the presence of acid.

4. The violet form is not stable, and may be irreversibly oxidized by excess reagent to colorless or weakly colored products.

Of importance in practical analysis are the following points:

(a) If diphenylamine is used as indicator in the titration of a reductant (such as ferrous iron) with dichromate, an equivalent amount of the latter is required to convert diphenylamine into diphenylbenzidine.

(b) In the titration of oxidants with ferrous solution using diphenylbenzidine as indicator, a correction is necessary since the violet holoquinoid is not entirely reduced to diphenylbenzidine, but is partly transformed into the green insoluble meriquinoid. The magnitude of this correction depends upon the time elapsed between indicator addition and observation of the end-point, since the holoquinoid is unstable in the presence of excess oxidant. If diphenylamine is used in place of diphenylbenzidine, the correction becomes still greater.

(c) Neither compound functions as a redox indicator in the presence of tungstate. In this respect, and also with regard to solubility, the sulfonic and carboxylic acid derivatives of diphenylamine or -benzidine have advantages.

Diphenylamine sulfonic acid: This compound was prepared and recommended for volumetric analysis by Kolthoff and Sarver.[52] The indicator is commercially available in the form of its barium salt, which is sufficiently soluble in water and dilute acids. The color change, from colorless through green to a red violet, is distinct and occurs at a potential of 0.80 volt (referred to the normal hydrogen electrode) in 1 N acid. Indicator corrections and other analytically important properties are discussed in Vol. II.

⁵² I. M. Kolthoff and L. A. Sarver, *J. Am. Chem. Soc.*, **53**, 2902, 2906 (1931).

Cohen and Oesper[53] prepared what appears to be a different isomer or isomeric mixture of diphenylamine monosulfonic acids. Their product also has good indicator properties, with a change from colorless to purple. In an investigation of tolylphenylamine monosulfonates, they found that only the o-tolylphenylamine derivative is satisfactory and that its color change to red may be erratic if hydrochloric acid stronger than about 0.1 N is present. Sulfuric acid does not interfere.

Diphenylbenzidine sulfonic acid: Since diphenylamine sulfonic acid is first oxidized to diphenylbenzidine sulfonic acid and then to the violet form, it is to be expected that diphenylbenzidine sulfonic acid used directly would have a smaller indicator correction. Sarver and von Fischer[54] prepared polysulfonic acids with up to 10 acid groups by sulfonation of diphenylbenzidine. A 0.1 per cent aqueous solution of the sodium salt is useful, and is stable for several months. For titrations with 0.01 or 0.001 N solutions (*e.g.*, ferrous), one drop is used; with 0.1 N solutions, ten drops are preferable. The color change to violet is reversible and takes place at the same oxidation potential as that of diphenylamine sulfonate. In general the indicator correction is negligible, corresponding to 0.1 ml. of 0.001 N reagent for 0.1 ml. of 0.1 per cent indicator solution. Partial oxidation produces a green form which is stable and which does not precipitate out on standing. The violet form is stable for a reasonable length of time in the presence of excess oxidant, but eventually fades. Bromine yields a rapidly fading blue.

Diphenylamine carboxylic acids: Syrokomskii and Stepin[55] recommended N-phenylanthranilic acid for which the normal potential is 1.08 volts, considerably higher than those of the sulfonic acids. The transition is reversible, from colorless through red to red-violet. Apparently the mechanism of the color change is comparable with that of the other diphenylamines.

The oxidation-reduction properties of the 2,2'-(o,o'-), 2,3'-(o,m'-) and 2,4'-(o,p'-) dicarboxylic acids of diphenylamine were investigated by Kirsanow and Tscherkassow.[56] These compounds, which should be used in strongly acid solution (15–20 N sulfuric acid) have color changes through green to blue or violet. *In hydrochloric acid no change takes place.* Of the oxidation products, the o,o' is quite stable, the o,p' is less stable, and the o,m' is labile. The acids are slightly soluble in water, fairly soluble in 15–20 N sulfuric acid. Generally 1.5 to 2.0 ml. of 0.001 M indicator are taken, and the indicator correction shown below should be applied for a solution volume of 100 ml.:

| | Diphenylamine dicarboxylic acid | | |
	o,o'	o,m'	o,p'
Redox potential	1.26	1.12	—
Correction, ml. 0.01 N $K_2Cr_2O_7$	1.5	4.2	2.8

[53] S. Cohen and R. E. Oesper, *Ind. Eng. Chem. Anal. Ed.*, **8**, 364 (1936); *cf.* also L. E. Straka and Oesper, *ibid.*, **6**, 465 (1934).

[54] L. A. Sarver and W. von Fischer, *Ind. Eng. Chem. Anal. Ed.*, **7**, 271 (1935).

[55] V. S. Syrokomskii and V. V. Stepin, *Zavodskaya Lab.*, **5**, 144 (1936), through *Chem. Abst.*, **30**, 4780 (1936); *cf.* also *Chem. Abst.*, **33**, 2061 (1939).

[56] A. V. Kirsanow and V. P. Tscherkassow, *Bull. soc. chim.*, [5], **3**, 2037 (1936).

Other Diphenylamine Derivatives.—Hammett, Walden and Edmonds[57] studied various substituted diphenylamines, recommending especially the *p*-nitro and 2,4-diamino derivatives.

p-Nitrodiphenylamine: Introduction of a nitro group raises the oxidation potential of diphenylamine by about 0.3 volt. Therefore, ferrous solution can be titrated with ceric sulfate in the presence of this indicator without addition of phosphoric acid. Since the indicator is further oxidized irreversibly, the back-titration is unsatisfactory. The direct titration of ferrous iron with dichromate is also unsatisfactory.

Polynitro derivatives have such high oxidation potentials that even very strong oxidants produce no color change.

p-Aminodiphenylamine: This compound[57] can be reversibly oxidized to a red-violet form, but the latter is easily destroyed by excess oxidant. (The potential for the color change in 1 M sulfuric acid is apparently somewhat below the ferrous-ferric potential.)

p-Acetylaminodiphenylamine: The oxidized form is greenish-blue and is somewhat more stable than that of the unacetylated product, but the indicator is still unsatisfactory. (The oxidation potential is about 0.06 volt lower than the ferric-ferrous potential.)

2,4-Diaminodiphenylamine: This indicator was prepared by Hammett and his coworkers[57] by reduction of the dinitro compound with tin and hydrochloric acid according to directions of Nietzki and Almenrader.[58] Its red-colored oxidized form is more stable than diphenylbenzidine violet. The oxidation potential in 1 M sulfuric acid is about 0.06 volt lower than the ferric-ferrous potential. Both the reduced and oxidized forms are sufficiently soluble in water and the indicator is satisfactory.

Reduction of 2,4-dinitro-4′-aminodiphenylamine and 2,4-dinitro-4′-methoxydiphenylamine with tin and hydrochloric acid yields compounds with indicator properties analogous to those of diaminodiphenylamine. The reduction products of tri- and tetranitrodiphenylamines do not behave as redox indicators.

p-Phenetidine[59] and *bi-ortho-anisidine*[60] have been recommended in place of diphenylamine and diphenylbenzidine. Further details concerning these indicators are given in Vol. III.

Phenanthrolines.—*o*-Phenanthroline dissolves readily in ferrous solutions, three molecules combining with one ferrous ion. The ferrous ion complex is intensely red in color. At room temperature it is very slowly decomposed by strong acids or by those ions with which

[57] L. P. Hammett, G. H. Walden, Jr. and S. M. Edmonds, *J. Am. Chem. Soc.*, **56**, 1092 (1934).

[58] R. Nietzki and K. Almenrader, *Ber.*, **28**, 2969 (1895).

[59] L. Szebelledy, *Z. anal. Chem.*, **81**, 97 (1930).

[60] Mary E. Weeks, *Ind. Eng. Chem. Anal. Ed.*, **4**, 127 (1932).

it forms a stable complex (Co^{++}, Cu^{++}, Ni^{++}, Cd^{++}, Zn^{++}). The ferrous complex, termed *ferroin*, is converted by strong oxidants into a blue ferric complex whose color intensity is so faint that the system behaves practically as a one-color redox indicator.

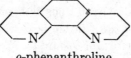

o-phenanthroline

The reaction

$$Fe(C_{12}H_8N_2)_3^{++} \rightleftarrows Fe(C_{12}H_8N_2)_3^{+++} + e$$

$$\text{(red)} \qquad\qquad \text{(light blue)}$$

is reversible. From the investigations of Walden, Hammett and Chapman,[61] the normal oxidation potential in 1 N sulfuric acid is 1.14 volts and the indicator changes to colorless at 1.2 volts.

Ferroin is commercially available and has become a very valuable indicator for titrations with strong oxidants such as ceric salts, dichromate and permanganate. The color change is distinct and reversible and the oxidized form is attacked only slowly by excess reagent, although more rapidly in acid solutions at higher temperatures. Indicator corrections and analytical applications will be discussed in Volume II.

Nitrophenanthroline: This compound, which forms a violet-red complex with ferrous ion, was obtained by Hammett, Walden and Edmonds[62] through nitration of *o*-phenanthroline. It is more stable toward acids than phenanthroline, but loses its color on boiling with a dilute acid; the color reappears after cooling. The oxidized form is a greenish-blue of very low intensity. The oxidation potential was estimated to be about 0.11 volt higher than that of ferroin.

α,α'-Dipyridyl Ferrous Complex: The ferrous complex of *α,α'*-dipyridyl has indicator properties[61] similar to those of ferroin. However, since it is more easily decomposed by acids, it is less useful as an indicator.

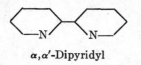

α,α'-Dipyridyl

---

[61] G. H. Walden, Jr., L. P. Hammett and R. P. Chapman, *J. Am. Chem. Soc.*, **55**, 2649 (1933). See also F. Blau, *Monatsh.*, **19**, 647 (1898).

[62] L. P. Hammett, G. H. Walden, Jr., and S. M. Edmonds, *J. Am. Chem. Soc.*, **56**, 1092 (1934).

p-Ethoxychrysoidine $(C_2H_5OC_6H_4N_2C_6H_3(NH_2)_2 \cdot HCl)$.—This water-soluble salt behaves also as an acid-base indicator (*cf.* page 92). Schulek and Rozsa[63] found that in strongly acid solution the red color is discharged by ceric sulfate or permanganate, the solution becoming a scarcely perceptible yellow. The red color is restored by strong reducing agents, and also by ferrous iron and trivalent arsenic or antimony provided that the solution is warmed slightly.

The behavior of the indicator toward bromine in 0.5 to 2 N sulfuric acid is very interesting. With a trace of bromine the red color becomes very intense and with a little more bromine the color is discharged. *This latter change is reversible.* Therefore *p*-ethoxychrysoidine is useful in titrations with bromate in acid medium. The authors do not give the oxidation potential of the indicator.

Triphenylmethane Derivatives.—Of the triarylmethane dyes studied by Knop and his coworkers,[64] only the diamino and triamino derivatives were found to have reversible oxidation-reduction properties. Useful as indicators were brilliant firn blue, cyanin B, cyanol fast green 2G, erioglaucin A, eriogreen B, patent blue A, setocyanin supra, setoglaucin O, setopolin, xylene blue AS, xylene blue VS and xylene cyanol FF. Upon oxidation in solutions from 0.4 to 1.2 N in sulfuric acid, the color change is from green or yellow to orange or pink-red. The oxidation potentials of all the indicators in acid medium are located between 1.0 and 1.1 volts. Each indicator is readily soluble in water. Below are listed the three most important representatives; their applications will be discussed in Volume II.

Erioglaucin A:

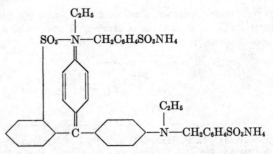

[63] E. Schulek and P. Rozsa, *Z. anal. Chem.*, **118**, 185 (1939).
[64] J. Knop, *Z. anal. Chem.*, **77**, 111 (1929); **85**, 253 (1931); J. Knop and O. Kubelková, *ibid.*, **77**, 125 (1929); **85**, 401 (1931).

Stock solution 0.1 per cent in water.   The blue color becomes yellow-green at a p_H of about 0.5.   At an oxidation potential of 1.0 volt the color changes reversibly to red.

Eriogreen B:

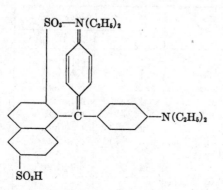

Stock solution 0.1 per cent in water.   This has a blue-green color.   Upon oxidation at a potential of 1.0 volt, in acid medium, the color changes slowly from yellow to orange.

Setoglaucin O:

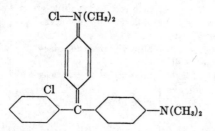

The aqueous solution is deep blue, becoming yellow-green in acid.   Oxidation at a potential of 1.06 volts changes the color to pale red, in acid medium.

Another triphenylmethane dye, *Patent blue V*, was studied by Yoe and Boyd.[65]   It is blue at $p_H = 3.0$, yellow at 0.8.   The yellow color changes reversibly to orange red in the presence of permanganate or ceric sulfate. Dichromate cannot be employed, and hydrochloric acid interferes in iron titrations.   The oxidation potential is about 0.7 volt.

8. Selected List of Oxidation-Reduction Indicators.—To summarize the foregoing sections on redox indicators, a list of the more useful compounds has been compiled.   Under π_0 are given the potentials

[65] J. H. Yoe and G. R. Boyd, Jr., *Ind. Eng. Chem. Anal. Ed.*, **11**, 492 (1939).

(referred to the normal hydrogen electrode) at which the indicators are "half-changed"; these potentials are those of solutions one normal in hydrogen ions.

SELECTED LIST OF OXIDATION-REDUCTION INDICATORS

Indicator	Color change		π_0 at $p_H = 0$
	(Ox)	(Red)	
Safranine T	red	colorless	0.24
Neutral red	red	colorless	0.24
Indigo monosulfonate	blue	colorless	0.26
Phenosafranine	red	colorless	0.28
Indigo tetrasulfonate	blue	colorless	0.36
Nile blue	blue	colorless	0.41
Methylene blue	green-blue	colorless	0.53
1-Naphthol-2-sulfonic acid indophenol	red	colorless	0.54
2,6-Dibromophenol indophenol	blue	colorless	0.67
Diphenylamine (diphenylbenzidine)	violet	colorless	0.76 ± 0.1
Diphenylamine sulfonic acid	red-violet	colorless	0.85
Erioglaucin A	red	green	1.0
Setoglaucin O	pale red	yellow-green	1.06
p-Nitrodiphenylamine	violet	colorless	1.06
o,m'-Diphenylamine dicarboxylic acid	blue-violet	colorless	1.12
o,o'-Diphenylamine dicarboxylic acid	blue-violet	colorless	1.26
o-Phenanthroline ferrous complex	pale blue	red	1.14 (distinct color change 1.20)
Nitro-o-phenanthroline ferrous complex	pale blue	violet-red	1.25 (color change 1.31)

9. Irreversible Indicators.—In oxidation-reduction titrations there are sometimes used indicators whose color changes are not reversible. Although indicators of this kind are not to be recommended in general, they can be of service under certain conditions, especially if they can reveal with great sensitivity the presence of an excess of reagent. Examples are methyl red and methyl orange, which are red in acid solution and are decolored by oxidants such as permanganate or bromine, and Bordeaux,[66] which is decolored by bromine (hypo-bromite) in acid, neutral or weakly alkaline solution. The disadvantage of such indicators is that they may be attacked by local excesses of reagent and decolored before the endpoint. Generally the titrations have to be performed slowly and carefully. Practical details concerning the use of these indicators, and data on their sensitivities, will be given in Volume III.

At the close of this chapter it is appropriate to emphasize that, while the theoretical considerations regarding indicators are of great importance for the establishment of favorable experimental conditions, still one should not be content with a result obtained merely by computation. *The theoretical deductions should always be subjected to experimental test.*

The sensitivity and other properties of an indicator are dependent upon several factors which are not readily calculable, such as the illumination, temperature, depth viewed, quantity of indicator, and subjective perception. All of these have to be considered in practical analysis. To arrive at a correct procedure, experimental verification is essential.

[66] See G. F. Smith and H. H. Bliss, *J. Am. Chem. Soc.*, **53**, 2091 (1931); I. M. Kolthoff and V. A. Stenger, *Ind. Eng. Chem. Anal. Ed.*, **7**, 79 (1935).

CHAPTER VI

TITRATION ERROR

1. Definition.—By the term "titration error" is meant primarily the error which occurs because an indicator changes a little before or after the equivalence-point. This is to be distinguished from the methodic errors caused by faulty calibration or improper handling of the measuring apparatus, which are not considered here.

The *drop error* will also be disregarded. Concerning this, Bjerrum[1] said: "In a titration one adds reagent until the last portion introduced, usually a drop, brings about a given effect in the solution. Even if the desired effect occurs quite sharply, for example with 0.001 ml. of reagent, still there is too much of the latter added. This is the drop error, and it has the order of magnitude of the last addition of reagent." It should be pointed out that for certain cases of very refined analyses the drop error may be determined experimentally, if color indicators show the change. In an acid-base titration, the hydrogen-ion concentration can be measured potentiometrically or colorimetrically, and the excess of reagent calculated. In titrations with permanganate it is a disadvantage that the pink color cannot be perceived with great sensitivity. The drop error in this case may be determined by iodimetric titration of the small excess, or by colorimetric estimation of the excess through comparison with a blank to which permanganate is added.

The *titration error* depends upon several factors such as the sensitivity of the indicator, the nature of the system to be titrated, temperature, and dilution. In order to formulate the theory as simply as possible, the factors involved in various cases will now be discussed. Estimations of the titration error may be made most readily in the case of precipitation reactions, hence these will be considered first.

2. The Titration Error in Quantitative Precipitations.—Suppose that a cation B^+ (for example, silver) is being titrated and that an

---

[1] N. Bjerrum, *Die Theorie der alkalimetrischen und acidimetrischen Titrierungen.* F. Enke, Stuttgart 1914, p. 74.

indicator is used whose sensitivity for this ion corresponds to a concentration a, expressed in gram-equivalents per liter.   If the volume of the liquid (in milliliters) is equal to v when the indicator changes, then the number of gram-equivalents of B^+ present will be $\dfrac{a}{1000} v$.

As a *first approximation*, it may be assumed that this number of equivalents of B^+ corresponds to the error of the titration.   If the total titration amounts to V ml. of B^+ solution of normality n, the total number of equivalents participating is $\dfrac{n}{1000}$ V.   Then the titration error, expressed in per cent, is

$$\text{T.E.} = \frac{av}{n\text{V}} \times 100 \text{ (approximately).} \qquad (125)$$

As mentioned above, this equation is only an approximation. Practically it may be used for most calculations, but in certain cases a more exact equation is desirable, principally when dilute solutions or large solubility products are involved.

The deviation of equation (125) from the actual titration error comes from the assumption that the sensitivity a is exactly equal to the concentration of B^+ ions, which are not titrated.   This is not exactly true, for at the equivalence-point $[B^+]$ is not zero, but is equal to $\sqrt{S}$, where S is the solubility product of the slightly soluble compound BA:

$$[B^+][A^-] = S.$$

Since $[B^+] = a$ when the indicator begins to change, one has:

$$[A^-] = \frac{S}{[B^+]} = \frac{S}{a}.$$

Now all the A^- ions present in the solution are those supplied by the precipitate, and since an equal number of B^+ ions is supplied in the same way, it follows that of the total concentration a of B^+ ions in solution at the endpoint, the concentration $\dfrac{S}{a}$ comes from the precipitate.   This has already been titrated, and the actual concentration of untitrated ions is $a - \dfrac{S}{a}$. Then the exact expression for the titration error (in per cent) becomes:

$$\text{T.E.} = \frac{(a^2 - S)v}{anV} \times 100. \tag{126}$$

If the composition of the precipitate is B_2A rather than BA, the actual concentration of B^+ ions remaining untitrated at the end-point is

$$a - \frac{2S_{B_2A}}{a}.$$

The magnitude of the titration error may thus be calculated in any case for which the solubility product, S, and the sensitivity, a, are known. Naturally the error will be positive or negative, depending upon whether A^- is titrated with B^+, or B^+ with A^-.

Illustration: In the titration of chloride according to Mohr's method, it has been found experimentally that a chromate concentration of 10^{-2} molar is satisfactory as an indicator. The solubility product of silver chromate is about 2×10^{-12}. Under these conditions the "theoretical" sensitivity of the indicator for silver ions amounts to

$$[Ag^+] = \sqrt{\frac{S_{Ag_2CrO_4}}{[CrO_4^=]}} = \sqrt{\frac{2 \times 10^{-12}}{10^{-2}}} = 1.4 \times 10^{-5}.$$

Although it is possible to demonstrate experimentally this theoretical sensitivity, the actual color change is so slight that it can be perceived only with great difficulty during a titration. In practice it is better to titrate to a silver-ion concentration of 3×10^{-5} corresponding to a p_{Ag} of 4.5, or in other words, to a *titration exponent* (p_T) of 4.5.

Suppose that 50 ml. of 0.1 N sodium chloride are titrated with 0.1 N silver nitrate. The values to be substituted in the equation for titration error are:

$$v = 100; \qquad a = 3 \times 10^{-5};$$

$$V = 50; \qquad n = 0.1;$$

$$S_{AgCl} = 10^{-10}.$$

Then according to equation (125):

$$\text{T.E.} = \frac{3 \times 10^{-5} \times 100}{50 \times 0.1} \times 100 = 0.06 \text{ per cent,}$$

or by the more exact equation (126):

$$\text{T.E.} = \frac{(9 \times 10^{-10} - 10^{-10}) \times 100}{3 \times 10^{-5} \times 0.1 \times 50} \times 100 = 0.05 \text{ per cent.}$$

In this case it makes very little difference which equation is employed. This is due to the fact that the solubility of silver chloride is almost negligibly small in the presence of excess silver ions. Had the solutions taken been only 0.01 N instead of 0.1 N, the value of n would have been 0.01 and the titration error would have been calculated as 0.6 per cent by the approximate equation or 0.5 per cent by the exact.

Inspection of equation (126) reveals that the titration error becomes smaller in accordance with the following conditions:

(1) The more sensitive is the indicator, that is, the smaller is a.

(2) The smaller is the solubility product, S.

(3) The smaller is the ratio $\dfrac{v}{V}$ of the final volume to the initial volume. Naturally the two volumes differ only by the amount of reagent and solvent (if any) added during titration. In order to keep the ratio small, it is desirable to use as concentrated a titer solution as is consistent with accuracy in measuring.

(4) The larger is n. Relatively less error is involved in the titration of concentrated solutions than in the titration of dilute solutions.

3. The Titration Error in Quantitative Neutralizations.

—In the neutralization of strong acids with strong bases, the titration error can generally be calculated with sufficient accuracy from the approximate equation derived for precipitations (p. 144).

Illustration: 50 ml. of 0.1 N hydrochloric acid are titrated with 0.1 N sodium hydroxide. If methyl yellow is used as indicator, the change will occur when the hydrogen-ion concentration is about 10^{-4}. In other words, p_T is about 4.0 and $a = -10^{-4}$.

$$\text{T.E.} = \frac{av}{nV} \times 100 = \frac{-10^{-4} \times 100}{50 \times 0.1} \times 100 = -0.2 \text{ per cent.}$$

If the titration is continued to the phenolphthalein endpoint, p_T is about 9 and p_{OH} is 5 (at room temperature). Then $[OH^-] = a = 10^{-5}$.

$$\text{T.E.} = +0.02 \text{ per cent.}$$

Therefore the change occurs about 0.2 per cent too soon with methyl yellow and 0.02 per cent too late with phenolphthalein, the difference between the two endpoints amounting to 0.22 per cent in the titration of 0.1 N solutions. This range can be confirmed experimentally if care is taken that the solutions are free from carbon dioxide.

In the titration of 0.01 N solutions the titration error becomes −2 per cent with methyl yellow or +0.2 per cent with phenolphthalein. It follows that methyl yellow is not suitable for this case; an indicator changing nearer to a p_H of 7 should be used. With methyl red, for example, if $p_T = 6$, then $a = -10^{-6}$ and the error is only −0.02 per cent.

The Titration of a Weak Acid or Base.—The simple equation is not adequate for the calculation of titration errors in the determination of weak acids or bases, in the displacement titration of salts of weak acids or weak bases, or in the titration of mixtures of acids or of bases. Here the ionization constants have to be considered. For example, in the titration of a weak acid HA, one has

$$\frac{[H^+][A^-]}{[HA]} = K_a, \tag{8}$$

$$\frac{[HA]}{[A^-]} = \frac{[H^+]}{K_a}.$$

From the rules of proportionality, it follows that

$$\frac{[HA]}{[A^-] + [HA]} = \frac{[H^+]}{K_a + [H^+]}, \tag{127}$$

and the titration error expressed in per cent is

$$\text{T.E.} = \frac{-100\,[HA]}{[A^-] + [HA]} = \frac{-100\,[H^+]}{K_a + [H^+]}. \tag{128}$$

This equation[2] neglects the part of [HA] furnished by hydrolysis of the salt, which would have to be considered for an exact result.

[2] It has been assumed here that the salt is completely dissociated, and that the activity of the anion is equal to the salt concentration.

Exact mathematical expressions for the titration error in acid-base titrations have been given by P. S. Roller, *J. Am. Chem. Soc.*, **54**, 3485 (1932). These calculations are of great theoretical interest, but are too involved for ordinary practical use, the more so since various factors affect the ionization constants of weak electrolytes (including indicators), as well as the activity coefficients of ions.

Illustration: 0.1 N acetic acid ($K = 1.8 \times 10^{-5}$) is titrated with 0.1 N alkali. If the titration is stopped at a p_T of 5, $[H^+] = 10^{-5}$, and the titration error is:

$$\text{T.E.} = \frac{-100 \times 10^{-5}}{1.8 \times 10^{-5} + 10^{-5}} = \frac{-100}{2.8} = -35.7 \text{ per cent.}$$

At $p_T = 6$, $[H^+] = 10^{-6}$:

$$\text{T.E.} = \frac{-100 \times 10^{-6}}{1.8 \times 10^{-5} + 10^{-6}} = \frac{-100}{19} = -5.26 \text{ per cent.}$$

At $p_T = 7$, $[H^+] = 10^{-7}$:

$$\text{T.E.} = \frac{-100 \times 10^{-7}}{1.8 \times 10^{-5} + 10^{-7}} = \frac{-100}{181} = -0.55 \text{ per cent,}$$

while at $p_T = 8$, $[H^+] = 10^{-8}$:

$$\text{T.E.} = \frac{-100 \times 10^{-8}}{1.8 \times 10^{-5} + 10^{-8}} = \frac{-100}{1801} = -0.055 \text{ per cent.}$$

Actually the error is slightly less in the last case, because part of the acetic acid comes from hydrolysis and this should be subtracted. At a p_H of 8 in the titration of 0.1 N acetic acid with 0.1 alkali, the concentration of acetate is practically 0.05 N, while that of the acetic acid is:

$$[HA] = \frac{[H^+][A^-]}{K_a} = \frac{10^{-8} \times 5 \times 10^{-2}}{1.8 \times 10^{-5}} = 2.8 \times 10^{-5}.$$

Hydrolysis takes place according to the equation:

$$A^- + H_2O \rightleftarrows HA + OH^-. \tag{20}$$

Equal concentrations of acid and hydroxyl ions are formed by this reaction. Since in this case $[H^+] = 10^{-8}$, $[OH^-]$ must be 10^{-6}, and the concentration of acetic acid formed by hydrolysis must also be 10^{-6}. Therefore the concentration of acetic acid which remains to be titrated is $2.8 \times 10^{-5} - 0.1 \times 10^{-5} = 2.7 \times 10^{-5}$. Obviously this difference is small enough to be neglected, and equation (128) is sufficiently accurate for most purposes.

It would appear from the foregoing that the titration error is generally independent of dilution. This applies in the case of acetic acid if the titration is carried to a p_H of 8 or 9; however, it is no longer true if the solution is weaker than 0.001 N. Hydrolysis, which under such conditions is relatively much greater, must then be considered in the calculations.

Whether or not an acid of given concentration can be titrated to a predetermined p_T, without exceeding a given error, may be ascertained simply if the ionization constant is known. Suppose that 50 ml. of 0.1 N weak acid are to be titrated with 0.1 N alkali. The total volume increases to 100 ml. If an error of -0.2 per cent is permissible, the titration can be stopped as soon as only 0.1 ml. of 0.1 N acid remains unneutralized. This corresponds to a concentration $[HA] = 10^{-4}$ N in the total volume.

Now, if it is desired to titrate to a p_T of 9, $[H^+]$ will be 10^{-9} and $[OH^-]$, 10^{-5}. The concentration of HA furnished by hydrolysis will also be 10^{-5} and the total concentration of HA becomes approximately:

$$[HA] = 10^{-4} + 10^{-5} = 1.1 \times 10^{-4}.$$

Near the end-point, $[A^-]$ becomes practically 5×10^{-2} N. Substituting these values, one finds for K_{HA}:

$$K_{HA} = \frac{[H^+][A^-]}{[HA]} = \frac{10^{-9} \times 5 \times 10^{-2}}{1.1 \times 10^{-4}} = 4.5 \times 10^{-7}.$$

Thus only acids with K_{HA} greater than 4.5×10^{-7} may be titrated with an error not to exceed -0.2 per cent, if 0.1 N solutions are used and the end-point is taken at $p_H = 9$. Were the end-point taken at $p_H = 10$, 0.1 N solutions of any acid with constant greater than 2.5×10^{-8} could be titrated within the same limit of error.

In the same manner it may be found that for titrations to a p_H of 9, exact to -0.2 per cent, an acid must have a constant of 2.5×10^{-7} or greater if the solution is 0.01 N, or of 4.5×10^{-8} or greater if the solution is 0.001 N.

From this one might conclude that the accuracy increases with decreasing concentration. This conclusion is not correct, for practically one does not titrate to a p_H of exactly 9.0, but has a possible deviation of at least ± 0.2. Furthermore, the color change is less distinct in dilute solutions so that the absolute accuracy is smaller. These practical details will be considered more extensively in Volume II.

In general, the possibility of titrating an acid or base with an error of not to exceed 0.2 per cent may be decided from the following data:

Titration Error Less Than 0.2 Per Cent

Titration of Weak Acids

$p_T = $ 9, K_{HA} must be greater than 3×10^{-7};
$p_T = $ 10, K_{HA} must be greater than 2×10^{-8}.

Titration of Weak Bases

$p_T = $ 5, K_{BOH} must be greater than 3×10^{-7};
$p_T = $ 4, K_{BOH} must be greater than 2×10^{-8}.

If the ionization constants are smaller than these, it is still possible in certain cases to obtain useful results by titrating to the p_H which the solution should have at the equivalence-point. Here one uses a reference solution of the correct p_H, containing the same quantity of indicator as the titrated solution. For example, a 0.1 N solution of a base, for which $K_{BOH} = 10^{-9}$, is titrated with 0.1 N acid. At the equivalence-point (see p. 21) the p_H becomes:

$$p_H = 7 - \tfrac{1}{2}p_b - \tfrac{1}{2}\log c = 7 - 4.5 + 0.65 = 3.15.$$

If one could titrate exactly to a p_H of 3.15, correct values could be found. However, the color change is not sharp and it is possible to make an error of ± 0.2 in the perception of p_H. This corresponds to a titration error of ± 1 per cent, since the p_H changes only gradually in the titration of such a weak base or acid (*cf.* p. 54).

In the manner described, one can determine the titration error for every titration of a weak acid or base, if the constants are known. The error caused by titration to a given exponent may be calculated closely and applied as a correction, but it should be noted that the observational error of p_H measurement is variable over the range of, say, ± 0.2 units.

Titration of a Weak Acid with a Weak Base.—Although one would not titrate a weak acid such as acetic directly with a weak base like ammonia, there are circumstances in which this in effect has to be done. For example, it might be necessary to determine acetic acid in a solution containing ammonium chloride. The problem also has significance for the preparation of solutions containing equivalent amounts of a weak acid and a weak base.

In the titration of acetic acid with ammonia, the equivalence-point lies at $p_H = 7.0$. If with the aid of a reference solution one can recognize the end-point within an error of ± 0.2 units, the titration error possible may be calculated easily from the p_H change in the vicinity of the equivalence-point. As was seen on p. 55, if the solutions are 0.1 N, 99.5 per cent of the acid is neutralized at a $p_H = 6.8$, while 0.5 per cent excess ammonia is present at $p_H = 7.2$. Therefore an observational error of 0.2 in p_H corresponds to a titration error of 0.5 per cent.

Titration of Dibasic Acids or Mixtures of Acids.—The calculation of titration error in the determination of a moderately strong acid in the presence of a weak one, or in the titration of a dibasic acid to its acid salt, has great practical importance. For illustration, consider the commonly performed titration of carbonic acid with alkali or of carbonate with acid, to the bicarbonate stage. To keep the derivation simple, approximate equations will be used.

For carbonic acid, K_1 is 3×10^{-7} and K_2 is 4.5×10^{-11}. The hydrogen-ion concentration of a bicarbonate solution may be calculated readily from equation (45), p. 27:

$$[H^+] = \sqrt{K_1 K_2} = 3.68 \times 10^{-9},$$

$$p_H = 8.43.$$

McCoy[3] found experimentally a p_H of 8.4, in good agreement with the theoretical value.

This p_H is the titration exponent to which one should titrate if carbonic acid or carbonate is being converted to bicarbonate. What error is to be expected if the titration of carbonic acid is stopped at a p_H of 8.0, or that of carbonate at 8.8? In the former case, the total concentration of carbonic acid at $p_H = 8.0$ may be calculated from the first ionization constant of carbonic acid. If the solutions were originally 0.1 N, the bicarbonate concentration will be 5×10^{-2} N at the end-point. Then:

$$[H_2CO_3] = \frac{[H^+][HCO_3^-]}{K_1} = \frac{10^{-8} \times 5 \times 10^{-2}}{3 \times 10^{-7}} = 1.67 \times 10^{-3}.$$

This quantity includes, in addition to the carbonic acid which remains untitrated, an amount formed by hydrolysis according to the equation:

$$2HCO_3^- \rightleftarrows H_2CO_3 + CO_3^{--},$$

[3] H. N. McCoy, *Am. Chem. J.*, **29**, 452 (1903); **31**, 503 (1904).

whereby the carbonate and carbonic acid formed are equivalent. The concentration of carbonate can be calculated from the second ionization constant:

$$[CO_3^-] = \frac{[HCO_3^-]}{[H^+]} K_2 = \frac{5 \times 10^{-2} \times 4.5 \times 10^{-11}}{10^{-8}} = 2.2 \times 10^{-4}.$$

Therefore the concentration of carbonic acid due to hydrolysis is also 2.2×10^{-4}, and this must be subtracted from the total. The concentration of carbonic acid which remains to be titrated is then:

$$(1.67 \times 10^{-3}) - (0.22 \times 10^{-3}) = 1.45 \times 10^{-3}.$$

This corresponds to 2.9 per cent of the original carbonic acid concentration (0.1 N = 0.05 M), hence the titration error is -2.9 per cent. It may be shown that in this case *the titration error is independent of dilution*, at least down to a concentration of 0.001 N. At smaller concentrations the equations are not strictly valid.

If the titration of carbonate is stopped at a p_H of 8.8 instead of 8.4, the error may be calculated in a similar way. At 8.8, $[H^+] = 1.6 \times 10^{-9}$, and the total concentration of carbonate ion is:

$$[CO_3^-] = \frac{[HCO_3^-]}{[H^+]} K_2 = \frac{5 \times 10^{-2} \times 4.5 \times 10^{-11}}{1.6 \times 10^{-9}} = 1.41 \times 10^{-3}.$$

Some of the carbonate comes from hydrolysis, and this part is equivalent to the free carbonic acid:

$$[H_2CO_3] = \frac{[H^+][HCO_3^-]}{K_1} = \frac{1.6 \times 10^{-9} \times 5 \times 10^{-2}}{3 \times 10^{-7}} = 2.7 \times 10^{-4}.$$

Subtracting this from the total, the concentration of carbonate remaining untitrated is found to be:

$$[CO_3^-] = (1.41 \times 10^{-3}) - (0.27 \times 10^{-3}) = 1.14 \times 10^{-3}.$$

Thus the titration error is -2.3 per cent, based upon a solution originally 0.1 N in carbonate ions; it is independent of dilution in this case also.

From these examples it follows that in titrations of carbonate to bicarbonate or of carbonic acid as a monobasic acid, to a p_H of 8.4, the titration error amounts to about ± 2.5 per cent if the endpoint can be perceived only within 0.4 of a p_H unit. Therefore these titrations can give satisfactory results only when definite precautions are taken, and accuracy to better than 1 per cent is not to be expected. Practical experience confirms this conclusion.

Phosphoric acid may be titrated as a monobasic or dibasic acid, and the most favorable conditions ascertained through the same type of reasoning. The ionization constants are:[4]

$$K_1 = 1.1 \times 10^{-2}, \qquad p_{K_1} = 1.96$$

$$K_2 = 1.4 \times 10^{-7}, \qquad p_{K_2} = 6.85$$

$$K_3 = 3.6 \times 10^{-13}, \qquad p_{K_3} = 12.44.$$

At the first equivalence-point ($H_2PO_4^-$),

$$p_H = \frac{1.96 + 6.85}{2} = 4.40.$$

By titrating to the yellow color of methyl orange or to an intermediate color of bromocresol green, preferably with the aid of a reference solution of $p_H = 4.4$, results accurate to within about 0.5 per cent may be obtained.

At the second equivalence-point (HPO_4^{--}),

$$p_H = \frac{6.85 + 12.44}{2} = 9.64,$$

and the titration exponent is thus 9.6. If phenolphthalein is used as indicator, a reference solution is unconditionally necessary. The pink color appears at a lower p_H and too little acid would be found if the titration were stopped at the first pink. It is better to employ thymolphthalein and titrate to a very faint blue. The liquid might also be half saturated with sodium chloride and titrated to a pale rose color of phenolphthalein. In Volume II the practical details will be entered into more fully.

The calculation of errors in the titration of polyacid bases or mixtures of bases is carried out in the same way as for polybasic acids. For example, quinine has the constants $p_{K_1} = 6.0$ and $p_{K_2} = 9.9$. At the first equivalence-point in the neutralization (if $K_w = 10^{-14}$),

$$p_H = 14 - \frac{(6.0 + 9.9)}{2} = 6.05,$$

[4] These constants are the older "concentration constants," whereas those given in the Appendix are activity products.

and the titration exponent is therefore 6.05. In practice, titration of the salt with a base may be carried just to the alkaline color of methyl red, or neutralization of the free alkaloid with an acid may be taken to the first change of this indicator from yellow to orange.

Hahn[5] sought to eliminate the titration error by performing a series of back-titrations, averaging results obtained by approaching the end-point in each direction. From a practical viewpoint, it would seem easier to determine the titration error experimentally and correct for it.

4. The Titration Error in Complex-Formation Titrations; The Determination of Iodide with Mercuric Salts.—From the complex dissociation constant and the sensitivity of the indicator, one can calculate titration errors in the same way as was done in the case of weak acids. As an illustration, consider the determination of iodide with a mercuric salt. Upon addition of mercuric chloride to an iodide solution, the latter remains clear while complex HgI_4 ions are being formed:

$$Hg^{++} + 4I^- \rightleftarrows HgI_4^=.$$

Near the equivalence-point a red turbidity of mercuric iodide appears:

$$HgI_4^= + Hg^{++} \rightleftarrows 2HgI_2 .$$

Provided that the solutions used are not too dilute, this turbidity anticipates the equivalence-point; that is, some of the complex decomposes according to the equation:

$$HgI_4^= \rightleftarrows HgI_2 + 2I^- .$$

Quantitatively the respective concentrations are governed by the complex dissociation constant K:

$$\frac{[HgI_2][I^-]^2}{[HgI_4^=]} = K = 10^{-7} \text{ (approximately}[6]).$$

[5] F. L. Hahn, *Mikrochim. Acta*, **3**, 9 (1938). An experimental method of computing titration blanks is given by B. Park, *Ind. Eng. Chem. Anal. Ed.*, **8**, 32 (1936); see also F. W. Glaze, *ibid.*, **12**, 14 (1940).

[6] According to M. S. Sherrill, *Z. physik. Chem.*, **47**, 104 (1904), K ranges from 1.7 to 3.2 × 10⁻⁷. F. Auerbach and W. Plüddemann, Experim. und krit. Beiträge zur Neubearbeitung der Vereinbarungen, Kais. Ges.-Amt. **1**, 209 (1909), consider the value to be 1 × 10⁻⁷; *cf.* also I. M. Kolthoff, *Pharm. Weekblad*, **57**, 836 (1920).

If in a solution of pure potassium mercuric iodide the concentration of mercuric iodide exceeds its saturation value, red mercuric iodide will separate out and the endpoint will appear too soon. However, one can calculate a correction for this. At the endpoint the liquid is just saturated with mercuric iodide; to reach the equivalence-point, as much more reagent would have to be added as would correspond to the quantity of mercuric iodide precipitated at the latter point; i.e., in a pure solution of the complex.

From the equation

$$HgI_4^- \rightleftarrows HgI_2 + 2I^-,$$

it is seen that at the equivalence-point the number of moles of mercuric iodide is equal to half the number of moles of iodide ion. Then the concentration k of the titrating agent, which would be needed for a correction, amounts to half of the iodide-ion concentration less the concentration c_{HgI_2} of a saturated mercuric iodide solution. The correction can be expressed in milliliters of reagent of any normality N, if the final volume v is known:

$$Correction = \frac{v \times k}{N}.$$

From the expression for the dissociation constant:

$$[I^-] = \sqrt{\frac{[HgI_4^-]}{c_{HgI_2}}K}.$$

It follows that the concentration k, needed to calculate the correction, is:

$$k = \frac{1}{2}\sqrt{\frac{[HgI_4^-]}{c_{HgI_2}}K} - c_{HgI_2}.$$

Taking K as 10^{-7} and using Sherrill's value[6] of 1.3×10^{-4} for the solubility, c_{HgI_2}, of mercuric iodide at 25°C., one finds that:

$$k = 1.4 \times 10^{-2}\sqrt{[HgI_4^-]} - 1.3 \times 10^{-4},$$

$$Correction \text{ (in milliliters)} = \frac{v}{N}(1.4 \times 10^{-2}\sqrt{[HgI_4^-]} - 1.3 \times 10^{-4}).$$

Illustration: Twenty-five ml. of 0.1 N potassium iodide are titrated with 0.05 M mercuric chloride. At the endpoint the volume v is about 37 ml., and the concentration of mercuric iodide ion, $[HgI_4^=]$ is $\dfrac{25}{37} \times \dfrac{0.1}{4} = 1.7 \times 10^{-2}$ molar.

$$k = 1.4 \times 10^{-2} \sqrt{1.7 \times 10^{-2}} - 1.3 \times 10^{-4} = 1.7 \times 10^{-3}$$

$$Correction = \frac{37 \times 1.7 \times 10^{-3}}{0.1} = 0.63 \text{ ml. of } 0.1 \text{ N } (0.05 \text{ M) reagent.}$$

The turbidity of mercuric iodide, therefore, appears too soon by about 0.63 ml. of 0.05 M mercuric solution, and this amount should be added to the observed titration as a correction. That the calculated figure agrees with the experimentally determined value can be seen in the accompanying table.

CORRECTION FOR THE TITRATION OF 25 ML. OF 0.1 N IODIDE WITH A MERCURIC SALT SOLUTION

Final volume v, ml.	Experimental correction, ml. 0.05 M	Calculated correction, ml. 0.05 M
37	0.60	0.63
50	0.73	0.70
75	0.91	0.86
100	1.05	1.02
125	1.14	1.07

For other dilutions, the corrections may be obtained by interpolation of these data.

As a final illustration, consider the practically important Liebig-Denigès titration of cyanide in ammoniacal medium, with silver nitrate as reagent and iodide as indicator. One wishes to know: (a) the silver-ion concentration at the endpoint; (b) whether the endpoint is found before or after the equivalence-point; and (c) the titration error.

Illustration: Suppose that 0.2 molar potassium cyanide is being titrated with 0.1 molar silver nitrate, and that the amounts of ammonia and iodide are so chosen that at the endpoint (not the equivalence-point) their concentrations are 0.1 M and 0.01 M, respectively. The constants necessary are:

$$[Ag^+][I^-] = 10^{-16},$$

$$\frac{[Ag^+][NH_3]^2}{[Ag(NH_3)_2^+]} = 7 \times 10^{-8},$$

$$\frac{[Ag^+][CN^-]^2}{[Ag(CN)_2^-]} = 10^{-21}.$$

(a) At the endpoint:

$$[Ag^+] = \frac{10^{-16}}{[I^-]} = \frac{10^{-16}}{10^{-2}} = 10^{-14}.$$

(b) At the equivalence-point:

$$[Ag(NH_3)_2^+] = \frac{[Ag^+][NH_3]^2}{7 \times 10^{-8}} = \frac{[Ag^+] \times 0.1^2}{7 \times 10^{-8}} = 1.43 \times 10^5 [Ag^+],$$

$$[Ag(CN)_2^-] = 0.05 - \{[Ag^+] + [Ag(NH_3)_2^+]\} = 0.05 \text{ (approx.)}.$$

From the above and the equation

$$Ag(CN)_2^- \rightleftarrows Ag^+ + 2CN^-,$$

it can be seen that:

$$[CN^-] = 2\{[Ag^+] + [Ag(NH_3)_2^+]\} = 2[Ag(NH_3)_2^+] \text{ (approx.)}.$$

$$[CN^-] = 2 \times 1.43 \times 10^5[Ag^+] = 2.86 \times 10^5[Ag^+].$$

Then

$$[Ag^+] = \frac{[Ag(CN)_2^-] \times 10^{-21}}{[CN^-]^2} = \frac{0.05 \times 10^{-21}}{2.86^2 \times 10^{10} [Ag^+]^2},$$

$$[Ag^+] = \sqrt[3]{0.611 \times 10^{-33}} = 0.85 \times 10^{-11} = 8.5 \times 10^{-12}.$$

Since it was found that at the endpoint $[Ag^+] = 10^{-14}$, it appears that under these conditions the endpoint occurs before the equivalence-point.

(c) At the equivalence-point, $[CN^-] = 2.86 \times 10^5 \times 8.5 \times 10^{-12} = 2.43 \times 10^{-6}$.

At the endpoint,

$$[CN^-]^2 = \frac{5 \times 10^{-2} \times 10^{-21}}{10^{-14}} = 5 \times 10^{-9},$$

$$[CN^-] = 7.07 \times 10^{-5}.$$

Making the assumptions that the final volume V remains unchanged between these two points, and that it is twice the initial volume, one has:

    Millimoles of cyanide at endpoint = 7.07×10^{-5} V
    Millimoles of cyanide at equivalence-point = 0.24×10^{-5} V
    Millimoles of cyanide not titrated at endpoint = 6.83×10^{-5} V

Since the number of millimoles of cyanide originally present was 0.1 V, the titration error in per cent is

$$\text{T.E.} = \frac{6.83 \times 10^{-5} \times 100}{0.1} = 0.07.$$

For practical reasons the foregoing calculations are only approximate. While it is possible to derive exact expressions, these become quite involved and are tedious to use. The calculations given are adequate for most purposes.

5. The Titration Error in Oxidimetry or Reductimetry.—In oxidation-reduction reactions the titration error depends upon the nature of the indicator as well as upon the characteristics of the system being titrated. In the preceding chapter two kinds of indicators were mentioned:

(a) *Specific indicators:* These react with the substance being titrated or with the titrating reagent. If the sensitivity of the indicator and the equilibrium constant of the system are known, the titration error may be calculated in the same way as has been done in previous paragraphs. The titration error increases with increasing dilution. In Volume II these practical points will be considered further in the applications of iodimetry and permanganate titrations.

(b) *Oxidation-reduction indicators:* Knowing the transition interval of the indicator and the oxidation potentials of the systems involved, the titration error can be ascertained readily. Although the change of oxidation potential in the neighborhood of the equivalence-point is independent of dilution, within wide limits, the titration error increases with dilution because a certain quantity of reagent is required to produce a color change in the indicator. This error will naturally increase if a larger amount of indicator is taken.

6. Summary.—In considering the sources of error in volumetric analysis, one should distinguish between the *methodic* or *technical errors*, from which no titration is entirely free regardless of its chemical nature, and the *intrinsic* or *specific error*, that is based upon the equilibrium constant of the reaction and the accuracy with which the equivalence-point can be perceived. The latter is designated here as the *titration error*. The methodic errors may be ascribed to imperfections in measuring apparatus and sensory organs, such as inaccuracies in the calibration of burettes, pipettes and volumetric flasks, faulty readings (parallax errors), effects of temperature variations, and errors in the drainage of vessels calibrated for delivery.

These methodic errors may be further classified as accidental or constant. The accidental errors, due to variable causes such as faulty readings, mechanical losses, errors of subjective perception, etc. affect the reproducibility or *precision* of a titration, and may be treated statistically if several determinations are made.[7] The constant errors include those due to inaccurate calibration and other consistent causes; these lower the absolute accuracy of an analysis without affecting the precision. All methodic errors have the common attribute of being diminishable by refinements in experimental technique. For example, weight burettes may be used and aliquots taken in terms of weight rather than volume, so that errors of reading, drainage and calibration are replaced by the much smaller errors of weighing. By such means the accuracy of a titration can be increased at the expense of simplicity and rapidity. Even the personal error of variations in endpoint recognition may be reduced by application of photometric methods.

The titration error, however, is independent of the experimental accuracy with which one works. Conforming solely to the chemical process involved and to the nature of the indicator, it is specific for each volumetric procedure. It cannot be diminished arbitrarily; the error is zero only if the indicator changes exactly at the equivalence-point. If the indicator is too sensitive, it changes before the equivalence-point, while if the sensitivity is slight the equivalence-point may be overstepped. The smaller the equilibrium constant of the underlying reaction (or the solubility product of a precipitate), the more abrupt is the change of ion concentrations near the equivalence-point. In such cases one may expect a sharp endpoint if a suitable indicator is used. On the other hand, when concentration changes in the region of the equivalence-point are relatively small, there is no sharp change and the result cannot be very exact.

Ordinarily the relative errors increase with increasing dilution, as has been explained previously. While the best conditions for keeping the titration error small may in general be deduced mathematically, they should always be tested experimentally. A correction obtained by calculation and confirmed empirically may be applied with confidence to an observed titration.

[7] A. A. Benedetti-Pichler, *Ind. Eng. Chem. Anal. Ed.*, **8**, 373 (1936).

CHAPTER VII

REACTION VELOCITY; CATALYSIS AND INDUCED REACTIONS

1. General Principles.—Reactions depending upon the union of ions, such as those met in neutralization and precipitation analyses, are practically instantaneous. While some crystalline precipitates separate rather slowly from their supersaturated solutions, this difficulty may be overcome by so modifying the medium that the precipitate becomes more insoluble. Thus the addition of alcohol or acetone hastens the precipitation of barium sulfate or calcium oxalate.

In contrast with ion-combination reactions, there are some oxidation-reduction processes that take place slowly. Although reactions of this kind may proceed practically quantitatively in a given direction, they may be unsuitable for volumetric purposes because of their low velocity. In such an instance it is of great advantage if one can add a material called a *catalyst*, which accelerates the reaction. One slow oxidation-reduction reaction is that of hydrogen peroxide with iodide in acid solution:

$$H_2O_2 + 2I^- + 2H^+ \rightleftarrows 2H_2O + I_2 .$$

This is especially slow in dilute solution, but molybdate acts as a strong positive catalyst so that in its presence the reaction is practically instantaneous. In the iodimetric titration of peroxide it is necessary to add a little molybdate solution if one wishes to titrate the liberated iodine with thiosulfate immediately after mixing the reagents.

Under certain conditions a reaction may be delayed by the presence of a suitable substance; such a material is called a *negative catalyst*. For example, the air oxidation of sulfite or bisulfite solution is retarded by the addition of ethyl alcohol, polyvalent alcohols or alkaloid salts. These compounds may be used to stabilize the standard solutions of sulfite or bisulfite that are employed in aldehyde determinations.

Closely related to catalytic reactions are *induced reactions*, which play an important role in various volumetric procedures. Leaving a more detailed discussion for a later section, one instance will serve as an illustration. Some reducing agents are only very slowly oxidized by air: thiocyanate and acid ferrous solutions are relatively stable. If a thiocyanate solution, however, is titrated with permanganate in the presence of air, a small portion of the thiocyanate reacts with atmospheric oxygen. This reaction is said to be *induced* by the rapid oxidation of thiocyanate with permanganate. A slow reaction between two substances may thus be accelerated if one of the two reacts rapidly with a third substance, the slow reaction being induced by the more rapid.

To analytical chemists, induced reactions are of interest chiefly because they are responsible for errors in certain titrations. Some strong oxidants which are fairly stable may decompose more rapidly with evolution of oxygen during a reduction process. Permanganate is a case in point. It would be desirable to have more information about such phenomena.

Heterogeneous catalysis (in which the catalyst is present as a separate phase) has only a subordinate part in volumetric analysis. It is manifest in the accelerated decomposition of permanganate solutions in the presence of finely divided manganese dioxide. Adsorption of reagents upon a surface may also result in a positive catalytic effect (contact action).

2. Theoretical Considerations.—To treat catalytic phenomena in a mathematical way and thereby to derive exact information concerning the possibility of errors in a titration would be the logical aim of this chapter. Unfortunately, the present knowledge of this subject enables one to predict very little about qualitative effects and practically nothing quantitatively. Therefore it is necessary to resort to empirically observed facts, and no attempt will be made to give an extensive theoretical discussion.

In general, one cannot tell in advance whether a substance will act as a catalyst in a given reaction, or if so, to what extent; neither is it possible to predict the occurrence of induced reactions. The latter, especially, seem to be accidental and arbitrary. For example, the reaction between permanganate and hydrochloric acid is noticeably induced during a titration of ferrous salts, yet it is normal during a titration of arsenious acid.

Since the effects of catalysis or induction are all expressed in terms of the speed of a given reaction, it is in order to consider first some conceptions of reaction velocity. Arrhenius[1] assumed that in a given system not all the molecules are capable of reacting, but only certain *active* ones. This postulates an equilibrium between inactive and active molecules, the effect of a catalyst being to displace the equilibrium in favor of the active variety. Such a deduction cannot be correct, for an increase in the number of active molecules would shift the equilibrium of the reaction being catalyzed. This would be contrary to experience. Therefore one can only assume, according to Arrhenius' theory, that a catalyst hastens the establishment of equilibrium between inactive and active molecules; but this is nothing more than saying that a catalyst influences the speed of reaction. The theory gives no adequate reason for the catalytic action, and on this account it is not a satisfactory working hypothesis.

A "radiation theory" has been developed by W. C. McC. Lewis and J. Perrin as a consequence of Arrhenius' theory. Lewis started with the hypothesis of Trautz, that a reaction takes place only when the molecules are activated through absorption of infra-red radiation. The energy of the molecules is increased to a critical point at which they become chemically active. The reaction velocity is therefore not dependent upon the total number of molecular collisions, but rather upon the number of collisions involving molecules which possess sufficient energy. The number of effective collisions is equal to the product of the total number of collisions and the probability that enough energy is present. A catalyst may then be considered to assist in the transfer of infra-red radiation to the reacting molecules. Induced reactions may be pictured in much the same way: a substance which by itself is capable of reacting only very slowly is activated by an accompanying process, thereby becoming able to react much more intensively. Although the radiation theory offered an attractive method of attacking the problem of catalytic action, later experiments failed to confirm that infra-red radiation plays an essential part in the phenomena.[2]

---

[1] S. Arrhenius, *Z. physik. Chem.*, **4**, 226 (1889).

[2] For discussions of the radiation theory, see *Trans. Faraday Soc.*, **17**, (1922); also W. C. McC. Lewis, *A System of Physical Chemistry*, Vol. III, Longmans, Green and Co., London 1919; E. K. Rideal and H. S. Taylor, *Catalysis in Theory and Practice*, 2nd Edition, The Macmillan Co., London 1926; H. S. Taylor and collaborators, *A Treatise on Physical Chemistry*, 2nd Edition, Vol. II, p. 984, D. Van Nostrand Co., New York, 1931; G. M. Schwab, *Catalysis from the Standpoint of Chemical Kinetics*, translation by H. S. Taylor and R. Spence, D. Van Nostrand Co., New York, 1937; W. Frankenburger, *Katalytische Umsetzungen.*, Akadem. Verlagsges., Leipzig 1937; *Twelfth Report of the Committee on Catalysis*, National Research Council, John Wiley and Sons, New York 1940.

Qualitatively one may regard a catalytic process as consisting in the union of the catalyst and one or more of the reagents to form a complex that is capable of reacting (as, for example, in the case of ester catalysis by hydrogen or hydroxyl ions). It is not possible to obtain a quantitative explanation of the changes in reaction velocity from this assumption, since it tells nothing of energy exchanges. Yet there may be a causal relationship between complex formation and variations in the ease with which energy changes take place.

Böeseken[3] proposed a theory of "molecular dislocation" for explaining catalytic behavior. That the catalyst forms an intermediate product with one of the reagents he regards as very unlikely, from experimental grounds; even if it does, the mechanism is still not clear. He pictures catalysis more as a physical than a chemical phenomenon: by collision of the catalyst with a reagent molecule the activity of the latter is increased. This change in activity is termed dislocation. Catalysts, which usually have a polar character and an open field of force, are able through a kind of induction to superimpose these properties on a screened system, so that this acts more or less polarized in subsequent collisions. Conversely it is also possible that negative catalysis takes place through a reduction in the polarization of a polar reagent.

According to this conception it is possible to understand why the catalytic effect upon a given substance varies widely for different catalysts: each catalyst produces a specific dislocation. For further details and examples, the reader is referred to Böeseken's articles.

A word should be said here of the important theory of chain reactions suggested by Christiansen.[4] This is of especial interest in the explanation of "negative catalysis" (better, "reaction retardation") and induced reactions. The reaction between sulfite and oxygen is a chain reaction. The process may be represented as follows: One molecule or ion (sulfite) having sufficient energy to be active in the Arrhenius sense, reacts with another (oxygen). The addition product so formed carries for an instant an abnormal amount of energy, not only the critical energy needed to bring about reaction, but also a considerable amount from the heat of reaction, which is characteristic of chain processes. Thus the particle has enough kinetic or poten-

[3] J. Böeseken, Chem. Weekblad, 25, 135 (1928); Trans. Faraday Soc., 24, 611 (1928).

[4] J. A. Christiansen, J. Phys. Chem., 28, 145 (1924), J. A. Christiansen and H. A. Kramers, Z. physik. Chem., 104, 458 (1928), Trans. Faraday Soc., 24, 596 (1928); see also H. L. J. Bäckström, Medd. Vetenskapsakad. Nobelinst., 6, Nos. 15 and 16 (1926-27), J. Am. Chem. Soc., 49, 1460 (1927); H. N. Alyea and H. L. J. Bäckström, ibid., 51, 90 (1929).

THEORETICAL CONSIDERATIONS

tial energy to "activate" another molecule or ion, which in turn reacts. In this way the reaction can be projected through a great number of collisions.

With the aid of the Christiansen theory many cases of inhibition phenomena can be understood. It has often been noted that in oxidation reactions those substances which act as inhibitors are themselves easily oxidizable, as polyvalent alcohols, hydroquinone, etc. These are able to break the reaction chain. If an activated molecule strikes an inhibitor molecule, the latter can become activated and react with oxygen, but the heat of reaction is so low or is taken up in such form that it is not transmitted to another particle. The main reaction is thereby stopped. It should be noted that the inhibitor is oxidized in the process; therefore it may not be considered as a negative catalyst in the sense of Ostwald's definition.

Some of the characteristics of induced reactions can be explained on the same grounds, although no quantitative information can be gained and in many cases it is not yet known whether the induced reaction proceeds by a chain mechanism or in some other way. The air oxidation of sulfite is without doubt a chain reaction, and it takes place quite rapidly. Arsenite is only very slowly oxidized, but can act as an inhibitor of sulfite oxidation and is thereby oxidized itself. If one mixes sulfite and arsenite, a noticeable air oxidation of arsenite occurs. Why should the sulfite-oxygen chain reaction induce the arsenite oxidation? Evidently if an arsenite ion is struck in the course of the chain reaction, it becomes activated and therefore is easily oxidized; the chain process is able to raise the energy state of arsenite ions.

Since the quantitative side of this promising theory has not yet been sufficiently developed, we must for the present be content with empirical facts in our considerations of the theoretical principles of quantitative analysis, giving up the attempt to explain catalytic action theoretically. With Ostwald and others, we shall define catalysts as substances which affect the velocity of a reaction without themselves undergoing a permanent change. As Ostwald[5] emphasized, it is only a question of intensity: "Fundamentally, every foreign material acts as a catalyst, i.e., alters the speed of reaction." The question as to whether or not a negative catalyst acts by neutralization or hindrance of positive catalysts will be left open.

[5] W. Ostwald, *Grundriss der allgemeinen Chemie*, 4th Edition, Theodor Steinkopf, Dresden 1909 p. 331.

From the above, one may surmise that there are several types of homogeneous catalysis. Although our present knowledge is meager, it is possible to make some generalizations which may be of practical importance in oxidation-reduction catalysis. It is widely true of the homogeneous catalysis of redox processes that the catalyst can exist in oxidized and reduced states, hence is a redox substance. The oxidized form of the catalyst must be able to react rapidly with the reducing agent of the main reaction, and the reduced form with the oxidizing agent. A simple example is the catalytic action of the iodide-iodine pair on the oxidation of thiosulfate by hydrogen peroxide in weakly acid solution. The stoichiometry and kinetics of the reaction are assembled in the following equations:

(1) $\qquad H_2O_2 + I^- \rightarrow IO^- + H_2O$ (measurable velocity)

(2) $\qquad IO^- + H^+ \rightleftarrows HIO$ (very rapid, reversible)

(3) $\qquad HIO + I^- + H^+ \rightleftarrows I_2 + H_2O$ (very rapid, reversible)

(4) $\qquad I_2 + I^- \rightleftarrows I_3^-$ (very rapid, reversible)

(5) $\qquad I_3^- + 2S_2O_3^- \rightarrow S_4O_6^- + 3I^-$ (rapid, apparently complex)

(6) $\qquad H_2O_2 + 2S_2O_3^- + 2H^+ \rightarrow S_4O_6^- + 2H_2O$ (stoichiometric).

The velocity of the stoichiometric reaction (6) is governed in the presence of the catalyst by equation (1), since the other reactions proceed rapidly. Another example of simple catalysis is found in the decomposition of peroxide, which in alkaline medium is strongly accelerated by iodide. If the reaction velocities of the various steps were known, one could predict what redox materials would be useful as catalysts for a desired reaction. Unfortunately, this information is usually not available, so that a catalyst has to be found by trial. In this empirical procedure the following rule is of great assistance:[6] The normal potential of the catalytic pair must lie between the normal potentials of the two reacting systems:

$$Ox_1 + ne \rightleftarrows Red_1, \pi_{01}$$

$$Ox_2 + ne \rightleftarrows Red_2, \pi_{02}$$

$$Ox_1 + Red_2 \rightleftarrows Red_1 + Ox_2.$$

---

[6] cf. W. C. Bray, *Chem. Rev.*, **10**, 161 (1932); see also I. M. Kolthoff and R. S. Livingston, *Ind. Eng. Chem. Anal. Ed.*, **7**, 209 (1935).

The normal potential of the catalyst pair therefore must lie between π_{0_1} and π_{0_2}. Although this rule alone does not permit one to predict which substances can serve as catalysts for a given reaction (since the reaction velocities must also be suitable), it can serve to simplify the problem, in that a large number of materials may be eliminated without the necessity for trial. An example is the reaction of arsenious acid with ceric sulfate in acid solution. In Figure 17 are shown the normal potentials, calculated from free energy data for the half

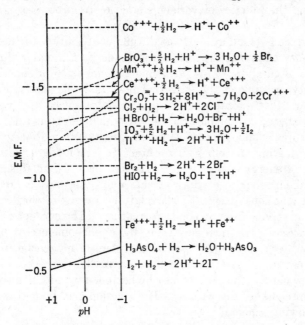

Fig. 17.—Normal Potentials for Several Reactions.

reactions, as a function of p_H over the range of -1 to $+1$. These potentials do not represent the theoretical normal potentials which would be determined by the activities of the reagents, but rather the normal potentials in concentration terms.

From the diagram it will be seen that the iodine-iodide pair can apparently exert almost no catalytic effect on the ceric sulfate-arsenious acid reaction, since at a p_H of zero the normal potential is too low. On the other hand, either the hypoiodite-iodine pair or the iodate-iodine pair might be useful. Actually it has been observed that iodide, iodine and iodate all have very strong catalytic influence.

The catalysis by iodide may be explained by the fact that it is first oxidized by ceric sulfate to hypoiodite or iodate. The bromine-bromide pair might also be active, but its catalytic effect is only very slight. Other possibilities would be the ferric-ferrous and thallic-thallous systems; practically they are ineffective, not showing suitable reaction rates. It would be unnecessary to try the cobaltous-cobaltic pair on account of its high potential. In connection with the search for useful catalysts, it is desirable to have available more details regarding the kinetics of various simple redox processes.

3. Induced Reactions.—A worthwhile contribution to the history and theory of induced reactions was made by Skrabal.[7] Just as in the case of catalysis, these phenomena of imparted or superimposed reactivity are among the long-known facts of chemistry. Lenssen and Löwenthal[8] pointed out long ago that Laplace and Berthollet had formulated a principle according to which "an atom set in motion by any force whatsoever can communicate its own motion to another atom with which it comes into contact." The modern view, that a transfer of energy occurs, is nothing more or less than this.

Schönbein[9] sought to draw a sharp line between catalytic and induced reactions, designating the latter as cases of the transfer of chemical activity from one body to another. The concept of "*chemical induction*" was introduced for these phenomena by Kessler,[10] while Luther and Schilow[11] set up a system of nomenclature for induced reactions. If a reaction between A and C proceeds by itself only very slowly, the process may be hastened by adding a substance B which reacts readily with A. The reaction may be represented by the following scheme:

$$A + C \rightarrow 0; \quad A + B \rightarrow +;$$

$$\begin{cases} A + B \rightarrow + \\ A + C \rightarrow + \end{cases}.$$

[7] A. Skrabal, *Die induzierten Reaktionen; ihre Geschichte und Theorie*, (Vol. 13, Samml. chem. und techn. Vorträge, Ahrens und Herz) Ferdinand Enke, Stuttgart 1908. Part of the material in Section 3 is taken from this clearly written volume.

[8] E. Lenssen and J. Löwenthal, *J. prakt. Chem.*, **86**, 215 (1862).

[9] C. F. Schönbein, *Pogg. Ann.*, **176**, 34 (1857).

[10] F. Kessler, *Pogg. Ann.*, **195**, 218 (1863).

[11] N. Schilow, *Z. physik. Chem.*, **42**, 643 (1903); R. Luther and N. Schilow, *Z. anorg. allgem. Chem.*, **54**, 1 (1907), *Z. physik. Chem.*, **46**, 777 (1903).

A is called the *actor* (Luther and Schilow) while B is the *inductor* (Kessler); C is the *acceptor*, according to Engler.[12] The spontaneous primary or inducing reaction between A and B accelerates the otherwise sluggish interaction of A and C.

In oxygen activation the oxygen may serve as either an actor or an acceptor. Mohr[13] found that a solution of arsenious acid in sodium bicarbonate is stable in air (although actually there is a slow oxidation). Under the same conditions, sulfite is oxidized quite rapidly. In a mixture of both solutions, arsenite is also oxidized. Here oxygen appears as the actor, according to Skrabal.[7] On the other hand, Löwenthal[14] found that the air oxidation of stannous chloride is strongly induced during titration with dichromate. Skrabal (*loc. cit.*, p. 9) says that in this case oxygen takes the place of an acceptor. It is in order to add here that the nomenclature is of more practical than theoretical significance in differentiating between actor, inductor and acceptor. These names do not express what really happens. Consider again the scheme of Luther:

$$A + B \rightarrow + \quad \text{and} \quad A + C \rightarrow 0, \text{ etc.}$$

The symbol 0 does not always indicate that the reaction does not occur at all, but in many cases that it proceeds very slowly. If the reaction of A with B takes place, one may assume either that part of the energy is transferred to C, or that both A and B are brought to an energy-rich condition in which they are more reactive. The inducing effect is not due solely to A or to B, but to the reaction between them. For instance, the reaction between A and B may also induce a reaction between C and D. Thus, according to Kessler,[15] the oxidation of arsenious acid by chromate induces that of tartaric acid by ferric salts. Expressed in more general terms:

$$A + B \rightarrow +; \quad C + D \rightarrow 0;$$

$$\begin{Bmatrix} A + B \rightarrow + \\ C + D \rightarrow + \end{Bmatrix}.$$

---

[12] C. Engler, *Ber.*, **33**, 1097 (1900).

[13] F. Mohr, *Lehrbuch chem.-anal. Titriermethoden*, Braunschweig 1855; *cf.* also W. P. Jorissen and C. v. d. Pol, *Rec. trav. chim.*, **44**, 805 (1925).

[14] J. Löwenthal, *J. prakt. Chem.*, **76**, 484 (1859).

[15] F. Kessler, *Pogg. Ann.*, **195**, 218 (1863).

The process may also be formulated in the following way:

$$A + B \to +; \quad A + D \to 0;$$

$$B + C \to 0;$$

$$\left\{ \begin{array}{l} A + B \to + \\ A + D \to + \\ B + C \to + \end{array} \right\}.$$

The assumption involved here, that intermediary energy-rich substances are formed during the rapid reaction between A and B, is really as old as the recognition of induction phenomena. Skrabal[16] made the statement that "In general, a strong oxidant can be produced by reduction, a strong reductant by oxidation." Manchot concluded from his thorough and valuable studies[17] that "In all oxidation processes there are formed primary oxides which have the character of peroxides"; this notion may also be traced back to Zimmermann.[18] The primary oxides often are not only stronger but also faster oxidizing (or reducing) agents than the materials from which they were formed, and they are unstable. Deviating from Manchot, Luther[11] clarified induction processes through the assumption that during reaction there arise unstable intermediate forms of the actor, whose other energetic and kinetic properties resemble those of the original form.

As an example of a simple induced reaction, the simultaneous oxidation of manganous ion and arsenious acid by chromate ion may be mentioned:

$$CrO_4^{-} + H_3AsO_3 + Mn^{++} + 6H^+$$

$$\to H_3AsO_4 + Mn^{+++} + Cr^{+++} + 3H_2O.$$

In the absence of arsenious acid the oxidation of manganous ion by chromate is very slow, but in its presence, and with otherwise favorable conditions, one mole (one equivalent) of manganous ion is oxidized for each mole (two equivalents) of arsenious acid oxidized.

---

[16] A. Skrabal, Z. anorg. allgem. Chem., **42**, 1 (1904), see also ref. 7.

[17] W. Manchot, Ann., **325**, 93 (1902).

[18] C. Zimmermann, Ann., **213**, 312 (1882).

This corresponds to a simple value of the "induction factor." The induction factor, F_i, gives the ratio of the equivalents of the induced reaction to those of the primary reaction. Denoting the actor's original valence state by A_0, its intermediate state by A_i and its final state by A_f, the following relation holds by definition:

$$F_i = \frac{A_i - A_f}{A_0 - A_i}.$$

Lang and Zwerina[19] found for this case an induction factor of 0.5. The equations below represent a possible, although by no means established, mechanism for the process:

(1) $CrO_4^- + H_3AsO_3 \rightarrow H_3AsO_4 + CrO_3^-$ (relatively rapid)

(2) $2CrO_3^- + H_3AsO_3 + 10H^+ \rightarrow H_3AsO_4 + 2Cr^{+++} + 5H_2O$

(slow, probably complex)

(3) $CrO_3^- + Mn^{++} + 6H^+ \rightarrow Mn^{+++} + Cr^{+++} + 3H_2O$

(rapid, probably complex)

The sum of equation (2) and twice equation (1) gives the stoichiometric expression for the primary reaction:

(4) $2CrO_4^- + 3H_3AsO_3 + 10H^+ \rightarrow 3H_3AsO_4 + 2Cr^{+++} + 5H_2O$

(stoichiometric).

When the reaction step shown in equation (3) proceeds much more rapidly than that in equation (2), an induction factor of 0.5 is realized and the total stoichiometric reaction is represented by equation (5), the sum of (1) and (3):

(5) $CrO_4^- + H_3AsO_3 + Mn^{++} + 6H^+ \rightarrow H_3AsO_4 + Mn^{+++} + Cr^{+++} + 3H_2O.$

In many of the practically important examples of this type of reaction, the oxidation of a reducing agent by atmospheric oxygen is greatly accelerated during its simultaneous oxidation by another reagent. A well known case is the air oxidation of stannous chloride during titration with dichromate. The value of the induction factor increases as the concentration ratio of dissolved oxygen to primary oxidant is increased. In practice this ratio depends on such factors

[19] R. Lang and J. Zwerina, *Z. anorg. allgem. Chem.*, **170**, 389 (1928); *cf.* also C. Wagner, *ibid.*, **168**, 279 (1927).

as order of mixing, rate of stirring, etc.   In some cases, the induction factor is also a function of the p_H , and even of the concentration of reducing agent.   If a proper choice of conditions results in a value of the induction factor much greater than unity, the induced reaction is said to be an example of "induced catalysis."[20]   If, on the other hand, the induction factor cannot be made to exceed a small value, the reaction is considered to be an instance of "simple coupling."

For all practical purposes, reactions of the induced catalysis type are of the greater importance.   A possible mechanism for this class consists in catalysis (of the reduction of oxygen) by means of a catalytic pair, one member of which is an intermediate in the primary reaction.   When the process is a chain reaction, induced catalysis may result from the starting of reaction chains by such an intermediate.   This mechanism has been clearly demonstrated in the atmospheric oxidation of sulfite induced by its primary oxidation with hydrogen peroxide.   Here the induction factor can be greatly decreased by addition of a suitable inhibitor.[21]

From the above it is evident that the mechanism of various types of induced reactions may be quite complicated.   An attempt to systematize the various types has been made by Bancroft and his coworkers.[22]   In general, one should be careful in the interpretation of induction factors.   Normal values may be found only in those cases in which no chain reactions occur.   For example, Manchot and Schmid[23] found that in the oxidation of ferrous iron by oxygen in the presence of hypophosphorous acid as acceptor, the oxygen consumption was about 17 equivalents while with arsenious acid as acceptor, only 2 equivalents of oxygen were used per equivalent of ferrous iron oxidized.   In the latter case the activation ratio is 1:1. From these and similar experiments Manchot concluded that in the oxidation of ferrous iron an intermediate unstable oxide of iron, FeO_2 , is formed.   This conclusion seems to be justified and is in agreement with investigations of Bray and Gorin[24] who independently

[20] W. C. Bray and J. B. Ramsey, *J. Am. Chem. Soc.*, **55**, 2279 (1933).

[21] H. L. J. Bäckström, *Medd. Vetenskapsakad. Nobelinst.*, **6**, 16 (1927).

[22] W. D. Bancroft, *J. Phys. Chem.*, **33**, 1184 (1929); W. G. Vannoy, *ibid.*, **33**, 1593 (1929); D. R. Hale, *ibid.*, **33**, 1633 (1929); see also W. C. Bray, *Chem. Rev.*, **10**, 161 (1932).   For a mathematical discussion of chemical induction see A. Skrabal, *Monatsh.*, **66**, 129 (1935).

[23] W. Manchot and H. Schmid, *Ber.*, **65**, 98 (1932).

[24] W. C. Bray and M. H. Gorin, *J. Am. Chem. Soc.*, **54**, 2124 (1932).

reported evidence for the existence of the FeO^{++} ion (derived from FeO_2).

In the succeeding paragraphs a few practically important induced reactions are discussed shortly. Skrabal, who carried out extensive studies on the reaction between permanganate and oxalic acid,[16] gives the following mechanism: If one adds a little permanganate to an acidified solution of oxalate, the permanganate color at first remains. At the beginning the reaction is very slow; this stage is known as the *incubation period*. As soon as some manganous ion is formed, or if a little is added, the reaction is strongly favored and proceeds almost instantaneously. Apparently permanganate reacts with manganous ion according to the following scheme:

$$Mn^{II} + Mn^{VII} \rightarrow Mn^{+++},$$

$$Mn^{+++} \rightarrow Mn^{III}.$$

Here the Roman numerals indicate the valence stages of manganese, while Mn^{+++} represents trivalent manganese ions. Part of these react with oxalate to form complex manganic oxalate (Mn^{III}) and the others oxidize oxalic acid:

$$H_2C_2O_4 + 2Mn^{+++} \rightarrow 2Mn^{++} + 2CO_2 + 2H^+.$$

In this way the manganous-permanganate reaction induces the oxalate-permanganate reaction. Manganous salt is formed during the incubation period, after which the *induction period* is entered. According to Luther's nomenclature, permanganate is the actor, manganous salt the inductor, and oxalic acid the acceptor. Near the expiration of the induction period, manganic salt decomposes at a measurable rate during what may be called the *end period*. According to Skrabal the manganic ion formed in the induction period would be a kind of primary oxide (or intermediate oxide), which Manchot said is formed in any oxidation process. This seems improbable, since manganic ion has a lower oxidation energy than permanganate. It may be more logical to assume the intermediate formation of a still higher oxide of manganese, which is very unstable.[25]

One might suppose that the rate of oxidation of oxalic acid would

[25] *Cf.* I. M. Kolthoff, *Z. anal. Chem.*, **64**, 185 (1924); A. Skrabal and J. Preisz, *Monatsh.*, **27**, 503 (1904).

be markedly increased by the addition of excess manganous salt as inductor. This does not turn out to be so; although the reaction between permanganate and manganous salt proceeds rapidly, the product is largely complex manganic oxalate which decomposes with measurable speed. If but little manganous salt is present, as is usually the case during a titration, the inducing reaction $Mn^{II} + Mn^{VII}$ goes more slowly and the manganic ions formed are reduced by oxalic acid before they are bound as a complex. From such observations Skrabal derived the following rule, which had earlier been formulated in a different way by Kessler:[26] *If induced reactions proceed through identical active intermediates and are therefore mutually comparable, the extent of induction is dependent entirely on the speed. If the induced reaction is spontaneous (but slow), the induction is greater the lower the velocity of the inducing reaction.*

A confirmation of this rule is found in the increased disturbance caused by hydrochloric acid during an oxalate titration. The reaction between hydrochloric acid and permanganate is in itself very slow, but it is noticeably induced by the permanganate-oxalate reaction. Especially in the incubation period, where the inducing reaction between oxalate and permanganate is sluggish, is the disturbance considerable. If one increases the velocity of the inducing reaction by adding manganous salt or titrating at a higher temperature (over 70°C.), the hydrochloric acid error may be eliminated. In Volume II the mechanism of the permanganate-oxalate reaction will be discussed in greater detail.

The presence of hydrochloric acid is also disturbing in the titration of ferrous iron with permanganate. As contrasted with the oxalate reaction, the oxidation of ferrous iron proceeds immeasurably faster. Yet, according to Skrabal,[16] one may assume by analogy three successive reaction periods, of which the incubation period is very short. Apparently during this inducing reaction there is formed a primary oxide, which induces the oxidation of hydrochloric acid by permanganate.[27] Through addition of manganous salt the incubation time is shortened and any primary oxide is reduced by manganous ions, so that it cannot exert an inducing effect on the oxidation of hydrochloric acid.

The error caused by the presence of hydrochloric acid is lessened,

[26] F. Kessler, *Pogg. Ann.*, **195**, 238 (1863).
[27] Compare the investigations of Bray and Gorin[24] and of Manchot and Schmid[23] on the intermediate formation of FeO^{++} or FeO_2.

though not entirely avoided, by titration at higher temperature. Also, the speed with which permanganate is added has an influence on the result, at room temperature. In slow titrations the error is almost negligible, while with rapid addition of permanganate it increases appreciably.

No hydrochloric acid interference has been noted in the titration of hydrogen peroxide with permanganate, although the incubation period is quite long, as in the titration of oxalic acid. Neither is chloride interference observed in the titration of ferrous iron with ceric sulfate, despite the fact that ceric ions in acid medium have at least as strong an oxidizing action as permanganate. The reduction of ceric cerium to the cerous state, however, occurs directly without formation of intermediary valence states.

At present one cannot predict whether or not a given reaction will induce another. Factors specific for the substances present play a great part. *Only by experiment can it be established whether a titration is accompanied by a disturbing induced reaction. If it is, the error may usually be diminished by a suitable change in the speed of the primary reaction.*

Under some conditions unexpected products may be formed through induction phenomena. Long ago it was known that a peroxide-like material, thought to be a carbon peroxide, forms during the titration of oxalic acid with permanganate. Kolthoff[28] found this to be hydrogen peroxide; *it is formed only if the solution being titrated contains dissolved oxygen.*[29] Here the reaction between permanganate and oxalic acid induces another by which oxygen is converted into peroxide. The more rapidly the oxalate is oxidized, the more peroxide is formed. This agrees with a rule formulated by Skrabal:[30] *"Stable end-products result when the reaction is sufficiently slow. With greater velocity, less stable products are formed, and from there on the formation of definite stable substances is much hindered."*

Until the mechanism of induced reactions is more clearly under-

---

[28] I. M. Kolthoff, *Z. anal. Chem.*, **64**, 185 (1924). On the other hand, E. Deisz, *Chem. Ztg.*, **50**, 399 (1926) assumes primarily the formation of peroxalic acid $\begin{array}{l} \text{O—COOH} \\ | \\ \text{O—COOH} \end{array}$

[29] K. Schröder, *Z. offentl. Chem.*, **16**, 270, 290 (1910).

[30] A. Skrabal, *Z. Elektrochem.*, **11**, 653 (1905); *Monatsh.*, **28**, 319 (1907); see also F. Oberhauser and W. Hensinger, *Ber.*, **61**, 521 (1928).

stood, we must be content with only practical rules. The following two may be derived in part from the above statements:

I. *If there are present in a solution two reducing agents A_R and B_R having very different oxidation potentials, so that, for example, A_R can be quantitatively oxidized to A_0 without much effect on B_R, then ordinarily a part of B_R will be oxidized along with A_R on account of induction phenomena.* Now, if the reaction

$$B_0 + A_R \rightarrow B_R + A_0$$

takes place rapidly, the induction cannot cause any disturbance, because B_R is formed again as would be expected from the oxidation potentials. However, if the speed of this back-reaction is small, A_R cannot be titrated accurately in the presence of B_R .

For this reason substances which are irreversibly oxidized or reduced are especially disturbing in titrations of other reductants or oxidants. This is often true of organic compounds.

II. *If a substance is slowly oxidized or reduced by a reagent, the velocity of such a process is increased during a concurrent rapid reaction between the reagent and another substance.* A confirmation of this rule is seen in the aforementioned disturbance of hydrochloric acid in permanganate titrations. Another example is the behavior of phosphite, which is but slowly oxidized by permanganate. An acid solution of phosphite treated with a little permanganate remains colored for a long time, yet if ferrous solution is titrated in the presence of phosphite, too much permanganate is required. Some is reduced by the phosphite.

Induced reactions in which atmospheric oxygen takes part are of great practical interest and several cases will be considered more closely. A solution of stannous chloride is rather slowly oxidized by air. Lenssen and Löwenthal[31] showed that this air oxidation is strongly favored during titration with permanganate or dichromate. The authors have noticed such interference during determinations with iodine or bromine.

It is peculiar that this increased oxidizability comes to light not only during reactions of oxidimetry, but also in quite different reactions, even during neutralizations. For example, Raschig[32] found that when bisulfite is neutralized with sodium hydroxide far more is

[31] E. Lenssen and J. Löwenthal, *J. prakt. Chem.*, **76**, 484 (1859).
[32] F. Raschig, *Z. angew. Chem.*, **17**, 580, 1407 (1904).

transformed into sulfate than would ordinarily be oxidized by exposure of normal sulfite to air. He showed a similar increase during the reverse process of converting sulfite to bisulfite. According to Luther's nomenclature, oxygen would here be the actor, hydrogen or hydroxyl ion the inductor, and sulfite or bisulfite the acceptor. A completely analogous induction occurs in the oxidation reaction of sulfite or bisulfite with iodine. While it is ordinarily said that iodine catalyzes the air oxidation of sulfite, actually the reaction between sulfite and oxygen is induced by the other more rapid reaction.

Another practically important example is the induced air oxidation of hydriodic acid by vanadic acid:

$$2HVO_3 + 3KI + 3H_2SO_4 \rightarrow 2VOSO_4 + KI_3 + K_2SO_4 + 4H_2O$$

$$O_2 + 6KI + 2H_2SO_4 \rightarrow 2KI_3 + 2K_2SO_4 + 2H_2O.$$

In case the acidity of the solution is less than 4 N, according to Edgar,[33] high results are obtained in the iodimetric determination of vanadate in the presence of air. Bray and Ramsey[20] investigated this induced process thoroughly. They concluded that the behavior of oxygen in redox reactions is quite specific, depending upon the particular oxidant and reductant involved. When one is indeed dealing with an induced reaction, the induction factor (Red. oxidized by O_2)/(Red. oxidized by Ox) increases without limit as the conditions are made more and more favorable for induction.

The induced air oxidation of thiocyanate during a titration with permanganate was mentioned at the beginning of this chapter.[34]

In general, though a reducing agent may itself be quite stable in air, if its oxidation potential is lower than that of atmospheric oxygen it will be oxidized more rapidly during a titration.

"Induced precipitations" are considered in the following chapter. The present discussion may well be concluded with a quotation from de Koninck:[35] "Beware of procedures which have been conceived by deduction, for reactions that are satisfactory for pure reagents separated from all others may no longer be so when applied to mixtures.'"

[33] G. Edgar, *J. Am. Chem. Soc.*, **38**, 2369 (1916).
[34] *Cf.* also K. Schröder, *Z. offentl. Chem.*, **15**, 321 (1909).
[35] L. L. de Koninck and C. Meineke, *Mineralanalyse*, Vol. I, XVI, Berlin, 1899. *Cf.* A. W. Skrabal.[7]

4. Examples of Catalytic Processes.—In this section will be mentioned several catalytically influenced reactions which can be used with advantage in volumetric analysis.

The reaction velocity of hydrogen peroxide with iodide in acid solution was studied by Noyes and Scott.[36] Two steps were distinguished, expressed by the equations:

$$(1) \quad H_2O_2 + I^- \rightarrow H_2O + OI^-$$

$$(2) \quad OI^- + 2H^+ + I^- \rightarrow H_2O + I_2$$

$$\overline{H_2O_2 + 2I^- + 2H^+ \rightarrow 2H_2O + I_2}$$

Step (1) goes slowly; according to the equation, hydrogen ions should have no influence, yet they appear to increase the speed catalytically. Step (2) takes place rapidly, especially in acid solution. Various workers have studied the effect of catalysts on the rate of the total reaction. Traube[37] recognized the strong catalytic influence of a mixture of copper and ferrous salts. Of especial analytical importance is the thorough investigation of Brode,[38] who showed that molybdic and tungstic acids bring about an unusually strong catalysis. He explained this as due to intermediate formation of per-acids, which can be detected in the mixture. If one adds molybdate to an acidified peroxide solution, it turns yellow.

Molybdate catalysis can be applied advantageously in the iodimetric determination of hydrogen peroxide. On account of the low reaction velocity, it was not clear in the older literature whether or not one could titrate peroxide quantitatively. In the presence of molybdate the reaction between iodide and peroxide in acid solution proceeds rapidly enough so that titration with thiosulfate may be started immediately after mixing the reagents. Even quite dilute solutions may be determined directly in this way.[39]

Peroxide and iodide react differently in neutral or alkaline solution:

$$(1) \quad H_2O_2 + I^- \rightarrow H_2O + OI^- \quad \text{(slow)}$$

$$(2) \quad H_2O_2 + OI^- \rightarrow H_2O + I^- + O_2 \quad \text{(rapid)}$$

$$\overline{2H_2O_2 \rightarrow 2H_2O + O_2.}$$

[36] A. A. Noyes and W. O. Scott, Z. physik. Chem., **18**, 118 (1895); **19**, 102 (1896).

[37] M. Traube, Ber., **20**, 1062 (1884).

[38] J. Brode, Z. physik. Chem., **37**, 257 (1901).

[39] I. M. Kolthoff, Z. anal. Chem., **60**, 400 (1921).

From this two-stage process it is evident that iodide ions catalytically favor the decomposition of peroxide into oxygen and water. Practical application of this fact can be made in the removal of excess peroxide from a solution. Upon addition of alkali and iodide to a solution containing hydrogen peroxide, the latter is rapidly decomposed. The second step of the reaction has been employed by Rupp[40] for the determination of peroxide with hypoiodite.

Catalysis by molybdate finds another use in the iodimetric titration of dilute bromate solutions. The reaction between bromate, iodide and acid can be summed up in the equation:

$$BrO_3^- + 6I^- + 6H^+ \rightarrow Br^- + 3I_2 + 3H_2O.$$

The velocity depends on many factors, which will be discussed in

THE EFFECT OF LIGHT AND CATALYSTS IN IODIMETRIC TITRATIONS OF 0.001 N DICHROMATE

Catalyst Added	Light Conditions	Ml. 0.001 N Thiosulfate
None	Dark	25.20
100 mg. ferrous sulfate	Dark	20.90
3 drops 3 per cent molybdate	Dark	27.00
None	Diffused light	26.00
100 mg. ferrous sulfate	Diffused light	22.90
3 drops 3 per cent molybdate	Diffused light	28.80
None	Direct sunlight	36.00
100 mg. ferrous sulfate	Direct sunlight	5.00
3 drops 3 per cent molybdate	Direct sunlight	45.50

Vol. II; in all cases it is strongly accelerated by molybdate.[41] The corresponding reaction of chlorate proceeds still more slowly. It is also catalyzed by molybdate, but the addition is not to be recommended here for it induces the air oxidation of iodide.

Dichromate, iodide and acid do not react instantaneously. In this case, molybdate actually retards the main reaction while inducing the oxidation of iodide by air. The mechanism appears to be very complicated, for light exerts a photochemical effect. Some figures showing this are given in the accompanying table; in each case the solution contained 5 ml. of 4 N hydrochloric acid, 25 ml. of 0.001 N

[40] E. Rupp, *Arch. Pharm.*, **245**, 6 (1907).

[41] W. Ostwald, *Z. physik. Chem.*, **2**, 137 (1888); N. Schilow, *ibid.*, **27**, 513 (1898); R. H. Clark, *J. Phys. Chem.*, **11**, 353 (1907); I. M. Kolthoff, *Z. anal. Chem.*, **60**, 348 (1921).

potassium dichromate, and 0.5 ml. of 1 N potassium iodide. After standing 15 minutes under the indicated conditions, the liberated iodine was titrated with 0.001 N thiosulfate.

In other tests the negative catalysis by molybdate could be demonstrated; high results shown in the table may be ascribed to increased oxidation by air. It should be noted that the catalytic effect of many substances depends on the hydrogen-ion concentration. An illustration of this is that under the conditions given above, ferrous iron exerts a negative catalytic action, whereas in weakly acid solution it serves as a positive catalyst.

Very interesting is the accelerating effect of osmic acid (OsO_4) on the reaction between arsenious acid and ceric sulfate in sulfuric acid solution. This otherwise extremely slow reaction proceeds almost instantly in the presence of a trace of osmic acid. The same catalyst is also effective in the reduction of chlorate by arsenite in acid solution. It is noteworthy that titration with ceric sulfate in the presence of osmic acid does not induce air oxidation of arsenite; yet if one determines chlorate by reduction with excess arsenite, using osmic acid as catalyst, air must be excluded or else high results will be obtained because of induced oxidation.[42] This case is typical of the complicated behavior of induced reactions.

The decided favorable action of zinc in the iodimetric determination of ferricyanide can be explained as a purely chemical effect:

$$2K_3Fe(CN)_6 + 2KI \rightleftarrows 2K_4Fe(CN)_6 + I_2$$

$$2K_3Fe(CN)_6 + 2KI + 2ZnCl_2 \rightleftarrows 2K_2ZnFe(CN)_6 + 4KCl + I_2.$$

In the presence of zinc salts, the reaction is shifted toward the formation of slightly soluble potassium zinc ferrocyanide.

The efficacy of corrosive sublimate in the determination of iodine number by Hübl's method[43] may be attributed to a somewhat similar cause. Iodine and mercuric chloride react forming the almost insoluble mercuric iodide:

$$2I_2 + HgCl_2 \rightarrow HgI_2 + 2ICl.$$

The iodine chloride thus developed is a more active addition agent than free iodine.

[42] K. Gleu, *Z. anal. Chem.*, **95**, 385 (1933).
[43] B. von Hübl, *Dinglers Polytech. J.*, **253**, 281 (1884).

In oxidation processes that involve persulfate, the catalytic action of silver ion is especially striking. According to R. Kempf,[44] silver peroxide, which is intermediate in the reaction, is continuously regenerated. Kempf made application of this to the determination of active oxygen in persulfate by reduction with oxalic acid.

From the examples that have been given it will be seen that catalytic activity may be of great assistance in accelerating or retarding reactions, but that the analytical chemist must constantly be on the alert to avoid interferences that may be caused by induction phenomena.

[44] R. Kempf, *Ber.*, **38**, 3963 (1906).

CHAPTER VIII

ADSORPTION AND COPRECIPITATION PHENOMENA

1. Coprecipitation and Postprecipitation.—In preceding chapters the changes of ion concentrations during precipitation titrations have been calculated. These calculations were made assuming that the precipitate which separates has its stoichiometric composition and is not contaminated by salts having an ion in common with the precipitate. However, it is very unusual for a precipitate to separate in pure form. This is the reason that calculated values of the ion concentrations generally differ from the actual values, especially in the neighborhood of the equivalence-point.

Several factors which affect the purity and the adsorptive properties of a precipitate will be discussed briefly in this chapter, insofar as they are of interest in volumetric analysis.

Various terms such as coprecipitation, carrying down, occlusion, inclusion and adsorption, are used in analytical chemistry to indicate that a precipitate has not exactly the composition indicated by its chemical formula, but that it is contaminated by impurities. These impurities can be located within the precipitate (*occlusion*) or on the surface (*adsorption*). In the following, the term *coprecipitation* will be used as a collective name indicating the *carrying down* of impurities within or on the surface of the precipitate. A distinction should be made between coprecipitation and *postprecipitation*. In cases of postprecipitation a second component separates out from the reaction mixture on standing, after precipitation of the desired constituent. In general, postprecipitation is characterized by the fact that the second precipitate is also slightly soluble in the reaction medium, but is slow to separate.

It has been frequently observed, especially in separating metals of the second and third groups of the qualitative analysis scheme, that the metal sulfides of group II may cause the appearance of the sulfides of group III in the precipitate under conditions which would not allow the precipitation of the latter if present alone. Such cases are often referred to as *induced precipitations*. The first precipitate formed *induces the postprecipitation* of the second. A characteristic of this process is that the amount of postprecipitation occurring increases with the time of standing prior to filtration. In the case of postprecipitation of zinc with copper sulfide[1] and with mercuric sulfide[2] in acid solution and also in other instances it was found that the sulfide with the smaller solubility product (CuS or HgS) primarily precipitates free from zinc, but on standing in the presence of a solution containing zinc ions and excess hydrogen sulfide more and more zinc sulfide is precipitated. Such postprecipitations are often responsible for the occurrence of impure precipitates in hydrogen sulfide separations.[3]

In volumetric analysis the interference caused by postprecipitation is limited. If a mixture 0.25 M in sulfuric acid and 0.025 M each in cupric and zinc sulfates is titrated with sodium sulfide (for example, potentiometrically), the primary precipitate consists of cupric sulfide; a large change of the sulfide concentration occurs after complete precipitation of the copper. Upon addition of excess sulfide a slow precipitation of zinc sulfide begins, its rate of formation being promoted by the presence of copper sulfide. Hence after some time of standing the precipitate will contain considerable zinc. On the other hand, in making a titration the copper sulfide separates uncontaminated by zinc and postprecipitation does not interfere if the titration is carried out directly to the endpoint.

2. Adsorptive Properties of Precipitates; Coprecipitation by Adsorption on the External Surface.—In this section only those adsorption phenomena which are of interest in volumetric analysis will be discussed. For a more complete presentation reference is made to the literature.[4]

Investigations on the structure of crystallized electrolytes have shown that these are built up from the individual ions in a lattice-like arrangement. According to conceptions developed by W. Kossel, M. Born and A. Landé,[5] electrostatic forces are responsible for

[1] I. M. Kolthoff and E. A. Pearson, *J. Phys. Chem.*, **36**, 549 (1932).

[2] I. M. Kolthoff and D. R. Moltzau, *J. Phys. Chem.*, **40**, 779 (1936).

[3] For a review and discussion of various postprecipitation phenomena see I. M. Kolthoff and D. R. Moltzau, *Chem. Rev.*, **17**, 293 (1935).

[4] K. Fajans and T. Erdey-Grúz, *Z. physik. Chem.*, **A158**, 97 (1931); I. M. Kolthoff, *J. Phys. Chem.*, **40**, 1027 (1936); O. Hahn, *Applied Radiochemistry*, Cornell University Press, Ithaca, New York 1936.

[5] *Naturwissenschaften*, **7**, 339 (1919); **8**, 373 (1920); **11**, 165 (1923); *Z. Krist.*, **61**, 18 (1925); *cf.* also K. Fajans and K. von Beckerath, *Z. physik. Chem.*, **97**, 478 (1921), K. Fajans and G. Joos, *Z. Physik.*, **23**, 1 (1924).

the stability of the lattice.   Figure 18 represents a schematic cross-section through a simple crystal of the common salt type; positive ions are denoted by $+$, negative by $-$.   Now a positive ion A within the crystal is subjected to attractive forces from the four neighboring negative ions a, b, c and d (as well as from those of parallel lattice planes).   In contrast, an ion B in the surface layer is attracted only by the three negative ions a, e and f.   Therefore the positive ions in the surface have free residual valence forces which can attract negative ions.   If adsorption takes place, the surface becomes negatively charged.   Conversely, negative ions in the surface may attract positive ions, so that the surface assumes a positive charge.   Adsorption is thus seen to be a surface action; the amount adsorbed increases

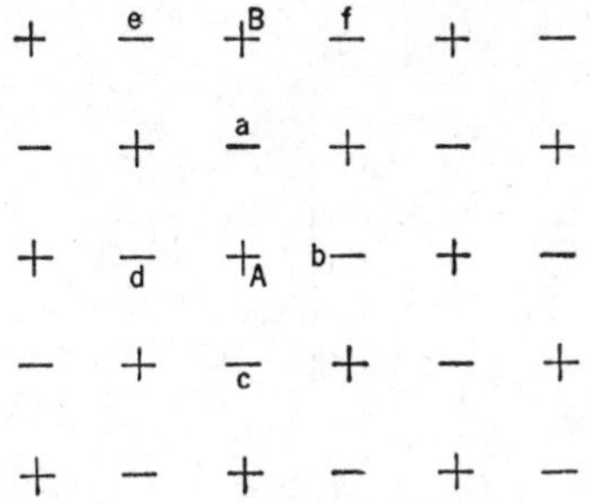

Fig. 18.—Crystal lattice

with increasing total surface area, that is, with increasing degree of dispersion of the precipitate.

Lottermoser and Rothe[6] demonstrated that pure silver iodide can adsorb either silver ions or iodide ions.   The process has been described as follows by Fajans and von Beckerath:[5] "Upon adsorption of silver ions, the surface becomes positively charged; the silver ions are included in the lattice structure of the silver iodide and at the same time lose their associated water molecules.

"Figure 19 indicates a neutral surface of silver iodide in contact with a solution of silver nitrate, (prior to adsorption); after adsorption of positive silver ions the situation is as shown in Figure 20. The adsorbed ions attract nitrate ions, which with their hydrate sheaths then function as the boundary medium (dielectric) of the Helmholtz double layer that is so formed.   Figure 21 represents the corresponding case of a precipitate negatively charged by adsorption of iodide from a potassium iodide solution.

[6] A. Lottermoser and A. Rothe, Z. physik. Chem., **62**, 359 (1908).

"That which has been illustrated for the case of a silver iodide precipitate in contact with a solution may be generally valid: if one adds a salt BA_{II} to a mixture of the solid salt BA_I and its saturated solution, *then in addition to the increased precipitation of BA_I corresponding to the solubility product principle, there will be a further adsorption of B caused by the residual valences of the lattice.* It is easy to see that the extent of this adsorption will, in general, be greater the less soluble is BA_I, in accordance with the adsorption rule of Paneth."[7]

Fajans and von Beckerath formulate Paneth's rule as follows: "An ionic lattice adsorbs easily those ions whose compounds with the oppositely charged constituent of the lattice are slightly soluble."

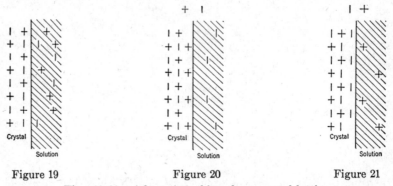

| Figure 19 | Figure 20 | Figure 21 |

Figs. 19–21.—Adsorption of ions by a crystal lattice

In addition they make the following remark which is of interest here: "It is to be expected that the less soluble a salt is, that is, the more easily a normal uncharged surface withdraws ions of both signs from water, the more easily will it take on an excess of its own ions. A difference between these two processes is that, on account of the deficiency in neighboring oppositely charged ions, the attractive forces between the lattice and the ion being adsorbed are smaller; on the other hand, less complete dehydration is necessary for adsorption than for precipitation."[8]

[7] F. Paneth, *Physik. Z.*, **15,** 924 (1914); K. Horowitz and F. Paneth, *Z. physik. Chem.*, **89,** 513 (1915); *Sitzber. Akad. Wiss. Wien*, **123** (IIa) 1819 (1914).

[8] Compare also O. Hahn, *Ber.*, **59,** 2014 (1926); *Naturwissenschaften*, **14,** 1196 (1926); *Applied Radiochemistry*, Cornell University Press, Ithaca, New York 1936; I. M. Kolthoff, *J. Phys. Chem.*, **40,** 1027 (1936).

From the foregoing it appears that a precipitate has a special tendency to adsorb its own ions. Errors caused by adsorption will be greater the larger the surface development of the primary precipitate. Quite generally, therefore, coprecipitation by adsorption on the external surface may be expected to be pronounced when the precipitate separates as a colloid or as an amorphous body.

The mechanism of adsorption indicator action (see p. 102) is easily explained by the concept shown in Figs. 18 to 21. When a suitable anion dye is used as adsorption indicator, in general it will be not at all or only very slightly adsorbed on the negative side of the isoelectric point, where the precipitate contains adsorbed lattice anions. Immediately after the equivalence-point is passed, the precipitate adsorbs lattice cations, with simultaneous adsorption of indicator anions. So long as the precipitate remains colloidal, the total surface of all the particles will be large. Upon flocculation, however, the total surface decreases rapidly, and a corresponding decrease of indicator adsorption results. On this account the color change at the endpoint will be less pronounced in the presence of ions that have a flocculating action.

In potentiometric titrations of halides (especially bromide and iodide) with silver, adsorption phenomena may be responsible for irregular changes of the potential near the equivalence-point, and for the fact that the endpoint does not coincide with the equivalence-point. Upon adding together equivalent amounts of iodide and silver, the precipitate does not have exactly the stoichiometric composition. At very small concentrations of dissolved ions, silver iodide has a greater tendency to adsorb iodide ions than silver ions. If pure silver iodide is shaken with a saturated aqueous solution of silver iodide, iodide ions are primarily adsorbed (with hydrogen ions as counter ions). Thus the precipitate acquires a negative charge. No adsorption, either of silver or of iodide ions takes place on pure silver iodide when the solution is 10^{-6} M in silver or 10^{-10} M in iodide (solubility product $S_{AgI} = 10^{-16}$). Under these conditions the precipitate remains uncharged. Hence the point of zero charge, or isoelectric point, of silver iodide is found at $p_{Ag} = 6$ or $p_I = 10$—in other words, when the silver-ion concentration is about 10,000 times the iodide-ion concentration.[9]

Due to this asymmetric location of the isoelectric point, the "equivalence-point" does not coincide with the stoichiometric end-

[9] E. J. W. Verwey and H. R. Kruyt, Z. physik. Chem., **A167**, 149 (1933).

point. As a matter of fact, it has been found[10] that upon mixing silver nitrate with potassium iodide at room temperature, the silver iodide at the equivalence potential contains 0.1 per cent of iodide in excess. That is, upon mixing equivalent amounts of silver and iodide the supernatant liquid retains a slight excess of silver and the precipitate a small amount of adsorbed iodide. Only at the isoelectric point is the precipitate free from adsorbed silver or iodide. The error in the above titration could be completely eliminated by slow precipitation at 95°C., or by the digestion at 95° of a precipitate formed at room temperature. Under such conditions a rapid *aging* of the precipitate occurs, accompanied by a large decrease of the surface and hence of the adsorption. This fact is of great analytical importance. When a colloidal precipitate is formed by adding an excess of reagent, some of the latter will be adsorbed by the precipitate. In many cases this adsorption can be reduced to practically zero, if the precipitate is digested (aged) before filtration.

The adsorption of silver ions by silver thiocyanate is evident in the Volhard titration of silver. During the titration silver ions are adsorbed and are given off again slowly. Close to the end-point the precipitate still contains adsorbed silver, while the amount of silver ions in solution is extremely small. Upon further dropwise addition of thiocyanate the solution may temporarily contain an excess of the latter while the precipitate still holds some adsorbed silver. Consequently if ferric alum has been added as indicator, the solution may turn red-brown before the equivalence-point is reached. The color disappears upon shaking the mixture, as silver ions are liberated from the precipitate and react with thiocyanate. With continued small additions of thiocyanate the process may be repeated until the precipitate is free of adsorbed silver. Hence in the Volhard titration of silver, thiocyanate should be added until the color remains even after energetic shaking of the mixture.[11]

Adsorption phenomena are also of great consequence in the titration of iodide with silver to the "clear-point." Lottermoser and coworkers[12] describe experiments in which 0.1 N silver nitrate is added to 500 ml. of 0.004 N iodide, dropwise and with vigorous stir-

[10] I. M. Kolthoff and J. J. Lingane, *J. Am. Chem. Soc.*, **58**, 1528 (1936).

[11] If silver is being back-titrated after a chloride precipitation, the silver chloride should first be removed; otherwise thiocyanate replaces chloride in the precipitate under these conditions (see Vol. II).

[12] A. Lottermoser, W. Seifert and W. Forstmann, *Kolloid Z.*, Zsigmondy Festschr., **36**, 230 (1925).

ring. The first few drops of silver nitrate cause hardly any opalescence, but yield a yellow green colloidal solution of silver iodide. Upon further addition an opalescence appears, which becomes more pronounced with increasing amounts of silver nitrate. Close to the equivalence-point the solution becomes turbid, and opaque when viewed under strong light. The next drop causes flocculation of silver iodide, but the supernatant liquid remains turbid. Continuing with small increments of silver nitrate, while shaking well, the precipitation becomes complete and the supernatant liquid appears perfectly clear. This stage is called the *clear-point* by Lottermoser. Its location depends somewhat on the dilution of the iodide and the speed of stirring. At high dilution and with vigorous agitation the clear-point and equivalence-point are said to coincide; on the other hand, the clear-point precedes the equivalence-point at greater concentrations. In the latter case, no iodide is found in solution at the clear-point, but the excess is adsorbed on the surface of flocculated particles. Naturally such a titration cannot be performed in the presence of higher valent cations which cause flocculation earlier in the titration.[13]

In the Mohr titration of iodide or thiocyanate the endpoint is unsatisfactory. The reason is that the silver salts remain partly in colloidal solution at the equivalence-point due to the peptizing effect of chromate ions, consequently the color change is difficult to observe. Addition of divalent cations, such as calcium or magnesium, favors flocculation, but then the color change is found too soon as a result of adsorption of iodide or thiocyanate ions on the precipitate. Contrary to this statement, Fajans and Frankenburger[14] claim that in the Mohr titration of bromide the color change occurs after the endpoint has been passed, the error amounting to about one per cent in titrations with 0.1 N solutions. They attribute the error to the fact that the precipitate adsorbs most of the excess silver ions, leaving too few to cause a color change at the equivalence-point. We have not been able to confirm this relatively large error.

Amorphous precipitates may be greatly contaminated by adsorption, due to the large surface development. In the precipitation of hydrous oxides from the metal salts, the endpoint may be observed long before the equivalence-point is reached. For example, upon addition of sodium hydroxide to a solution of ferric chloride until all

[13] A clear-point titration of molybdate with lead solution is also possible; practical details are given in Volume II.

[14] K. Fajans and W. Frankenburger, *Z. physik. Chem.*, **105**, 255 (1923).

iron is precipitated, the solid formed has not exactly the composition $Fe(OH)_3$, but it contains some chloride. Hence the endpoint is found before the equivalence-point. If anions of higher valence are present, the error becomes greater, as these are adsorbed more strongly than univalent anions. Similar difficulties are encountered in acidimetric titrations of the salts of aluminum, copper, zinc, etc. It is sometimes possible to improve the results by titrating at boiling temperatures, under which conditions the precipitates become aged fairly rapidly. However, exact results are not to be expected. It has also been recommended that excess alkali be added and back-titrated with acid. Under these conditions the adsorbed acid may be completely removed, but another error may arise through adsorption of base. Most of the hydrous oxides are amphoteric in character; on the acid side of their isoelectric points they adsorb hydrogen ions (acids) and on the alkaline side, hydroxyl ions (bases).

From the above it is evident that an understanding of the properties of colloidal solutions is necessary for the interpretation of results of titrations in which a precipitate remains in colloidal form. In the following section some of the more important properties of hydrophobic colloids or sols are shortly reviewed from the analytical standpoint.

3. Stability and Flocculation of Colloids.—The stability of a sol is connected with the electrical charge of the disperse phase. If a silver iodide sol is prepared from silver nitrate and an excess of potassium iodide, the silver iodide particles remain colloidal because they are capable of adsorbing iodide ions. Through adsorption the surface of the particles becomes negatively charged. An equivalent quantity of positive ions is distributed around the particles, maintaining the electrical neutrality of the solution as a whole. There is thus formed a diffuse double layer, whose properties determine the stability of the system.

The adsorbed iodide ions are firmly held on the surface; they are no longer mobile, whereas the surrounding cations have lost only a little of their mobility. Colloidal particles, called *micelles*, are continuously in vigorous motion (Brownian movement). Yet they do not join together, for they bear charges of the same sign and hence repel each other. If the diffuse double layer around the particles is destroyed, the particles will attract one another and combine into larger aggregates which become visible as flocs. This flocculation of a sol can be caused by the addition of a suitable electrolyte.

The flocculating effect of ions with a charge opposite to that of the colloidal particles rapidly increases with increasing valence of these ions, and with increasing adsorbability. Negatively charged colloids are easily flocculated by higher valence cations and by univalent aromatic cations. On the other hand, positive particles are flocculated by higher valence anions and by aromatic anions such as picrate.[15] For example, the flocculation of a certain negatively charged arsenic trisulfide sol could be brought about by 50 millimoles of potassium chloride, 0.69 millimoles of barium chloride, or 0.093 millimoles of aluminum chloride per liter. The anion valence of these flocculating salts is of subordinate influence.

Micelles undergoing flocculation retain the ions to which their original charge was due. Thus a negative silver iodide sol is stable by virtue of the fact that the particles have adsorbed iodide ions. Upon coagulation, the adsorbed ions are carried down and an equivalent amount of flocculating cations is carried down (adsorbed) also. Although the flocculation values of individual electrolytes are quite variable, the amount of this secondary adsorption (expressed in equivalents) might be expected to be constant for a given sol. However, according to reliable studies of Weiser and his associates,[16] such an equivalence rule does not apply exactly. Weiser and Middleton[17] determined, for a positive aluminum oxide sol, the flocculation values of various anions and the amounts of the latter adsorbed. Their results are shown in the following table:

FLOCCULATION AND ADSORPTION OF AN ALUMINUM OXIDE SOL

(Weiser and Middleton)

Anion	Flocculation value, milli-equivalents per liter	Milli-equivalents adsorbed per gram of Al_2O_3
Ferrocyanide	0.375	1.281
Thiosulfate	0.375	0.819
Ferricyanide	0.400	1.214
Sulfate	0.538	0.997
Oxalate	0.700	1.142
Phosphate	1.038	2.427
Chromate	1.300	0.870
Dithionate	1.625	0.657
Dichromate	1.775	0.629

---

[15] H. Schulze, *J. prakt. Chem.*, **25**, 431 (1882); **27**, 320 (1883).

[16] H. B. Weiser and coworkers, *J. Phys. Chem.*, **21**, 315 (1917); **23**, 205 (1919); **24**, 30, 630 (1920); **25**, 399 (1921); **29**, 955 (1925).

[17] H. B. Weiser and E. B. Middleton, *J. Phys. Chem.*, **24**, 630 (1920).

The observed deviations from *equivalent adsorption* cannot be attributed to experimental errors. Weiser and Middleton postulate that the coagulated particles—which are practically uncharged—may again adsorb ions. However, if electrolyte is added in a quantity sufficient to produce flocculation, it is hard to understand how the particles can again become charged.

It is of analytical importance that the *stabilizing ion*, which determines the charge of the sol, *is always adsorbed during flocculation*. Upon addition of silver nitrate to iodide solution, there is formed a silver iodide sol whose stability is due to adsorbed iodide ions. As more silver nitrate is added, more iodide ions are withdrawn from solution. Just before the equivalence-point the concentration of iodide ions becomes so low that the sol can no longer remain dispersed, but flocculates out. Yet the precipitate retains in adsorbed state a clearly detectable amount of iodide ion.

If the silver iodide is now filtered and washed, the adsorbed flocculating electrolyte is largely removed. Because of the iodide ions enclosed by the precipitate, a portion of the silver iodide may revert to colloidal form; this process is called *peptization*. In analytical work peptization can be very disturbing during the washing of precipitates such as ammonium phosphomolybdate or aluminum hydroxide, but these disturbances may be avoided by adding suitable electrolytes to the wash water. Conversely, peptization may be caused by ions that are strongly adsorbable: it has been observed that chromate ion exerts a peptizing action upon coagulated silver iodide. This is the reason that under certain conditions silver iodide is not flocculated at the equivalence-point in the Mohr iodide titration, but remains dispersed under the stabilizing effect of chromate. On this account iodide and thiocyanate cannot be determined by the usual procedure according to Mohr.

Another interesting phenomenon, easily perceptible with silver iodide, is the so-called *reversal of micellar charge*. If one adds a slight excess of silver nitrate to an already flocculated silver iodide sol, it again goes partly into colloidal solution.[12] The silver iodide, which originally had a negative charge due to adsorbed iodide ions, now becomes positively charged by adsorption of silver ions.[18] The sign of the charge is therefore independent of the particle's chemical nature and is determined only by the kind of ions adsorbed.

[18] Concerning the adsorption of silver salts by silver iodide, see J. S. Beekley and H. S. Taylor, *J. Phys. Chem.*, **29**, 942 (1925).

Many materials—especially hydrophilic colloids like gelatin, dextrin or gum arabic—are capable of hindering the coagulation of sols by electrolytes. Such substances are known as *protective colloids*. If, for example, a silver salt-egg albumin combination (protargol) is treated with iodide, the solution remains clear. Silver iodide is formed, as may be shown potentiometrically, yet it remains in colloidal solution under the protective action of albumin. In several cases it is possible to make analytical application of this effect. In titrating with adsorption indicators, the best color changes are obtained when the precipitates are kept in colloidal form. Flocculating ions can be made harmless by addition of gum arabic or agar to the solution which is to be titrated.

Quite generally the surface of flocculated particles decreases markedly on aging; the reactivity of such particles toward various reagents decreases accordingly. If flocculation is prevented by a suitable hydrophilic colloid, the reactivity may remain large. Use of this fact is made in a volumetric determination of mercury based on reduction to the metal with formaldehyde in alkaline solution, followed by re-oxidation with standard iodine. The mercury globules formed during reduction rapidly combine to larger drops, consequently the rate of reaction with iodine is small. Addition of a protective colloid before reduction prevents the globules from agglomerating and the reaction velocity remains large.

4. Coprecipitation and Occlusion.—Usually a precipitate does not separate in entirely pure form, but is contaminated by impurities which it carries down. In this section the phenomena of co- and postprecipitation will be discussed only from the standpoint of volumetric analysis.[19] The carrying down of foreign materials, such as water and foreign salts, is of great consequence in gravimetric analysis, but does not lower the accuracy of a volumetric determination. As a rule, it is only the co- or postprecipitation of salts having an ion in common with the precipitate which affects the accuracy of a precipitation titration. The various types of contamination may be classified under several headings, for convenience.

A. Adsorption on the External Surface of a Precipitate.—This kind of coprecipitation, which has been discussed in a previous sec-

---

[19] More complete discussions are presented in modern texts of quantitative analysis; *e.g.* I. M. Kolthoff and E. B. Sandell, *Textbook of Quantitative Inorganic Analysis*, The MacMillan Co., New York 1936.

tion, becomes of importance when the precipitate is amorphous or of a colloidal nature, that is, when there is a large surface development. Errors caused by it can in general be reduced if the precipitate is given an opportunity to age in contact with solution near the equivalence-point.

B. Coprecipitation by Compound Formation With an Excess of Reagent.—As a rule this type of coprecipitation is of no consequence when the titration is carried out to the equivalence-point. It assumes importance when excess reagent is added and later back-titrated in the filtrate. Under such conditions relatively large errors may arise as a result of double salt formation. For example, in the precipitation of lanthanum oxalate with an excess of alkali oxalate, double salts having the general formula $La_2Ox_3 \cdot Alk_2Ox \cdot xH_2O$ may be obtained.[20] Upon addition of oxalate to a lanthanum solution, lanthanum oxalate first separates in pure form. However, when the excess of alkali oxalate becomes greater than 0.005 to 0.01 M, lanthanum oxalate is no longer stable and it is transformed into the double salt. The error can be eliminated by working with oxalic acid rather than with alkali salts. Another example is found in the precipitation of oxalate with an excess of lead halide.[21] During the titration lead oxalate separates, but with excess lead halide it is transformed into a double salt $PbOx \cdot Pb(Hal)_2$. In the precipitation of lead with an excess of potassium sulfate greater than 0.022 molar, a double salt $PbSO_4 \cdot K_2SO_4$ may be formed.[22] The double salt is not formed with sodium sulfate.

Precipitates of varying composition may result from the reaction of certain metal ions with alkali ferrocyanides. In the precipitation of zinc with sodium or potassium ferrocyanide the precipitate has the composition $Zn_3Fe(CN)_6$. With sodium ferrocyanide in excess the compound remains unchanged, whereas with potassium ferrocyanide it is rapidly transformed into $K_2Zn_3[Fe(CN)_6]_2$. With an excess of cesium ferrocyanide a compound $Cs_2ZnFe(CN)_6$ is formed. Treadwell and Chervet[23] carried out interesting studies in this field.

The ability of an alkali ion to enter into a complex precipitate depends upon its hydration and ionic volume. The smaller its vol-

[20] I. M. Kolthoff and Ruth Elmquist, *J. Am. Chem. Soc.*, **53**, 1232 (1931).

[21] Z. Karaoglanov and B. Sagortschev, *Z. anorg. allgem. Chem.*, **199**, 7 (1931).

[22] M. Randall and D. L. Shaw, *J. Am. Chem. Soc.*, **57**, 427 (1935).

[23] W. D. Treadwell and D. Chervet, *Helv. Chim. Acta*, **5**, 633 (1922); **6**, 550 (1923); W. D. Treadwell, *ibid.*, **6**, 559 (1923).

ume, the easier it is for an ion to penetrate into the crystal lattice, and the less soluble is the resulting ferrocyanide. Since the ion also loses its water of hydration upon entering the precipitate, one may expect that the least hydrated ions will be taken up most readily. The hydration of alkali ions increases in the order:

$$Cs < K < Na < Li.$$

Therefore cesium (and also rubidium) should be taken up more easily than lithium.

This conclusion is confirmed by the experiments of Treadwell and Chervet, who obtained, from cobaltous solution and the various alkali ferrocyanides, precipitates having the following compositions:

$$Li_4Fe(CN)_6 \rightarrow Co_2Fe(CN)_6$$

$$Na_4Fe(CN)_6 \rightarrow Na_2Co_3[Fe(CN)_6]_2$$

$$K_4Fe(CN)_6 \rightarrow K_2Co_3[Fe(CN)_6]_2 + K_2CoFe(CN)_6$$

$$Cs_4Fe(CN)_6 \rightarrow Cs_2CoFe(CN)_6.$$

In addition, Treadwell notes that while the alkali ion loses its water of hydration with consequent expenditure of energy, the displaced heavy metal ion becomes hydrated. The difference between the free energies of these two processes perhaps serves as a driving force in the exchange reaction. Since the energies of hydration for most heavy metal ions are not known exactly, these considerations have only qualitative significance and they will not be discussed further.

C. Coprecipitation as a Result of Mixed Crystal Formation.— Coprecipitation due to the formation of mixed crystals cannot be eliminated; the amount of coprecipitation, however, depends somewhat on the conditions during precipitation. A case of practical importance is the titration of a mixture of bromide and chloride with silver nitrate, which will be considered in a following section. Silver bromide and chloride form a continuous series of mixed crystals over the entire range. Calculations on the classical basis of the mass action law do not yield good results, for the solid phase is neither pure silver bromide nor a mixture of the two pure silver halides, but consists of silver bromide and chloride mixed crystals, whose composition changes during the titration.

D. Coprecipitation as a Result of Adsorption During the Growth of a Microcrystalline Precipitate. Occlusion.—This type of coprecipitation is fairly general and may cause errors of more or less consequence. One should keep in mind that in the precipitation of barium or lead with sulfate, or vice versa, there may arise occlusion errors of the order of one per cent or more. Hence, even though indicators are available for such precipitation titrations (see Volume II), these determinations cannot yield accurate results. This is quite broadly true of titrations in which a microcrystalline precipitate separates.

It has been mentioned that a precipitate tends to adsorb salts which have an ion in common with the lattice. Such an adsorption may occur during the growth of a crystalline precipitate, and if the adsorbed salt does not have an opportunity to escape it will remain in the occluded state. The following rules[24] are of importance with regard to the amount of occlusion:

a. Occlusion of foreign cations may be expected to predominate when the solution contains an excess of lattice anions during the precipitation. The amount of occlusion increases with increasing concentration of lattice anions and decreases (often to zero) if the precipitation is made from a solution containing an excess of lattice cations. The reverse holds true for the occlusion of lattice anions.

b. The amount of occlusion increases with increasing adsorbability of the salts present. It should be remembered that, in general, the adsorbability of a salt having an ion in common with the lattice increases with decreasing solubility and decreasing electrolytic dissociation of the adsorbed compound.

c. The amount of coprecipitation is greater the more concentrated is the solution during formation of a precipitate—in other words, the greater is the relative supersaturation. Ordinarily precipitation from hot dilute solution yields a purer solid phase than precipitation from more concentrated solution at room temperature. The latter conditions are more often applied in volumetric analysis, however.

d. Digestion of the precipitate at higher temperatures and in contact with the liquid phase generally results in a distinct purification, the solid undergoing recrystallization and giving contaminants an opportunity to redissolve. Moreover, the specific surface decreases markedly as the precipitate ages. Usually the purification and

[24] I. M. Kolthoff, *J. Phys. Chem.*, **36**, 860 (1932).

decrease in specific surface during digestion are more pronounced the more imperfect the primary precipitate. In precipitation titrations in which an excess of reagent is back-titrated in the filtrate, the errors of occlusion can as a rule be lessened by a digestion at 90 to 100°C., before filtration. The digestion process should not be applied, however, if an interfering chemical reaction can occur between the solid and liquid phases.

5. The Formation of Mixed Crystals.—If two compounds AC and BC can form mixed crystals, the interaction between the crystals and ions in solution may be represented by the equation:

$$AC + B \rightleftarrows BC + A,$$

in which A and B are either cations or anions of the same charge. When to a solution containing A and B there is added a solution of the precipitant, C, mixed crystals consisting of AC and BC are formed. If these crystals are in equilibrium with the solution, the distributions of A and B between solid and solution are related by the expression:

$$\left(\frac{aB}{aA}\right)_s \left(\frac{aA}{aB}\right)_l = D'. \tag{1}$$

In this equation aA denotes the activity of A ions and aB that of B ions, in the solid state (s) and in the liquid (l). Since the activities are proportional in an ideal solution to the molar concentrations, and in an ideal solid to the mole fractions N_A and N_B, one obtains:

$$\frac{N_B[A]}{N_A[B]} = D. \tag{2}$$

Here D is the so-called distribution coefficient. If the ions do not behave in ideal fashion, D will vary with the composition of the solid phase.

Suppose that there are taken a equivalents of A, b of B and m of C, in a volume V. Suppose further that there is such an excess of B (macro component) compared with A (micro component) that on addition of C the precipitate, practically speaking, consists entirely of BC. Let x represent the number of equivalents of A precipitated; them $m - x$ equals the number of equivalents of B precipitated, provided that m does not exceed b. At equilibrium, equation (2) applies:

$$\frac{[A]}{N_A} = \frac{[B]}{N_B} D;\tag{2}$$

$$N_A = \frac{x}{2m}, \qquad N_B = \tfrac{1}{2},$$

$$[A] = \frac{(a - x)}{V}, \qquad B = \frac{(b - m + x)}{V};$$

therefore:

$$\frac{2m(a - x)}{xV} = \frac{2(b - m + x)D}{V}$$

$$\frac{(a - x)}{x} = \frac{(b - m + x)}{m} D.\tag{3}$$

In equation (3), $(a - x)$ is the number of equivalents of A left in solution, while $(b - m + x)$ is the number of equivalents of B left in solution. If enough reagent is added to precipitate 99 per cent of B (that is, $b = 1$, $(b - m + x) = 0.01$, and $m =$ approximately 0.99), then

$$\frac{(a - x)}{x} = \frac{.01}{.99} D.$$

If the value of D is about 100, one would find 50 per cent of A in the solution and 50 per cent in the precipitate. On the other hand, after 99.9 per cent of B is precipitated:

$$\frac{(a - x)}{x} = \frac{.001}{.999} \times 100 = 0.1.$$

About 91 per cent of A would be in the solid and 9 per cent in the solution. In this case an excess of C would have to be added in order to get a quantitative precipitation of A with BC. Conversely, when D is smaller than 1 there is an enrichment of A in the precipitate during the early stages of precipitation. For example, if D is equal to 0.01 and enough reagent is added to precipitate 50 per cent of B, the distribution of A becomes:

$$\frac{(a - x)}{x} = \frac{0.50}{0.50} \times 0.01 = 0.01.$$

that is, 99 per cent of A is found in the precipitate. The distribution of microcomponent A between solid and solution under equilibrium conditions is given in the following table for various values of D and percentages of B precipitated:

DISTRIBUTION OF MICROCOMPONENT A BETWEEN SOLUTION AND PRECIPITATE BC

(Homogeneous distribution)

Per cent of B precipitated	Per cent of A in precipitate		
	D = 100	D = 1	D = 0.01
9	0.1	9	91
50	1	50	99
91	9	91	99.9
99	50	99	99.99
99.9	91	99.9	99.999
99.99	99	99.99	99.9999

If A is not a micro constituent, but is present in an amount comparable with that of B, the mole fraction of B in the solid becomes $\frac{(m - x)}{2m}$, and in place of equation (3) one obtains:

$$\frac{(a - x)}{x} = \frac{(b - m + x)}{(m - x)} D. \tag{4}$$

In the special case where $a = b = m$, it can be shown that:

$$\frac{(a - x)}{x} = \sqrt{D} \quad \text{and} \quad \frac{(b - m + x)}{(m - x)} = \sqrt{\frac{1}{D}}.$$

For example, if D is 100, 9 per cent of A will be precipitated and 91 per cent will be in the solution. The situation of B will be just the reverse. There is enrichment of B in the precipitate when D is greater than 1, and enrichment of A in the precipitate when D is less than 1 (under these conditions of incomplete precipitation).

When dealing with microcrystalline precipitates, the latter will not generally be in thermodynamic equilibrium with the liquid phase at various stages during the precipitation. If the reaction is carried out so slowly that each new layer of BC which separates on the surface is in equilibrium with the liquid phase, and if there is no aging of the precipitate, distribution will take place according to the logarithmic expression of Doerner and Hoskins:[25]

$$\log \frac{y}{a} = K \log \frac{n}{b} \tag{5}$$

in which a and b are the original amounts of A and B in the solution and y and n the final amounts. If the distribution really occurs under the ideal conditions specified, K is equal to $\frac{1}{D}$. In equation (5), $\frac{y}{a}$ multiplied by 100 represents the percentage of A left in solution and $\frac{n}{b} \times 100$ that of B left in solution, after addition of a certain amount of reagent. Hence the percentages of A and B precipitated are $100 \frac{(a - y)}{a}$ and $100 \frac{(b - n)}{b}$, respectively.

For example, taking K equal to 2 it appears that after precipitation of 10 per cent of B:

$$\frac{n}{b} = 0.90,$$

$$\log \frac{y}{a} = 2 \log 0.90 = -0.092 = \bar{1}.908,$$

$$\frac{y}{a} = 0.81.$$

In other words, 81 per cent of A remains in solution while 19 per cent is precipitated. When K is greater than 1 there is enrichment of A in the crystal during the early stages of precipitation: when K is smaller than 1 the reverse is true. This is also evident from the following table:

[25] H. A. Doerner and Wm. H. Hoskins, *J. Am. Chem. Soc.*, **47**, 662 (1925).

Distribution of A between Solution and Precipitate BC

(Heterogenous distribution according to Doerner and Hoskins; $K = \dfrac{1}{D}$)

Per cent of B precipitated	Per cent of A in precipitate		
	$K = 100$	$K = 2$	$K = 0.025$
1	63.7	2.0	0.025
10	99.998	19	0.27
50	(100)	75	1.7
90	(100)	99	5.6

The distribution of A between precipitate and solution, therefore, is quite different when heterogeneous mixed crystals are formed according to the expression of Doerner and Hoskins than when the crystals are homogeneous. One can decide which distribution is approached the more closely if values for D (or K) can be found. Kolthoff and Yutzy,[26] by shaking well-aged precipitates of silver bromide for a long time in the presence of solutions containing chloride and determining the amount of bromide which went into solution, obtained a value of about 460 for D. Similarly Kolthoff and Eggertsen[27] reported a value of 393 in the case of a colloidal silver bromide. These figures refer to a homogeneous distribution of chloride in the silver bromide precipitates, when in equilibrium with the solution.

Suppose now that an equimolecular mixture of chloride and bromide is being titrated with silver nitrate. At the first equivalence-point the quantity of reagent taken, m, will be equal to a and to b. In a homogeneous distribution, one would find:

$$\frac{(a - x)}{x} = \sqrt{D} = \sqrt{393} = 19.8$$

$$x = \frac{a}{20.8}.$$

Taking a as 100 in order to express the result simply in percentage, it appears that 4.8 per cent of the chloride would be coprecipitated. However, if the distribution were heterogeneous, equation (5) would

[26] I. M. Kolthoff and H. C. Yutzy, *J. Am. Chem. Soc.*, **59**, 916 (1937); see also F. W. Küster, *Z. anorg. allgem. Chem.*, **19**, 81 (1899); H. Flood, *ibid.*, **229**, 76 (1936); H. Flood and B. Bruun, *ibid.*, **229**, 85 (1936).

[27] I. M. Kolthoff and F. T. Eggertsen, *J. Am. Chem. Soc.*, **61**, 1036 (1939).

apply; here $y = a - x$ and $n = b - m + x$, but since $a = b = m$, n becomes equal to x:

$$\log \frac{(a - x)}{a} = K \log \frac{x}{a}$$

$$\log (a - x) - \log a = K \log x - K \log a$$

$$\log (a - x) = K \log x + (1 - K) \log a.$$

This equation may be solved by trial. For small values of K, the term $K \log x$ does not affect the equation greatly and it may be omitted by assuming $x = 1$. Then, with a as 100:

$$\log (100 - x) = 2(1 - K)$$

$$K = \frac{1}{D} = \frac{1}{393} = 0.00254$$

$$\log (100 - x) = 1.9949$$

$$100 - x = 98.83$$

$$x = 1.17.$$

The value of 1.17 is close enough to the assumed value of 1 so that a second approximation is unnecessary. A coprecipitation of 1.17 per cent of the chloride would thus be expected under conditions of heterogeneous distribution. It is evident that in this case the latter type of distribution would be the more advantageous from the analytical viewpoint. Now if an actual titration were carried out, with $a = b = m$, and the amount of coprecipitation were determined analytically, one could tell whether the observed percentage corresponded more closely to that calculated for homogeneous or for heterogeneous distribution.

In the titration of mixtures, a will not generally be equal to b, but if the compound BC is less soluble than AC it is axiomatic that at the first equivalence-point m will equal b. The next table shows the calculated percentages of A coprecipitated and of B left in solution at the first equivalence-point, for various values of K and ratios of a to b:

COPRECIPITATION OF A WITH BC AT FIRST EQUIVALENCE-POINT

K	D	a:b	Per cent A pptd.		Per cent B left in solution	
			Hetero-geneous distribution	Homo-geneous distribution	Hetero-geneous distribution	Homo-geneous distribution
.0050	200	10.	1.10	1.98	11.0	19.8
"	"	1.	1.95	6.6	1.95	6.6
"	"	0.1	2.88	19.8	0.29	1.98
.00254	393	10.	0.68	1.47	6.8	14.7
"	"	1.	1.13	4.8	1.13	4.8
"	"	0.1	1.63	14.7	0.16	1.47
.00143	700	10.	0.44	1.12	4.4	11.2
"	"	1.	0.69	3.6	0.69	3.6
"	"	0.1	0.98	11.2	0.10	1.12

From the analytical standpoint it is also of interest to consider the conditions in the neighborhood of the first equivalence-point. Assume that $a = b = 100$ milli-equivalents and that $K = 0.00254$. This value of K holds closely for the silver bromide-chloride system. If the amount of silver nitrate added is 1 per cent in excess of that corresponding to the first equivalence-point, m will equal 101, and the Doerner-Hoskins expression becomes:

$$\log \frac{(100 - x)}{100} = K \log \frac{(x - 1)}{100}.$$

Solution of this equation (by trial and error) indicates that $x = 1.39$, or that 1.39 per cent of chloride is in the precipitate and 0.39 per cent of the bromide remains in solution. If the distribution were homogeneous, the amount of bromide remaining in solution would have been 4.33 per cent. A few more figures corresponding to the situation in the region of the first equivalence-point are given in the following table:

PRECIPITATION OF A WITH BC IN VICINITY OF FIRST EQUIVALENCE-POINT
(a = b = 100; K = 0.00254)

m	Per cent of A precipitated		Per cent of B left in solution	
	Hetrogenous distribution	Homogenous distribution	Heterogenous distribution	Homogenous distribution
99	0.99	4.33	1.99	5.33
100 (first equiv.-pt.)	1.13	4.80	1.13	4.80
101	1.39	5.33	0.39	4.33
102	2.03	5.90	0.03	3.90
104	4.0	7.20	0.00001	3.20

The large difference between homogeneous and heterogeneous distribution is particularly striking when the reagent is added in excess. Thus heterogeneous conditions call for only 0.03 per cent of the bromide to remain in solution after addition of a 2 per cent excess of reagent, while with homogeneous distribution 3.9 per cent of the bromide would remain unprecipitated. In actual practice it is very difficult to realize either mode of distribution exclusively. Conformance to the Doerner-Hoskins expression requires that each new layer of the growing crystal be in equilibrium with the solution, but that no recrystallization (aging) take place. In homogeneous mixed crystal formation, on the other hand, the primary precipitate must recrystallize so rapidly and frequently that the solid phase maintains thermodynamic equilibrium with the liquid.

Kolthoff and Eggertsen[27] investigated the distribution of bromide between precipitate and solution during the titration of a mixture of chloride and bromide with silver nitrate. In general, they found that if the precipitate were kept in the colloidal state, homogeneous distribution would be approached quite closely. However, with the addition of aluminum ions to flocculate the precipitate as it formed, and with very slow addition of silver nitrate, it was possible to approach heterogeneous distribution. Nevertheless, the amount of bromide remaining in solution was always somewhat higher than would be expected according to the Doerner-Hoskins expression, since it was not possible to prevent aging entirely. Another factor is that in the presence of flocculating ions each newly formed layer does not come into equilibrium with the solution. For example, near the first equivalence-point the solution is very weak in bromide and local excesses of silver ion react first with chloride. The silver chloride is quickly flocculated and does not have sufficient opportunity to attain equilibrium with the liquid.

It is of practical interest to mention that the distribution coefficient D for the silver bromide-chloride system increases greatly with decreasing temperature. Therefore the coprecipitation of chloride will be considerably less if the precipitation is made at near zero degree rather than at room temperature. This is true for either mode of distribution. Thus Kolthoff and Eggertsen found 2.9 per cent coprecipitated at about 10°C. compared with 4.7 per cent at about 30°, under conditions of homogeneous distribution and at the first equivalence-point. In the presence of aluminum ions (heterogeneous distribution), the corresponding percentages were 1.5 and 2.16, respectively. For experimental details and further data on this silver halide system, the reader is referred to the original publication.[27] The observations mentioned above are of great consequence in the interpretation of potentiometric curves obtained in the titration of bromide-chloride mixtures.[28] In the potentiometric determination of bromide in the presence of chloride, it should be advantageous to cool the mixture in an ice-bath during titration.

In concluding this chapter it may be pointed out that mixed crystal formation can be put to analytical use in some cases for the quantitative precipitation of traces of ions from solution. Amounts of arsenate so small that ordinarily they would precipitate only very slowly (if at all) in the presence of magnesia mixture, can be precipitated completely if a little phosphate is added. Magnesium ammonium arsenate forms mixed crystals with magnesium ammonium phosphate, so that the latter carries down all the arsenate. Kolthoff and Carr[29] made use of this fact, accumulating arsenate in the precipitate and determining it volumetrically. Coprecipitation with lead as the sulfide can also serve to gather mercury from very dilute solutions, and there will doubtless be found various other applications of occlusion or adsorption.

[28] *Cf.* H. Flood and E. Sletten, *Z. anal. Chem.*, **115**, 30 (1938); H. Flood, *Z. anorg. allgem. Chem.*, **229**, 76 (1936); H. Flood and B. Bruun, *ibid.*, **229**, 85 (1936).

[29] I. M. Kolthoff and C. W. Carr, unpublished experiments.

CHAPTER IX

VOLUMETRIC METHODS OF ORGANIC ANALYSIS

1. Introduction.—Organic compounds may be classified as electrolytes or non-electrolytes. To the former group belong organic acids, bases and their salts; since members of this class can generally be determined by means of ionic reactions which have already been discussed, they will not be considered further. The non-electrolytes present a different problem, in that methods for their determination are based on molecular reactions. These do not proceed instantaneously, but ordinarily have a measurable velocity that depends upon factors of widely varying character.

Determinations involving *hydrolysis*, for example, are quite different from those resting on the *formation of addition products*, while methods of *oxidation-reduction* comprise a still different type which is of great analytical value. It is therefore expedient to consider the individual titrimetric procedures separately, inquiring whether physico-chemical principles can also be of help in developing volumetric methods of this kind.

Specialized procedures in which elements are titrated after conversion to inorganic form will not be discussed in this chapter.

2. Methods of Saponification or Hydrolysis of Esters.—The term *saponification* denoted originally the conversion of fats (glycerine esters of fatty acids) into glycerine and the alkali salts of fatty acids. The idea of saponification has since been extended to the splitting of esters in general as well as to other similar processes, so that under this heading may be included the decomposition of phenol ethers, imide ethers, acid amides and nitriles.[1] Saponification is a kind of hydrolysis; by taking up water an ester separates into an alcohol and an acid.

As saponifying agents one may use water, acids, or alkalies, in-

---

[1] *Cf.* for example W. Vaubel, *Die physikalischen und chemischen Methoden der quant. Bestimmung organischer Verbindungen*, Vol. II, p. 109, Julius Springer, Berlin 1902.

cluding hydrolyzed salts. Alkalies are the most important for analytical purposes. Theoretical considerations regarding their use will be given briefly, without regard to special cases such as the effect of neutral salts. If ethyl acetate is treated with an aqueous solution of a base, reaction takes place gradually according to the equation:

$$CH_3COOC_2H_5 + NaOH \rightleftarrows CH_3COONa + C_2H_5OH.$$

This is the classical example of a bimolecular reaction. Letting a and b represent the original concentrations of base and ester, and x the amount decomposed after time t, the velocity of the reaction is given by the expression:[2]

$$\frac{dx}{dt} = k(a - x)(b - x).$$

Upon integration, the reaction velocity constant is found to be:

$$k = \frac{1}{(a - b)t} \, ln \, \frac{(a - x)b}{(b - x)a},$$

and after converting the natural logarithms to Briggsian, this becomes:

$$k = \frac{2.303}{(a - b)t} \log \frac{(a - x)b}{(b - x)a}.$$

Equilibrium in the case of the above reaction is not reached until the ester has been almost completely saponified.

Viewed in the light of the electrolytic dissociation theory, the saponification process consists in the action of hydroxyl ions upon ester molecules and may be better expressed by the equation:

$$CH_3COOC_2H_5 + OH^- \rightleftarrows CH_3COO^- + C_2H_5OH.$$

The cation of the base has no part in the change. The larger the hydroxyl-ion concentration, that is, the stronger the base, the greater is the rate of reaction. This is shown by the data of Reicher,[3] who first studied systematically the velocity of saponification reac-

---

[2] Consult any standard text on physical chemistry.
[3] L. T. Reicher, *Ann.*, **228**, 257 (1885), **232**, 103 (1885).

tions. He found the following values for the reaction velocity constant k in the saponification of ethyl acetate at 9°:

Base used	k	Base used	k
NaOH	2.307	Sr(OH)$_2$	2.204
KOH	2.298	Ba(OH)$_2$	2.144
Ca(OH)$_2$	2.285	NH$_4$OH	0.011

Before potentiometric or colorimetric methods of determining p_H came into general use, concentrations of H^+ and OH^- were frequently measured by the rate of saponification of esters. It is evident from the above values that ammonia behaves as a very weak base.

The velocity of saponification being dependent upon the strength of the base, it might be concluded that in all cases the speed should be smaller in solvents having less ionizing power than water. However, another consideration also enters: apparently the solvent is not excluded from the reaction, but exerts a specific effect upon the velocity. The nature of the solvent has the most influence over the molecular state of dissolved materials. On this account the rate of saponification in aqueous solution does not necessarily exceed that in other solvents.

In another sense also the nature of the solvent is of importance. Many esters, such as fats, are insoluble in water, and in these cases other solvents are naturally preferable. In practice, an ethyl alcohol solution of sodium or potassium hydroxide is warmed with the ester until the reaction is complete. The temperature greatly influences the rate.[4] Thus Reicher[3] established that the velocity constant for ethyl acetate with sodium hydroxide is 2.307 at 9.4°, and 21.65 at 45°; the ratio for a ten-degree temperature rise is 1.89. Obviously the saponification should proceed much more rapidly in higher boiling solvents than in ethyl alcohol, for example in propyl, butyl or even benzyl alcohol solutions at their boiling points. This is confirmed by experiment and finds practical application in the saponification of relatively stable compounds such as many kinds of waxes.[5]

[4] *Cf.* J. H. van't Hoff, *Vorlesungen über theoretische und physikalische Chemie*, Part 1, Die chemische Dynamik, Braunschweig 1898.

[5] The use of propyl alcohol as a solvent during saponifications was recommended by L. W. Winkler, *Z. angew. Chem.*, **24**, 626 (1911); see also J. Prescher, *Pharm. Zentralhalle*, **58**, 456 (1917). Other proposals include benzyl alcohol, H. F. Slack, *Chemist and Druggist*, **87**, 673 (1915); isobutyl alcqhol, A. M. Pardu, R. L. Hasche and E. E. Reid, *Ind. Eng. Chem.*, **12**, 481 (1920), I. M. Kolthoff, *Chem. Weekblad*, **17**, 348 (1920); isopropyl alcohol, H. A. Schuette and P. M. Smith, *Ind. Eng. Chem.*, **18**, 1242 (1926).

In saponifications the speed of reaction is directly proportional to the concentration of each reacting substance. It is therefore in order to chose a solvent in which the ester is readily soluble; otherwise the ester is replaced rather slowly after decomposition and the concentration remains small. Most fats are only slightly soluble in ethyl alcohol, but this can be partly overcome by adding some soap to the mixture, as Rusting[6] proposed. According to N. Schoorl the reagent may be prepared as follows: Dissolve 45 gms. of potassium hydroxide in 45 grams of water; add 56 grams of coconut oil and 750 ml. of strong ethyl alcohol, and warm the mixture gently. Allow to stand overnight, then dilute to one liter with alcohol. The solution will be about 0.5 N in potassium hydroxide; it decomposes on standing and on boiling, so that a blank determination should be carried through the procedure.

A readily saponifiable fat like olive oil may be quantitatively decomposed by boiling for three minutes with this reagent. The favorable effect of soap is apparently to be explained on the basis of its emulsifying action. The speed of solution of the fat is increased and a heterogeneous reaction may also occur, alkali attacking the surface of finely divided fat particles.

To summarize, the most favorable conditions for rapid saponification consist in having a large concentration of hydroxyl ions, a homogeneous solution, and a high temperature.

Apparently a small amount of water is necessary. Obermüller[7] was able to show that with the use of reagents as nearly anhydrous as possible and with special precautions for excluding atmospheric moisture, the saponification did not take place completely. Also, the esterification of certain difficultly saponifiable waxes with sodium alcoholate seems to proceed more rapidly in the complete absence of water than when a trace is present.[8]

Saponification by water may be catalyzed by specific enzymes. Although analytical use of such enzyme actions is rarely made in the determination of saponification values, there are other cases of hydrolysis in which enzymes are of great assistance. A common example is the hydrolysis of urea with the aid of the enzyme urease.[9]

$$(NH_2)_2CO + 2H_2O \rightarrow (NH_4)_2CO_3.$$

[6] N. Rusting, *Pharm. Weekblad*, **45**, 433 (1908).

[7] K. Obermüller, *Z. physik. Chem.*, **16**, 152 (1892).

[8] A. Beythien, *Pharm. Zentralhalle*, **38**, 850 (1897).

[9] *Cf.* for example J. Y. Yee and R. O. E. Davis, *Ind. Eng. Chem. Anal. Ed.*, **7**, 259 (1935).

In the decomposition of nitriles, the corresponding acid and ammonia are formed:

$$CH_3C{\equiv}N + 2H_2O \rightarrow CH_3COOH + NH_3 \rightleftarrows CH_3COONH_4 + H_2O.$$

Either acids or bases favor this hydrolysis, acids having the stronger action.

There are many substances which though not themselves saponifiable may be converted into saponifiable compounds. In this category are the alcohols, phenols, and compounds of basic character such as amines. Practically, the methods of acetylation or of benzoylation are adopted, whereby acetyl (CH_3CO^-) or benzoyl ($C_6H_5CO^-$) groups are introduced into the compound. Either of two procedures may be followed: the excess of reagent may be back-titrated after quantitative substitution, or it may be removed and the saponification number of the new compound determined. The latter is the more commonly used.

Suitable reagents for acetylation are acetic anhydride or acetyl chloride, perhaps with addition of sodium acetate. Acetic acid may also be used, but its action is slower. The rate of acetylation of phenols may be increased by adding a drop of concentrated sulfuric acid as a catalyst. According to Smith and Bryant,[10] a mixture of acetyl chloride and pyridine is well suited for the determination of hydroxyl groups in a wide range of compounds.

Benzoylation may be carried out with benzoyl chloride, benzoic anhydride with or without addition of sodium benzoate, or with substituted benzoyl compounds such as o-, m- or p-bromobenzoyl chloride. Bruner and Tolloczko[11] investigated the reaction velocity during esterification of aliphatic alcohols with benzoyl chloride. The velocity constants were found to decrease markedly with increasing molecular weight of the alcohol. Otherwise the mechanism of ester formation remains uncertain. According to the equation,

$$C_6H_5COCl + ROH \rightleftarrows C_6H_5COOR + HCl,$$

the reaction should be bimolecular, yet Bruner and Tolloczko observed that the velocity coefficient decreases steadily. Possibly the dissociation of hydrochloric acid is involved. A more exact theoreti-

[10] D. M. Smith and W. M. D. Bryant, *J. Am. Chem. Soc.*, **57**, 61 (1935).
[11] L. Bruner and L. Tolloczko, *Chem. Ztg.*, **24**, 59 (1900).

cal knowledge of the processes would be of great practical value, since the determination of acetyl or benzoyl number is frequently called for in technical analysis.

In the general application of esterification methods some caution is necessary, as several sources of error exist. One of these in the case of hydroxy acids is the tendency toward formation of inner esters (lactones), which makes the observed acetyl number too small. According to Grün[12] most of the literature values are erroneous on this account. He suggests that all errors can be avoided if the esters or free acids are first converted into methyl esters, and the acetyl numbers of the latter determined.

Somewhat related in principle to methods involving acid hydrolysis is the practically important procedure for determination of methoxy or ethoxy groups proposed by Zeisel.[13] The alkoxyls react with hydriodic acid:

$$ROR' + 2HI \rightleftarrows RI + R'I + H_2O$$

$$\phi OR + HI \rightleftarrows RI + \phi OH.$$

These equilibria are shifted toward the formation of alkyl iodides through continuous removal of the latter by distillation. Passage of the vapors through bromine water liberates iodine which may be determined volumetrically as iodate.[14]

3. The Formation of Addition Products.—Many organic compounds are capable of forming addition products, especially those substances which possess a carbonyl group or a double bond between carbon atoms. Between an addition compound and its constituents there may exist a reversible equilibrium, as in the case of addition at the carbonyl group. In other instances the reaction may be irreversible. The two types are different in principle as well as in their analytical applications and will therefore be considered separately.

---

[12] A. Grün, *Analyse der Fette und Wachse*, Julius Springer, Berlin 1925, p. 159.

[13] S. Zeisel, *Monatsh.*, **6**, 989 (1885); for the application to alkimides see T. Herzig and H. Mayer, *Ber.*, **27**, 319 (1894), *Monatsh.*, **15**, 613 (1894), **16**, 599 (1895), **18**, 379 (1897).

[14] F. Viebock and A. Schwappach, *Ber.*, **63**, 2819 (1930); Viebock and C. Brecher, *ibid.*, **63**, 3207 (1930).

A. REVERSIBLE ADDITION REACTIONS

Addition of Bisulfite to the Carbonyl Group.—Of the several types of addition to the C=O group, the reaction with bisulfite has especial analytical importance since it is a basis for the determination of many aldehydes and some ketones. Characteristically, there are in the literature many contradictory statements about the accuracy of bisulfite or sulfite methods. This is because the methods have been applied or studied only empirically, without regard for theoretical considerations. As will be seen in what follows, one can calculate on theoretical grounds the conditions under which an aldehyde or ketone will enter into a quantitative reaction with bisulfite, and the magnitude of the error resulting from incomplete addition. The reaction furnishes a good demonstration of how a proper regard for physico-chemical principles can benefit the practical application of a volumetric procedure.

Upon addition to an aldehyde or ketone, sulfurous acid or bisulfite is, strictly speaking, "bound" directly. There is formed an

α-hydroxy sulfonic acid, R—CH$\begin{smallmatrix}\diagup \text{OH} \\ \diagdown \text{SO}_3\text{H}\end{smallmatrix}$ (or its salt), which is stable toward oxidizing agents. Such "bound acids" and their salts are, in aqueous solution, split to a certain degree into their components. The extent of this decomposition depends upon the strength of the union between the components (which is a function of the temperature), as well as upon the concentration of the solution.

The equilibrium reaction may be, for example:

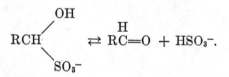

The decomposition of the addition product into bisulfite and aldehyde increases significantly with rising temperature and diminishing concentration.

If iodine is added to an aqueous solution of the sodium salt of an aldehyde-sulfurous acid compound, as much of the oxidant is reduced as corresponds to the quantity of bisulfite formed by dissociation. When this bisulfite is oxidized, further dissociation produces more in accordance with the law of mass action, until equilibrium is restored.   The velocities of such equilibrium shifts are quite different in equivalent solutions of various aldehyde salts, and for a given salt the rate depends upon the dilution and the temperature.   W. Kerp[15] carried out thorough studies on the conditions suitable for different carbonyl-bisulfite compounds.   Two factors have especial analytical importance:

(a) The *dissociation constants* of the salts.

(b) The *speed* with which equilibrium is established.

A new equilibrium is never established instantly.   In determining an aldehyde, one may always titrate the excess of bisulfite iodimetrically, for the iodine color remains long enough at the endpoint so that it may be recognized.   Only after longer standing is the excess iodine reduced by newly dissociated bisulfite.   On the other hand, the mixture of aldehyde and bisulfite should be allowed to stand long enough, before back-titration, for the reaction to approach completion.   This reaction time depends upon several conditions, especially upon the nature of the aldehyde and upon the concentrations of the reactants.   According to Kerp, it amounts in the case of acetaldehyde to about an hour with 0.1 to 0.5 N solutions, or two hours with 0.01 N solutions.

Dissociation Constants of Aldehyde-Bisulfite Compounds.—On application of the law of mass action to the equation previously given for the decomposition of an aldehyde-bisulfite salt, the expression for the dissociation constant, K, is seen to be:

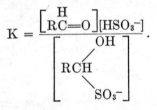

Rounded values for K at 25°C., as determined by Kerp and his collaborators, are assembled in the following table along with figures giving the percentage of the total concentration that is present as free sodium bisulfite, in pure solutions of the sodium salts:

[15] W. Kerp, *Arb. kaiserl. Gesundh.*, **21**, 180 (1904); see also A. W. Stewart, *J. Chem. Soc.*, **87**, 185 (1905).

DISSOCIATION CONSTANTS OF ALDEHYDE-BISULFITE COMPOUNDS AND PERCENTAGES DECOMPOSED IN SOLUTIONS OF THE SODIUM SALTS AT 25°C.

Compound	K at 25° (rounded)	Per cent decomposed at indicated total concentration		
		1N	0.1N	0.033N
Formaldehyde sodium sulfite	1.2×10^{-7}	0.034	0.097	0.155
Acetaldehyde sodium sulfite.....	2.5×10^{-6}	0.17	0.45	0.71
Benzaldehyde sodium sulfite.....	1.0×10^{-4}	2.07	2.98	4.90
Acetone sodium sulfite...........	$3.5{-}4.0 \times 10^{-3}$	5.73	14.58	23.67
Furfural sodium sulfite..........	7.2×10^{-4}			
Chloral sodium sulfite...........	3.5×10^{-2}			
Arabinose sodium sulfite.........	3.5×10^{-2}			
Glucose sodium sulfite...........	2.2×10^{-1}	42.32	74.61	81.9

From the studies of Kerp and Bauer[16] it may be concluded (a) that the free acids of aldehyde-bisulfite compounds are very strong electrolytes, and (b) that the decomposition constants rise rapidly with the temperature. Thus the constant for acetaldehyde sodium sulfite is five times as great at 37.5° as at 25°. If the constants generally increase five-fold with a 12.5° rise in temperature, then at 0° they should have only one twenty-fifth of their value at 25°. It might then be possible to determine even substances like acetone and furfural with some degree of accuracy.

Kerp and Wöhler[17] carried out a thorough investigation of the addition of bisulfite to unsaturated aldehydes, especially citronellal and cinnamic aldehyde. Citronellal has the formula:

$$H_2C{=}C(CH_3)CH_2CH_2CH_2CH(CH_3)CH_2\overset{\text{H}}{C}{=}O.$$

Addition can take place at either the double bond or the carbonyl group. In the latter case there is formed the usual bisulfite compound which splits only very slowly into its components. The dissociation does not come to an equilibrium, for on one hand citronellal "induces" the air oxidation of bisulfite, and on the other, bisulfite attacks the double bond:

$$H_2C{=}\overset{R'}{C}R + HSO_3^- \rightleftarrows H_3C{-}\overset{R'}{\underset{\underset{SO_3^-}{|}}{C}}R .$$

[16] W. Kerp and E. Bauer, *Arb. kaiserl. Gesundh.*, **26**, 231 (1907).
[17] W. Kerp and P. Wöhler, *Arb. kaiserl. Gesundh.*, **32**, 138 (1909).

As a result of these processes, compounds may be formed with one mole of bisulfite per mole (at either group), or with two moles of bisulfite per mole (one at each group). In the combined reaction, the sodium citronellal di-bisulfite which is formed has a decomposition constant of 8×10^{-7}.

The following constants were measured for cinnamic aldehyde:

$$\begin{matrix} & & \text{H} & \\ \text{C}_6\text{H}_5\,\text{CH}{=}\text{CH}{-}\overset{|}{\underset{|}{\text{C}}}\text{OH}, & & K = 1.02 \times 10^{-3}; \\ & & \text{SO}_3^- & \end{matrix}$$

$$\begin{matrix} & \text{H} & \text{H} & \\ \text{C}_6\text{H}_5\,\text{CH}_2{-}\overset{|}{\underset{|}{\text{C}}}{-}{-}\overset{|}{\underset{|}{\text{C}}}\text{OH}, & & & K = 4.06 \times 10^{-6}. \\ & \text{SO}_3^- & \text{SO}_3^- & \end{matrix}$$

From an analytical standpoint it is noteworthy that *the addition compound of bisulfite at the double bond is thoroughly stable,* and does not split off sulfurous acid even on warming with dilute sulfuric acid, in contrast with the aldehyde-bisulfite product.[18] Further, from the values above one can conclude that introduction of bisulfite at the double bond strongly represses the dissociation of carbonyl bisulfite. Therefore the following findings of Bauer and Wöhler have especial interest for analytical practice:

(a) That one mole of an unsaturated aldehyde can combine with two moles of bisulfite, and that addition of bisulfite to the double bond strongly increases the stability of the complex (decreases K).

(b) That in the addition of bisulfite to unsaturated aldehydes the hydrogen-ion concentration must play an important part.

On theoretical grounds it might be expected that the two types of addition would be influenced in different ways by the concentration of hydrogen ions. In this respect the exact investigations of Stewart and Donnally[19] on the reaction of benzaldehyde and bisulfite at varying p_H are of interest. These workers studied the velocity of association of benzaldehyde and bisulfite, as well as the dissociation rate of

---

[18] Concerning the addition of sulfite to the double bond see also E. Hägglund and A. Ringborn, *Z. anorg. allgem. Chem.,* **150,** 231 (1926); **169,** 96 (1928); also J. M. van der Zanden, *Dissertation,* Gröningen, (1926), *Rec. trav. chim.,* **45,** 424 (1926).

[19] T. D. Stewart and L. H. Donnally, *J. Am. Chem. Soc.,* **54,** 2333, 3555, 3559 (1932).

the compound formed, over a wide p_H range and at several temperatures. The specific velocity constants, k_1 for dissociation and k_2 for association, increase rapidly with decreasing hydrogen-ion concentration, while the equilibrium constant K reaches a minimum between p_H values of 3 and 4 (in other words, when the sulfurous acid is present mainly as bisulfite). The expression for the equilibrium constant may be written as:

$$K = \frac{[\sum H_2SO_3][\sum C_6H_5CHO]}{[\sum C_6H_5CH(OH)SO_3H]} \, ,$$

in which the summation signs denote total concentrations of the particular components without regard to ionization effects; that is, $\sum H_2SO_3$ includes sulfite, bisulfite and free sulfurous acid, all uncombined with aldehyde. In the following table are given the various constants as observed by Stewart and Donnally at 21°C.

CONSTANTS FOR THE BENZALDEHYDE-BISULFITE REACTION AT 21°C.

p_H	k_2 (min.$^{-1}$)	k_1 (min.$^{-1}$)	$K \left(= \frac{k_1}{k_2} \right)$
0.0	6.62	3.26×10^{-2}	4.88×10^{-3}
1.0	11.8	5.34×10^{-3}	4.53×10^{-4}
2.0	27.0	3.32×10^{-3}	1.23×10^{-4}
3.0	1.01×10^2	9.89×10^{-3}	9.78×10^{-5}
4.0	7.99×10^2	7.85×10^{-2}	9.85×10^{-5}
5.0	7.67×10^3	7.65×10^{-1}	1.00×10^{-4}
6.0	6.98×10^4	7.63	1.09×10^{-4}
7.0	3.76×10^5	7.63×10	2.02×10^{-4}
8.0	6.74×10^5	7.20×10^2	1.07×10^{-3}
9.0	7.30×10^5	4.50×10^3	6.16×10^{-3}
10.0	7.35×10^5	9.65×10^3	1.31×10^{-2}
11.0	7.15×10^5	1.09×10^4	1.52×10^{-2}
12.0	4.90×10^5	1.10×10^4	2.24×10^{-2}
13.0	1.22×10^5	1.10×10^4	9.05×10^{-2}

These changes in equilibrium and velocity constants with the p_H of the solution are connected with changes in the dissociation states of the different components. Within certain p_H regions, the main reactions are as indicated below:

p_H 0-1 $C_6H_5CHO + H_2SO_3 \rightleftarrows C_6H_5CH(OH)SO_3^- + H^+$

p_H 3-7 $C_6H_5CHO + HSO_3^- \rightleftarrows C_6H_5CH(OH)SO_3^-$

p_H 10–12 $\qquad$ $C_6H_5CHO + SO_3^- \rightleftarrows C_6H_5CH(O^-)SO_3$

p_H 12–13 $\qquad$ $C_6H_5CHO + OH^- \rightleftarrows C_6H_5CH(O^-)(OH)$

$$C_6H_5C(O^-)OH + SO_3^- \rightleftarrows C_6H_5C(O^-)SO_3^- + OH^-$$

Benzaldehyde sulfonic acid behaves as a strong monobasic acid; its second ionization constant is 7.0×10^{-10}. Benzaldehyde is a very weak acid with an ionization constant of 5×10^{-13}.

As the following table shows, the equilibrium constant rises sharply with increasing temperature:[19]

INFLUENCE OF TEMPERATURE AND p_H ON BENZALDEHYDE-BISULFITE EQUILIBRIUM CONSTANT

$p_H = 1.91$		$p_H = 5.21$		$p_H = 7.18$	
Temp. °C.	$K \times 10^5$	Temp. °C.	$K \times 10^4$	Temp. °C.	$K \times 10^4$
3.2	2.20	3.5	0.24	3.4	1.12
20.3	13.1	20.3	1.07	20.9	3.3
34.6	57.4	32.3	2.10	46.2	10.2
37.3	60.8	33.0	2.21	53.1	12.5

It would be of advantage to have similar data on other aldehydes. From the figures of Stewart and Donnally, one could expect to obtain the best results in a determination of benzaldehyde by maintaining a p_H of 3 to 4 and back-titrating at a low temperature.

The Titration Error Due to Dissociation of an Aldehyde-Bisulfite Compound.—For analytical purposes, it is of importance to find from the decomposition constants of the addition compounds, the fraction of aldehyde or ketone that remains unreacted (or free in the solution) in the presence of excess bisulfite. From this one can estimate the accuracy of such a determination. The expression for the equilibrium constant may be written:

$$K = \frac{[RCHO][HSO_3^-]}{[RCH(OH)SO_3^-]}.$$

If a ml. of aldehyde of molarity n are added to b ml. of m molar bisulfite, the total volume becomes $(a + b)$ ml. Provided that no reaction took place, dilution would bring the molarities of aldehyde and bisulfite to the following values, respectively:

$$\frac{an}{a + b} \quad \text{and} \quad \frac{bm}{a + b}.$$

However, by the reaction enough aldehyde-bisulfite compound is formed to make its concentration x, and the other concentrations are diminished accordingly. The equilibrium may then be expressed as:

$$K = \frac{\left(\dfrac{an}{a+b} - x\right)\left(\dfrac{bm}{a+b} - x\right)}{x}.$$

Although this quadratic equation can be solved for x, it is simpler to make an approximation. Since an excess of bisulfite is taken, the concentration of aldehyde-bisulfite formed may be set equal to the original aldehyde concentration without introducing a serious error. Then:

$$[RCH(OH)SO_3^-] = \frac{an}{a+b},$$

and

$$[HSO_3^-] = \frac{bm}{a+b} - \frac{an}{a+b} = \frac{bm - an}{a+b}.$$

The concentration of unbound aldehyde thus becomes:

$$[RCHO] = K\frac{[RCH(OH)SO_3^-]}{[HSO_3^-]} = K\frac{an}{bm - an}.$$

With the aid of this equation one can calculate the error due to incomplete binding of the aldehyde. Initially the number of millimoles of aldehyde present was $n \times a$; at equilibrium the number is:

$$K\frac{an(a+b)}{bm - an}.$$

Therefore the percentage remaining unreacted, that is, the per cent of error, becomes:

$$\text{Per cent error} = 100K\frac{an(a+b)}{an(bm - an)} = 100K\frac{(a+b)}{(bm - an)}$$

(K = decomposition constant, a = original milliliters of n molar aldehyde, b = original milliliters of m molar bisulfite.) This equation, though based on an approximation, is useful even if as much as 5 per cent of the aldehyde remains unbound. If more than this remained, the exact quadratic equation would have to be employed, but under such conditions the volumetric determination would be correspondingly poor.

From the above equation it can be seen that the relative error decreases with decreasing values of K, with increasing excess of bisulfite, and with increasing concentration of both reagents.

In the table on page 221 are listed titration errors calculated for various conditions that may be encountered. In these calculations it has been assumed that the equilibrium does not shift during back-titration, an assumption justified by the studies of Kerp (loc. cit.). The table shows that aldehydes whose bisulfite compounds have dissociation constants of about 10^{-7} react quantitatively in practically all cases. Even 0.001 molar solutions show an error of only 0.4 per cent when the excess of bisulfite amounts to 5 per cent. These relationships correspond to those of formaldehyde.

With compounds for which K is about 10^{-6}, a 50 per cent excess of bisulfite is necessary if 0.001 molar solutions are to be titrated with only 0.5 per cent error. This point has to be considered in the determination of acetaldehyde (K = 2.5×10^{-6}), for example. As the constants increase, the limits within which the titration can give good results become more restricted. Thus benzaldehyde (K = 10^{-4}) requires a bisulfite excess of 50 per cent in the titration of 0.1 molar solutions, if the error is not to exceed 0.5 per cent. The relationships are still less favorable for acetone and furfural. These considerations explain the conflicting statements which have appeared in the literature, regarding the determination of aldehydes and ketones with bisulfite.

In general, to lessen the error due to incomplete reaction one should work at low temperatures, thereby decreasing the decomposition constant (cf. pages 215 and 218). On the other hand, the establishment of equilibrium then requires a longer time, so that the determination becomes more tedious. In practice, a compromise between accuracy and speed may be necessary.

Errors Due to Incomplete Reaction in the Bisulfite Determination of Aldehydes or Ketones

K = decomposition constant
a = ml. of aldehyde solution of molarity n
b = ml. of bisulfite solution of molarity m

a	n	b	m	[RCHO] at equilibrium	Error, per cent
			$K = 10^{-7}$		
10	0.1	15.0	0.1	2.0×10^{-7}	0.0005
10	0.1	10.5	0.1	2.0×10^{-6}	0.004
10	0.01	15.0	0.01	2.0×10^{-7}	0.005
10	0.01	10.5	0.01	2.0×10^{-6}	0.04
10	0.001	15.0	0.001	2.0×10^{-7}	0.05
10	0.001	10.5	0.001	2.0×10^{-6}	0.4
			$K = 10^{-6}$		
10	0.1	15.0	0.1	2.0×10^{-6}	0.005
10	0.1	10.5	0.1	2.0×10^{-5}	0.04
10	0.01	15.0	0.01	2.0×10^{-6}	0.05
10	0.01	10.5	0.01	2.0×10^{-5}	0.4
10	0.001	15.0	0.001	2.0×10^{-6}	0.5
10	0.001	10.5	0.001	2.0×10^{-5}	4.
			$K = 10^{-5}$		
10	0.1	15.0	0.1	2.0×10^{-5}	0.05
10	0.1	10.5	0.1	2.0×10^{-4}	0.4
10	0.01	15.0	0.01	2.0×10^{-5}	0.5
10	0.01	10.5	0.01	2.0×10^{-4}	4.
10	0.001	15.0	0.001	2.0×10^{-5}	5.
10	0.001	50.0	0.001	2.5×10^{-6}	1.5
			$K = 10^{-4}$		
10	0.1	15.0	0.1	2.0×10^{-4}	0.5
10	0.1	10.5	0.1	2.0×10^{-3}	4.
10	0.01	15.0	0.01	2.0×10^{-4}	5.
10	0.01	40.0	0.01	3.0×10^{-5}	1.7
10	0.01	50.0	0.01	2.5×10^{-5}	1.2
			$K = 10^{-3}$		
10	0.1	15.0	0.1	2.0×10^{-3}	5.0
10	0.1	25.0	0.1	6.7×10^{-4}	2.3
10	0.1	40.0	0.1	3.0×10^{-4}	1.7
10	0.1	50.0	0.1	2.5×10^{-4}	1.2
10	0.01	40.0	0.01	3.0×10^{-4}	17.

In seeking the most favorable hydrogen-ion concentration, it must be remembered that while the addition compounds are strong electrolytes (sulfonic acids), the first dissociation constant of sulfurous acid is only 1.7×10^{-2}. Therefore if bisulfite is added to an acidified aldehyde solution, some sulfurous acid may be lost through volatilization. The equilibrium would shift unfavorably and furthermore the formation of addition product would be retarded. The studies of Stewart and Donnally[19] bear on this matter.

The optimum p_H for the addition is about 4, $i.e.$, the p_H of a bisulfite solution. Since the conditions are less favorable at higher alkalinities, just as at higher acidities, methods involving sodium sulfite are less useful than those in which bisulfite is employed. The alkalimetric determination, based upon back-titration of free alkali liberated in the reaction

$$RCHO + Na_2SO_3 \rightleftarrows RCH(OH)SO_3Na + NaOH,$$

cannot give good results unless the decomposition constant of the bisulfite compound is very small. It would be better to add a bisulfite solution of which a separate portion had been titrated with alkali, using thymolphthalein as indicator, and to back-titrate the excess, after establishment of equilibrium, to the same p_H. During this process the aldehyde sodium sulfonate behaves as a neutral salt. A systematic study of such methods would be desirable.

Addition of Mercuric Salts to Unsaturated Compounds.—Mercury salts are taken up by organic compounds possessing double bonds. The composition of the product depends upon the particular mercury salt chosen and the experimental conditions. With mercuric sulfate, propylene and its homologues give amorphous yellow precipitates, formulated according to Denigès[20] as molecular compounds

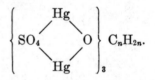

By treatment with acids these salts decompose into mercurous salts and compounds with aldehyde properties. Hofmann and Sand[21] have shown that under other conditions one can obtain two series of salts, differing in molecular size, of which one is derived from mercury-

[20] G. Denigès, *Compt. rend.*, **126**, 1145, 1868 (1898); *Ann. chim. phys.*, [7], **18**, 382 (1899).

[21] K. A. Hofmann and J. Sand, *Ber.*, **33**, 1340, 1358, 2692 (1900); J. Sand, *ibid.*, **34**, 1385 (1901); J. Sand and F. Breest, *Z. physik. Chem.*, **59**, 424 (1907).

substituted alcohols and the other from mercury-substituted ethers, for example:[22]

$$HOCH_2CH_2HgX \quad \text{and} \quad (CH_2CH_2HgX)_2O.$$

Biilmann and Hoff[23] studied mercury addition compounds from the physico-chemical standpoint. According to their findings, mercuric salts unite with ethylene derivatives, whereby —Hg(I) or —Hg(II)X enters at the double bond. In this way may be formed complexes stable enough so that the mercury no longer reacts with hydrogen sulfide. With maleic acid and its derivatives the complexes formed are soluble in alkali without decomposition.

The addition process may be written as a molecular reaction (a), or in part as an ionic reaction (b). Thus the addition of a mercuric salt to crotonic acid may be expressed by either of the equations:

(a) $\quad CH_3CH{=}CHCOOH + HgX_2 + H_2O \rightarrow$

$$CH_3CHOHCH(HgX)COOH + HX,$$

(b) $\quad CH_3CH{=}CHCOOH + Hg^{++} + H_2O \rightarrow$

$$CH_3CHOHCH(Hg^+)COOH + H^+.$$

According to Biilmann the reaction is reversible and the law of mass action applies:

$$K = \frac{[ROH\,R'\,Hg^+][H^+]}{[R{=}R'][Hg^{++}]} .$$

Through determinations of the concentrations of hydrogen ions and mercuric ions (potentiometrically), Biilmann and Hoff were able to obtain the equilibrium constants for several reactions:

Compound	K
Allyl alcohol complex	8.7×10^8
Allyl acetate complex	9.5×10^8
Crotonic acid complex	5.1×10^4
Maleic acid complex	3.0×10^3

[22] For further details see Victor Meyer and P. Jacobson, *Lehrbuch der org. Chem.* 2nd Ed., p. 833, Leipzig, 1907 ; F. C. Whitmore, *Organic Compounds of Mercury*, Chemical Catalog Co., New York, 1921, p. 31. Concerning the reaction of mercuric acetate with ethylenes in methanol, see G. F. Wright, *J. Am. Chem. Soc.*, **57**, 1993 (1935).

[23] E. Biilmann and Agnes Hoff, *Rec. trav. chim.*, **36**, 289 (1916); see also E. Biilmann, *Ber.*, **33**, 1641 (1900), **35**, 2571 (1902), **43**, 573 (1910); *Ann.*, **388**, 259 (1912).

The direct formation of mercury addition products has not yet been applied to the volumetric determination of unsaturated organic compounds, although new titration methods might well be based on such reactions.

Qualitative studies of the behavior of various compounds when treated with an alcoholic solution of mercuric chloride, in the presence of sodium ethoxide, have been carried out by Connor and Van Campen.[24]

The catalytic action of mercuric sulfate has been applied by Lucas and Pressman[25] in the determination of unsaturated compounds with bromate-bromide. This catalysis may be due to the ease with which mercury adds to the double bond and is subsequently replaced by halogen. On the other hand, it may be due to the increase in oxidation potential caused by combination of bromide ions with mercuric ions.

Biilmann and Thaulow[26] utilized the formation of an addition compound for the determination of mercuric mercury in its salts other than halides. The salt is digested with excess allyl alcohol and neutralized to phenolphthalein:

$$C_3H_5(OH)_2HgX + NaOH \rightleftarrows C_3H_5(OH)_2HgOH + NaX.$$

This free base is not strong enough to redden phenolphthalein. Upon addition of an alkali bromide, a stable complex (slightly dissociated salt) is formed:

$$C_3H_5(OH)_2HgOH + KBr \rightleftarrows C_3H_5(OH)_2HgBr + KOH.$$

The equivalent amount of free base may then be titrated.

B. HALOGEN ADDITION COMPOUNDS

The addition of iodine to unsaturated oils, fats and fatty acids is known to take place incompletely in organic solvents. According to investigations of van der Steur,[27] if one dissolves an oil or fat in carbon tetrachloride containing excess iodine, a condition of equi-

[24] R. Connor and J. H. Van Campen, *J. Am. Chem. Soc.*, **58**, 1131 (1936).

[25] H. J. Lucas and David Pressman, *Ind. Eng. Chem. Anal. Ed.*, **10**, 140 (1938); R. H. Frieman, E. R. Kennedy and H. J. Lucas, *J. Am. Chem. Soc.*, **59**, 722 (1937).

[26] E. Biilmann and K. Thaulow, *Bull. soc. chim.*, **29**, 587 (1921).

[27] J. P. K. van der Steur, *Rec. trav. chim.*, **46**, 278, 414, 409 (1927). Concerning bromine addition see K. H. Bauer, *Ber.*, **37**, 3317 (1904); *Chem. Umschau Fette, Öle, Wasche Harze*, **28**, 163 (1921).

librium is attained after several days. The process actually appears to be reversible:

$$R{=}R' + I_2 \rightleftarrows RR'I_2 .$$

The equilibrium constant K for oleic acid at 0°C. is given by van der Steur as

$$K = \frac{[R{=}R'][I_2]}{[RR'I_2]} = 1.05 \times 10^{-2}.$$

From the value of this constant it is evident that one cannot expect to obtain complete conversion to the iodine addition compound. However, van der Steur was able to make an approximate determination of oleic acid in the presence of elaidic acid. The latter has a still larger equilibrium constant, 2×10^{-1} at 0°.

At higher temperatures the constants increase; thus at 19.5° the value of K for oleic acid is 3.82×10^{-2}, and for elaidic acid, 5×10^{-1}. With benzene instead of carbon tetrachloride as solvent, the respective constants at 19.5° are 1.05×10^{-1} and 1.7, indicating that the equilibrium is even less favorable in benzene. Glycerine esters of these acids are said to have constants of the same magnitude.

It would be of great practical interest to know the equilibrium conditions for additions of bromine, iodine chloride, iodine cyanide, etc., in order to be able to calculate the extent to which such reactions take place. There appears to be a certain dependence between the ease of addition and the ease of removal of halogens.

The following discussion of additions to unsaturated compounds, taken from Meyer and Jacobson,[28] is quoted here because of its interest to analytical chemists:

"For the explanation of additions, Thiele[29] assumes that the so-called double bond results from the affinities of two neighboring carbon atoms, as was previously generally assumed, but that doubling does not completely equalize the forces. Rather there remains for each carbon atom a residual affinity—'partial valence'—indicated by the dots directed downward in the following formula:

[28] V. Meyer and P. Jacobson, *Lehrbuch der organischen Chemie*, 2nd edition, Part I, Leipzig 1907, p. 792.

[29] J. Thiele, *Ann.*, **306**, 87 (1899); **319**, 132 (1901).

According to Thiele, the ability of an unsaturated compound to react with halogens depends upon these unsatisfied partial valences. The addition process may be thought of as follows: the substance to be added takes first a partial valence and then a complete affinity quantity, for example:

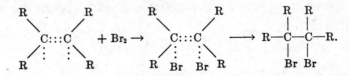

"To this hypothesis of partial valence, Thiele added a further assumption relating to valences in *conjugated systems*, that is, systems in which two or more double bonds connect neighboring atoms without any one atom sharing in more than one double bond:

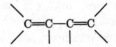

If such a molecule takes up two univalent atoms of reagent in an addition reaction, one might expect addition to be confined to one double linkage leaving the other untouched:

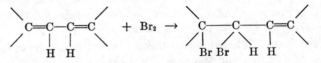

"Contrary to this expectation, experience has shown that in many cases[30] addition does not take place at only one double bond, but at the ends of the conjugated system. Hence the equation given above should be replaced by the following:

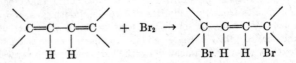

in which the added bromine atoms enter the 1, 4 positions rather than the 1, 2. Instead of the two double bonds originally thought to be present, one new double bond appears in the 2, 3 position. To account for this behavior, Thiele

---

[30] For examples and literature references see C. T. H. Allen and A. H. Blatt, "Unsaturation and Conjugation," Chapter 6 in *Organic Chemistry, An Advanced Treatise*, edited by H. Gilman, Vol. I, John Wiley and Sons, New York 1938.

assumed that in the vicinity of two double linkages the inner partial valences neutralize each other:

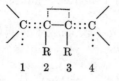

$$\begin{array}{cccc} 1 & 2 & 3 & 4 \end{array}$$

In this mode of presentation a double bond would surely be formed between carbon atoms 2 and 3, but it would differ from an ordinary double bond by the lack of unsatisfied partial valences; the capacity of atoms 2 and 3 to take on atoms is restricted and the bond is said to be 'inactive.' Unsatisfied valences are present only at atoms 1 and 4, hence addition occurs there and the 2, 3 inactive bond goes over into an ordinary active one with partial valences:

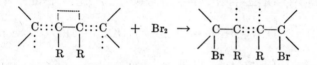

To be sure, there are frequent exceptions to this rule; cases of addition at the 1, 2 or 3, 4 positions are known.[30]

"According to Hinrichsen,[31] addition in the 1, 4 position takes place only if the two adding atoms (or groups) are similar and repel one another because of their like polarities (for example, in bromine addition), and if, besides, the qualitative relations between individual parts of the molecule favor the entrance of the two adding groups into positions as far separated as possible. For the actual course of addition, the deciding factor is that the new arrangement of atoms shall best equalize the affinities.[32] Thiele's theory, however, still fails to explain the fact that the 2, 3 double bond formed in a conjugated system takes up no more bromine."

Because of their ability to add, free halogens, especially iodine and bromine (usually an acidified solution of bromate and bromide) are often employed for the quantitative determination of double bonds in organic compounds. For this purpose also thiocyanogen, $(CNS)_2$, has been recommended by Kaufmann.[33]   In place of the free halogens,

[31] F. W. Hinrichsen, Z. physik. Chem., **39**, 308 (1902); Ann., **336**, 182 (1904).

[32] See, for example, K. G. Falk, Chemical Reactions; Their Theory and Mechanism, D. van Nostrand Co., New York 1920.

[33] H. P. Kaufmann, Arch. Pharm., **263**, 645 (1925); Seifensieder-Z., **55**, 297 (1928); Ber., **59**, 1390 (1926); H. Stadtlinger, Pharm. Ztg., **53**, 340 (1928); A. Krassilchik, Chem. Abstr., **30**, 1023 (1936). Concerning the application of thiocyanogen iodide see H. P. Kaufmann and H. Grosse-Oetringhaus, Ber., **69B**, 2670 (1936); **70B**, 911 (1937).

one can use compounds of the halogens with each other, such as iodine monochloride (in acetic acid, Wijs solution), iodine mono-bromide (Hanus solution) or iodine cyanide. Hypoiodous acid, HOI, adds rapidly, according to Wijs.

From the valuable investigations of Wijs and others[34] it appeared that iodine adds to fats in the form of hypoiodous acid rather than as free halogen or as a compound with another halogen. The more favorable are the conditions made for the formation of hypoiodous acid, the more rapidly does the addition reach completion. The addition compound can then react with hydrochloric acid so that the total effect is the same as if iodine chloride had been taken up directly. The process can be represented by the equations:

$$C_{17}H_{33}COOH + HOI \rightarrow C_{17}H_{33}OHICOOH \quad \text{(primary)},$$

$$C_{17}H_{33}OHICOOH + HCl \rightarrow C_{17}H_{33}ClICOOH + H_2O \quad \text{(secondary)}.$$

The product may further decompose with separation of hydrochloric acid:

$$C_{17}H_{33}ClICOOH \rightarrow C_{17}H_{32}ICOOH + HCl,$$

so that the over-all reaction is quite complicated.

On the contrary, Ingle[35] demonstrated that no addition of HOI comes into question, but that iodine chloride as such is the active agent. He explained the formation of free acid as due to hydrolysis of the addition product:

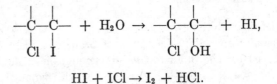

$$HI + ICl \rightarrow I_2 + HCl.$$

[34] J. J. A. Wijs, Z. anal. Chem., 37, 277 (1898); Z. angew. Chem., 11, 298 (1898); Ber., 31, 750 (1898). See also B. M. Margosches, L. Friedmann and E. Neufeld, Chem. Umschau Fette, Öle, Wachse Harze, 32, 221 (1925); Z. deut. Öl- u. Fett-Ind., 45, 605 (1925); Ber., 58, 794, 1064 (1925); 59, 325, 375 (1926); Z. angew. Chem., 37, 334, 982 (1924); E. André, Chimie et industrie, Special No. 435 (Sept., 1925); D. Holde and A. Gorgas, Ber., 59, 113 (1926). For other literature up to 1925 cf. A. Grün, Analyse der Fette und Wachse, Julius Springer, Berlin 1925.
[35] H. Ingle, J. Soc. Chem. Ind., 21, 587 (1902); 23, 422 (1904).

According to the last equation free iodine is formed during the process, as is evident in practice.

Böeseken and Gelber[36] carried out thorough studies on the determination of the iodine number. They showed that many compounds known to contain double bonds react only partially or not at all in the usual methods of iodine addition, whereas in other cases the iodine numbers found are far higher than the theoretical values. Besides, it has often been pointed out in the literature that various procedures give different iodine numbers for the same commodity. High results are generally attributed to "substitution" occurring along with the desired addition, hydrogen being replaced by a halogen. According to Böeseken and Gelber, however, the addition proceeds normally and deviations from theory are to be ascribed to other causes. The nature of the solvent, the excess of iodine chloride employed, and especially the presence of certain groups in the molecule influence the speed of the addition reaction. So-called "negative" groups, like $COOH$, C_6H_5, $COCH_3$, COC_2H_5, COC_6H_5, retard the reaction so that one has to wait eight hours before reaching the correct iodine number, even if a 50 per cent excess of iodine chloride is present. This holds for systems with one double bond, or with more if they are not conjugated. With conjugated double bonds, the 1,4 carbon atoms are attacked first and only after a very long time are the resulting 2,3 double bonds saturated.

In the views of Böeseken and Gelber, the 1,4 carbons react with chlorine. Therefore upon treatment of a conjugated system with iodine chloride, the solution is darkened by iodine:

$$-\overset{|}{C}=\overset{|}{C}-\overset{|}{C}=\overset{|}{C}- + 2ICl \rightarrow -\overset{|}{\underset{Cl}{C}}-\overset{|}{C}=\overset{|}{C}-\overset{|}{\underset{Cl}{C}}- + I_2 \quad \text{(rapid)},$$

$$-\overset{|}{\underset{Cl}{C}}-\overset{|}{C}=\overset{|}{C}-\overset{|}{\underset{Cl}{C}}- + ICl \rightarrow -\overset{|}{\underset{Cl}{C}}-\overset{|}{\underset{Cl}{C}}-\overset{|}{\underset{I}{C}}-\overset{|}{\underset{Cl}{C}}- \quad \text{(very slow)}.$$

During back-titration of the excess iodine, it is sometimes noted that the color returns. This is caused by a side reaction which tends to give low values for the iodine number, the addition compound

[36] J. Böeseken and E. T. Gelber, *Rec. trav. chim.*, **46**, 158 (1927); **48**, 377 (1929).

decomposing to liberate iodine. Van Duin[37] investigated such reactions for brominated compounds. He advanced the following mechanism:

$$-\overset{|}{\underset{Br}{C}}-\overset{|}{\underset{Br}{C}}- \ + \ 2KI \ \rightarrow \ -\overset{|}{\underset{I}{C}}-\overset{|}{\underset{I}{C}}- \ + \ 2KBr,$$

$$-\overset{|}{\underset{I}{C}}-\overset{|}{\underset{I}{C}}- \ \rightarrow \ -\overset{|}{C}=\overset{|}{C}- \ + \ I_2.$$

According to van Duin the velocity of this reaction depends upon the group adjacent to the double bond:

$$COCH_3 > C_6H_5 > COOC_2H_5 > COOCH_3 > COOH > H > Br.$$

Potassium iodide may react similarly with the addition products of iodine chloride. The amount of interference caused is dependent upon the constitution of the organic compound and upon the solubility relationships of the iodo-chloride formed. In solvents which permit dissociation (alcohol, acetic acid), decomposition proceeds to a greater extent than in non-ionizing media (carbon tetrachloride, chloroform, benzene, ether).

For this reason, Böeseken and Gelber prefer carbon tetrachloride to acetic acid as a solvent. The reagent of Marshall,[38] consisting of a solution of iodine chloride in carbon tetrachloride, is to be recommended since side reactions are less disturbing. Böeseken and Gelber remove the excess of iodine chloride (after addition) with calomel or silver, filter, add alcoholic sodium iodide to the filtrate, and after ten minutes titrate the liberated iodine with thiosulfate.

In some cases the halogens are taken up rapidly enough so that a direct titration is possible, as, for example, in the reaction of allyl alcohol with bromine. Generally, however, the reaction is sluggish and the reagent must be added in excess. After equilibrium is reached, the excess is titrated iodimetrically.[39]

[37] C. F. van Duin, *Rec. trav. chim.*, **45**, 345 (1926); see also R. T. Dillon, *J. Am. Chem. Soc.*, **54**, 952 (1932).

[38] A. Marshall, *J. Soc. Chem. Ind.*, **19**, 231 (1900).

[39] Concerning the catalytic effect of mercuric sulfate, see the references given on page 224.

In order to avoid various errors, Buckwalter and Wagner[40] recommend bromination at a definite temperature with a solution of bromine in carbon tetrachloride. They remove excess bromine, and any hydrogen bromide formed, by aerating with a stream of dry nitrogen and trapping the vapors in aqueous potassium iodide. The iodine is titrated with thiosulfate, as is the acid also after addition of iodate. (Each equivalent of acid formed is considered to represent the loss of two equivalents of bromine through substitution, provided that no cleavage of HBr from the brominated compound has occurred). The optimum temperature of bromination varies with different substances. Buckwalter and Wagner tested a number of compounds between 0° and 75°C., for details of which the reader is referred to their paper.

Below are summarized several of the errors that can arise in the determination of halogen addition values:

(a) If an excess of halogen is employed, substitution as well as addition may take place:

$$RH + Br_2 \rightarrow RBr + HBr.$$

Proportionately more bromine is then used than corresponds to the double bond.[41]

(b) The halogens and their hydrolysis products (hypo acids) are strong oxidants. Therefore if the substance being determined contains oxidizable groups (unsaturated aldehydes, etc.), too much halogen may be used under certain conditions. Generally light accelerates these side reactions markedly.

In connection with the titer stability of halogens in an organic solvent, the oxidizability of the latter is also of interest. Unless, for example, the glacial acetic acid or carbon tetrachloride used in the preparation of a reagent is free from oxidizable impurities, the titer diminishes rapidly.

(c) As has already been mentioned (page 226), the addition of halogens to a conjugated system leads to the formation of a new and more stable double bond.

(d) Some unsaturated compounds react only slowly with halogens,

[40] H. M. Buckwalter and E. C. Wagner, J. Am. Chem. Soc., 52, 5241 (1930).
[41] Concerning the action of chlorine on butene, see G. G. Gustavson, J. prakt. Chem., 42, 495 (1890); J. Kondakow, Ber., 21, 440 (1888); 24, 932 (1891); C. Hell and M. Wildermann, Ber., 24, 216 (1891); G. Pogozzelski, Chem. Zentr., 1905, I, 667.

while a few others seem hardly to be attacked at all.   The temperature plays a part in such cases.[40]

(e) In some instances cleavage of hydrogen halide from the addition compound occurs.[40]   If this happens and the resulting acidity is calculated as though due to substitution, the substitution correction will be too high and consequently the corrected addition value will be low.

(f) Decomposition of the addition compound may yield free iodine during back-titration, causing low results (see page 230).

(g) Certain compounds that do not contain double bonds are still capable of reacting with halogens.   Thus the alkaloids and some other substances, though differing from true unsaturated compounds, form halogenated products whose components may not be present in stoichiometric proportions.   They are therefore not well suited for analytical use.   One must seek special conditions, under which reproducible results can be obtained.

In general, alkaloids form perbromides or periodides with solutions of halogens in halide salts.   Gomberg[42] investigated in a quantitative way the behavior of caffeine, especially, toward bromine and iodine solutions.   He found compounds of various compositions, among which $C_8H_{10}N_4O_2HI \cdot I_4$ appeared to be the most stable.   He also obtained a di-iodine product, $C_8H_{10}N_4O_2HI \cdot I_2 \cdot 3H_2O$, and a penta-iodine derivative as well as similar compounds with bromine.

A systematic investigation of halogen addition reactions from the physico-chemical standpoint is much to be desired.

4. The Formation of Condensation Products.—Many organic compounds unite through carbon linkages to form condensation products. Numerous applications of condensation processes are known, both in qualitative and in quantitative analyses, particularly in cases where the product is slightly soluble.   Aldehydes, ketones, phenols, amines, etc., can be determined in the form of difficultly soluble condensation products by various methods.   Unfortunately, these analytical procedures have largely been developed only empirically, without testing whether the law of mass action holds for such reactions.   On this account the methods still lack an exact systematic basis; their applicability and most advantageous working conditions cannot be estimated in advance.

[42] M. Gomberg, *J. Am. Chem. Soc.*, **18**, 358 (1896).

Suppose that two compounds, A and B, undergo a reversible condensation reaction:

$$A + B \rightleftarrows AB.$$

After equilibrium is established, one has:

$$\frac{[A][B]}{[AB]} = K.$$

If the condensation product AB is slightly soluble, as is generally the case in analytical methods, its concentration may be considered constant, so that:

$$[A][B] = K' = S.$$

Just as the solubility product of a slightly soluble uni-univalent electrolyte is defined as the product of the ion concentrations in a saturated solution, the solubility product of the condensation compound AB is given by the product of the concentrations of its free components, A and B, in a saturated solution.

In the more general case

$$nA + mB \rightleftarrows A_n B_m,$$

the mass law expression becomes:

$$\frac{[A]^n[B]^m}{[A_n B_m]} = K,$$

in which K is the dissociation constant. If the solution is saturated with respect to $A_n B_m$:

$$[A]^n[B]^m = S_{A_n B_m}.$$

Side reactions may accompany the process of condensation so that direct application of the mass action law is not permissible. However, in many cases the condensation proceeds to a reversible equilibrium, and then a knowledge of the solubility product and dissociation constant is obviously desirable. From their values one may calculate the amounts of AB dissolved with various excesses of A or B.

Illustration: Hydroquinone and quinone when mixed in aqueous solution form an equimolecular compound, quinhydrone, of low solubility. Letting [Q] represent the concentration of quinone, [HQ] that of hydroquinone and [QH] that of quinhydrone, the equilibrium expression becomes:

$$\frac{[Q][HQ]}{[QH]} = K.$$

It has been shown[43] that a saturated solution of quinhydrone is more than 90 per cent dissociated. Granger[44] found a value of 0.29 for K at 25°. The total solubility of quinhydrone at 25° is 1.78×10^{-2} molar. Upon solving the above expression as a quadratic equation, one finds that in the saturated solution the undissociated quinhydrone concentration [QH] is 9.8×10^{-4} molar; therefore $S = K \times 9.8 \times 10^{-4} = 2.9 \times 10^{-4}$.

In order to calculate the solubility of quinhydrone in the presence of an excess of quinone or hydroquinone, the procedure is the same as that given for slightly soluble univalent electrolytes (p. 32). For example, if the excess hydroquinone added corresponds to a concentration of 0.3 molar and if this is increased by an amount x from the dissociation of quinhydrone, one has:

$$(0.3 + x)x = 2.9 \times 10^{-4},$$

$$x = 9.7 \times 10^{-4}.$$

Since the concentration of undissociated quinhydrone in a saturated solution is 9.8×10^{-4}, the total solubility is $(9.7 + 9.8)\ 10^{-4} = 1.95 \times 10^{-3}$ molar. Granger found 1.89×10^{-3} experimentally. It is evident that addition of 0.3 molar hydroquinone represses the total solubility of quinhydrone to about one-tenth of its value in pure water.

Many analytical applications are made of the reactions of phenyl hydrazine and its derivatives (*p*-nitrophenyl hydrazine, *p*-bromo-phenyl hydrazine, *p*-tolyl hydrazine, etc.) especially in the determination of aldehydes and ketones. Compounds having the carbonyl group react with phenyl hydrazine to form slightly soluble hydrazones:

$$R_2C{=}O + H_2NNHC_6H_5 \rightarrow R_2C{=}NNHC_6H_5 + H_2O.$$

The hydrazone may be determined gravimetrically, or the excess of phenyl hydrazine may be titrated.[45]

[43] R. Luther and A. Leubner, *J. prakt. Chem.*, **85**, 314 (1912).

[44] F. S. Granger, *Oxidation and Reduction in Organic Chemistry from the Standpoint of Potential Differences, Dissertation*, New York 1920.

[45] Concerning practical procedures see, for example, W. Vaubel, *Die physikalischen und chemischen Methoden der quantitative Bestimmung organischer Verbindungen*, Vol. 2, Berlin 1902, p. 291; E. R. Ardagh and G. J. Williams, *J. Am. Chem. Soc.*, **47**, 2983 (1925).

According to the thorough studies of Bodforss,[46] intermediate products occur in the formation of hydrazones. Grassi[47] had already found from velocity measurements that the reaction of phenyl hydrazine with l-menthone, an optically active ketone, is monomolecular, although from the equation a bimolecular reaction would be expected. Bodforss assumes that the carbonyl compound and phenyl hydrazine rapidly form a condensation product which slowly decomposes into hydrazone and water:

$$R_2CO + \text{Phenyl hyd.} \rightleftarrows \text{Cond. (instantaneous)};$$

$$\text{Cond.} \rightleftarrows \text{Hydrazone} + H_2O \text{ (measurable).}$$

If aldehyde is present in excess, the decomposition of the condensation product takes place as a monomolecular reaction, determining the order of the overall reaction.   However, if the phenyl hydrazine is in excess, the decomposition follows a more complicated course.

Bodforss studied principally aromatic aldehydes, but also experimented with an aromatic ketone (acetophenone).   Here in singular manner the formation of the condensation product is the order-determining step.   The velocity decreases measurably according to the rule for bimolecular reactions, yet with excess of phenyl hydrazine it is apparently monomolecular.   The mechanism is therefore quite complicated.

The reactions are accelerated catalytically by hydrogen ions, but the way in which hydrogen-ion concentration governs the equilibrium conditions is not clear.   Possibly in acid solution the reaction proceeds more rapidly, though less completely.[48]

Sugars having free carbonyl groups are distinguishable from lower aldehydes and ketones in that the sugars first yield hydrazones which then react with more phenyl hydrazine to form difficultly soluble osazones:

$$\underset{O}{\underset{\|}{RCHOHCH}} + H_2NNHC_6H_5 \rightarrow \underset{N-NHC_6H_5}{\underset{\|}{RCHOHCH}} + H_2O$$

$$\text{hydrazone}$$

---

[46] S. Bodforss, $Z.\ physik.\ Chem.$, **109**, 223 (1924).

[47] N. Grassi, $Gazz.\ chim.\ ital.$, **40**, 139 (1910).

[48] Concerning the influence of p_H in the osazone reaction see G. Quagliarello and A. Caponetto, $Chem.\ Abstr.$, **21**, 1967 (1927).

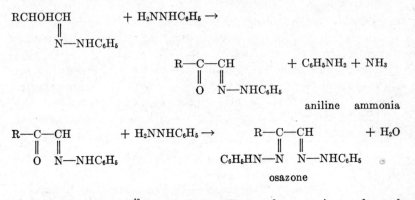

aniline   ammonia

osazone

Schoorl and Milius[49] found that aniline and ammonia are formed quantitatively in accordance with the above equation. With most sugars, the mixture must be warmed; mannose, in contrast, forms a slightly soluble osazone even in the cold.

Phenyl hydrazine reacts also with polyhydroxy phenols yielding compounds of low solubility. Seyewetz[50] based a method for the determination of orcinol upon this reaction:

$$C_6H_3 \begin{matrix} (1)\ OH \\ (3)\ OH \\ (5)\ CH_3 \end{matrix} + 2H_2NNHC_6H_5 \rightarrow C_6H_3 \begin{matrix} OH \cdot H_2NNHC_6H_5 \\ OH \cdot H_2NNHC_6H_5 \\ CH_3 \end{matrix}$$

Reactions of phenyl hydrazine with the chlorides, anhydrides and esters of organic acids produce difficultly soluble hydrazides.

Aldehydes and ketones condense also with other hydrazines, according to the general reaction:

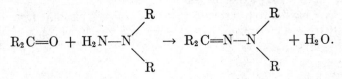

Other compounds finding analytical application in place of phenyl hydrazine are semicarbazide, $H_2NCONHNH_2$, and its derivatives (forming semicarbazones), as well as thiosemicarbazide, $H_2N-CSNHNH_2$.

A condensation process of importance from both the analytical and

[49] H. C. Milius and N. Schoorl, *Pharm. Weekblad*, **53**, 1249 (1916).

[50] A. Seyewetz, *Compt. rend.*, **113**, 264 (1891); *Z. anal. Chem.*. **31**, 329 (1892).

technical viewpoints involves the reaction of aldehydes with phenols. Upon such condensations rest methods for the determination of formaldehyde, furfural, etc., with phloroglucinol as reagent. The reaction between formaldehyde and phloroglucinol may be expressed as follows:

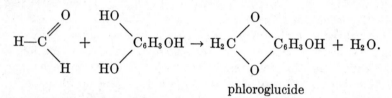

$$\text{phloroglucide}$$

Here it would be interesting to know how far the process is subject to the law of mass action.[51]

The carbonyl group also yields condensation products with other compounds; with hydroxylamine, for example, giving oximes:

$$R_2C{=}O + H_2NOH \rightarrow R_2C{=}NOH + H_2O.$$

Derivatives of hydroxylamine (of which hydrazine may be considered as one) are also used analytically. The oximes are inclined to polymerize.

An acidimetric determination of aldehydes is possible through their reaction with hydroxylamine salts. If hydroxylamine hydrochloride is used, an equivalent quantity of hydrochloric acid is liberated and may be titrated:

$$R_2C{=}O + H_2NOH{\cdot}HCl \rightarrow R_2C{=}NOH + H_2O + HCl.$$

Apparently the reaction proceeds to a condition of equilibrium, hydrogen ions tending to retard or oppose the process. According to Ölander,[52] an intermediate product is formed at first, in the case of acetone perhaps $(CH_3)_2C{-}NOH$. In studies of the gross reac-
$$\qquad\qquad\qquad\quad \underset{OH\ \ H}{|\ \ \ |}$$
tion it appeared that free hydroxylamine unites only slowly with acetone. The hydroxylammonium ion reacts more rapidly, having a

[51] For technical studies on the condensation of various phenols with formaldehyde see F. S. Granger, *Ind. Eng. Chem.*, **24**, 442 (1932); **29**, 860, 1125, 1305 (1937).

[52] A. Ölander, *Z. physik. Chem.*, **129**, 1 (1927).

velocity constant of 84 at 20°C. At a p_H of 4.5 the rate attains a maximum (in 0.003 N solution at 20°C.). Only when the p_H is greater than 7 does the reaction become complete, but under these conditions it proceeds very slowly.

Of great analytical importance for the determination of aldehydes and ketones with hydroxylamine, phenylhydrazine or semicarbazide are the studies of Conant and Bartlett.[53] The oximes are less hydrolyzed than the phenylhydrazones or the semicarbazones. Conant and Bartlett investigated especially the hydrolysis and formation of the latter. One has to consider that both the rate of formation and the equilibrium constant depend upon the p_H. The optimum p_H for velocity of formation, however, does not coincide with the optimum for quantitative reaction. The formation of acetone-semicarbazone shows a velocity optimum at p_H 4.5. It was also noted that in addition to hydrogen ions, undissociated acids (in the Brönsted sense[54]) exert a similar effect. For the quantitative formation of a condensation product one has to take into account the fact that hydrolysis of the product increases with rising hydrogen-ion concentration, thereby reversing the reaction:

$$R_2C{=}O + H_2NNHCONH_2 \underset{\text{hydrolysis}}{\overset{\text{formation}}{\rightleftarrows}} R_2C{=}NNHCONH_2 + H_2O$$

Since the analytical reactions have not yet been worked out in detail, further discussion is omitted for the present.

The behavior of ammonia, amines and amides toward aldehydes and ketones is interesting. If one brings such compounds together, they generally unite at first:

$$\begin{array}{ccc}
\text{OH} & \text{OH} & \text{OH} \\
| & | & | \\
\text{R—C—H} & \text{R—C—H} & \text{R—C—H} \\
| & | & | \\
\text{NH}_2 & \text{NR} & \text{NR}_2 \\
 & \text{H} & \\
\end{array}$$

Aldehyde-ammonia	Aldehyde amines or amides	
I	II	III

---

[53] J. B. Conant and P. D. Bartlett, *J. Am. Chem. Soc.*, **54**, 2881 (1932).
[54] J. N. Brönsted, *Chem. Rev.*, **5**, 231 (1928).

These addition products usually are unstable, easily separating into their components or rearranging with the loss of water (from I or II):

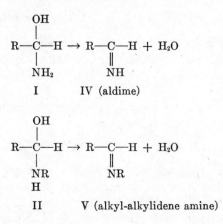

$$\begin{array}{c} \text{OH} \\ | \\ \text{R—C—H} \\ | \\ \text{NH}_2 \\ \text{I} \end{array} \rightarrow \begin{array}{c} \text{R—C—H} \\ \| \\ \text{NH} \\ \text{IV (aldime)} \end{array} + \text{H}_2\text{O}$$

$$\begin{array}{c} \text{OH} \\ | \\ \text{R—C—H} \\ | \\ \text{NR} \\ \text{H} \\ \text{II} \end{array} \rightarrow \begin{array}{c} \text{R—C—H} \\ \| \\ \text{NR} \\ \\ \text{V (alkyl-alkylidene amine)} \end{array} + \text{H}_2\text{O}$$

The latter compounds (V) are often called "Schiff's bases"; they have very weak basic properties.

In volumetric analysis such reactions are used to advantage for the titration of amino acids. If one tries to titrate the carboxyl groups, the basic amino groups interfere so that with phenolphthalein as indicator the color change occurs much too soon. However, if a neutral formaldehyde solution is added, a Schiff's base is formed:

$$\text{H}_2\text{C}\!\!=\!\!\text{O} + \text{H}_2\text{NRCOOH} \rightleftarrows \text{H}_2\text{C}\!\!=\!\!\text{NRCOOH} + \text{H}_2\text{O}.$$

Thus the basic character is so markedly decreased that usually the acid carboxyl groups may be titrated without difficulty. Because the reaction is reversible, formaldehyde must be added in great excess. In Volume II we shall discuss further this method (Sörensen's formol titration[55]), which is of especial importance in physiological investigations. It furnishes still another instance in which a correct application of theoretical principles contributes to the development of an analytical procedure.

In the action of ammonia upon formaldehyde there is formed at

[55] S. P. L. Sörensen, *Z. physiol. Chem.*, **64**, 120 (1909).

first an aldehyde-ammonia, which later polymerizes into hexamethylene tetramine. The total process is:

$$6H_2CO + 4NH_3 \rightarrow C_6H_{12}N_4 + 6H_2O.$$

Through back-titration of the excess ammonia one can determine the quantity that has combined with aldehyde. Since the product acts as a very weak base, an indicator appropriate to the conditions must be selected.

Aldehydes yield condensation products also with aromatic amines; for example, aniline:

$$C_6H_5NH_2 + H_2C{=}O \rightleftarrows C_6H_5N{=}CH_2 + H_2O.$$

The product being only slightly soluble, both gravimetric and volumetric methods[56] for the determination of aniline or formaldehyde are based upon this reaction. Experiments indicate that an equilibrium is reached, hence that an excess of the reagent is needed to bring about quantitative reaction. Formaldehyde enters into complex compounds (polymerization products) with various other amines also. Details concerning such condensations are to be found in texts on organic chemistry. Here it is necessary only to emphasize that physico-chemical studies of a reaction are of the greatest importance in determining its suitability for analytical purposes.

In concluding this section there will be described briefly several titrations based on irreversible reactions. These methods, although limited in general application by complicating factors and by the lack of information as to their physico-chemical characteristics, nevertheless are widely used in industrial organic laboratories. *They are based on the formation of diazo compounds from primary amines and nitrous acid, and, further, upon the coupling of such diazotized amines with aromatic amino or hydroxyl compounds to form dyes.* Two procedures are used:[57]

(a) The determination of primary amines with nitrite.

(b) The determination of aromatic amines or phenols with diazo solution.

The Determination of Amines with Nitrite.—Primary aromatic

---

[56] B. Tollens, *Ber.*, **17**, 652 (1884); M. Klar, *Pharm. Ztg.*, **40**, 611 (1895).

[57] The presentation given here is based on that of R. Möhlau and H. T. Bucherer, *Farbenchemisches Praktikum*, 3rd Edition, Gruyter and Co., Berlin and Leipzig 1926, in which more detailed descriptions are to be found, especially on and following page 88.

amines may be quantitatively converted by nitrous acid (nitrite in acid solution) into diazo compounds:

$$RNH_2 \cdot HCl + HNO_2 \rightarrow 2H_2O + RN\!\equiv\!N.$$
$$\underset{Cl}{|}$$

The endpoint of diazotization is reached with the first slight excess of nitrous acid which remains for some time, and may be recognized with starch-iodide paper as external indicator. Because iodide reacts instantaneously with nitrous acid it cannot be added directly to the mixture, in which the nitrous acid and amine react less rapidly. The reaction is followed by placing a test drop on starch-iodide paper a short time after each addition of reagent. Excess nitrous acid, of course, colors the paper blue. The nitrite solution may be standardized against permanganate solution of known strength.

The time required for complete diazotization varies according to the amine in question. Para nitro aniline and α-naphthylamine may be diazotized with relative ease, whereas sulfanilic acid and especially the slightly soluble naphthylamine sulfonic acids react much more slowly.

This titration procedure is useful for primary monoamines and for diamines of which each group may be diazotized (benzidine, tolidine), but not for compounds such as m-diamines in which coupling takes place to form dyestuffs. With o-diamines the formation of azoimides interferes, while certain diamines are partially oxidized by HNO_2 so that the reaction is not stoichiometric. Secondary amines interfere. by forming nitrosamines, and tertiary amines in which one or more groups are aromatic yield p-nitrosoaniline derivatives.

Conditions essential to the success of nitrite titrations are:

(1) That interfering reactions be avoided.

(2) That the temperature maintained be low enough to prevent loss of nitrous acid from the mixture.

(3) That the reaction proceed completely and rapidly enough so that the endpoint does not appear too soon. (With some slowly reacting compounds it is necessary to work at room temperature or even slightly higher, less error being introduced through loss of nitrous acid than through an incomplete reaction. Decomposition of the diazo compound into a phenol is not of consequence.)

The Determination of Aromatic Amines and Phenols with Diazo Solutions.—This method is based on the fact that under suitable conditions diazonium compounds are able to condense with reactive aromatic amines or phenols (coupling components) in molecular proportions, forming azo dyes:

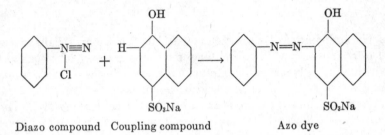

Diazo compound   Coupling compound   Azo dye

Many diazo solutions are unstable, decomposing readily with liberation of nitrogen:

$$C_6H_5N_2Cl + H_2O \rightarrow C_6H_5OH + N_2 + HCl.$$

Naturally, for a reagent to be suitable it must be stable enough at the working temperature not to decrease in strength during a titration. Mohlau and Bucherer[57] in describing the preparation of reagents recommend diazotized p-nitroaniline, $O_2NC_6H_4N_2Cl$.

Coupling compounds may be classified according to their auxochromic groups, as amino-, hydroxy-, amino-hydroxy, etc. Compounds lacking such a group are not capable of coupling (at least in simple and normal manner); neither are those in which a hydrogen atom from the auxochrome has been replaced by an acid radical as in acetanilide or phenyl benzoate.

The conditions under which the coupling reactions proceed to completion vary widely for different substances. A striking fact is that mineral acids strongly retard the rate of reaction, even in relatively small concentrations. Nevertheless it is frequently necessary to work with strongly acidified solutions in order that a monoazo dye be produced, excluding the possible coupling at two positions when two auxochrome groups are present. Besides, it may be desirable to salt out the dye immediately after its formation, to prevent further reaction with the diazo compound. Therefore the acidity and other conditions must be modified to suit the particular case.

The titration procedure is generally as follows: After one adds a certain amount of titer solution, stirs thoroughly and waits a short time, a drop of the reaction mixture is transferred to filter paper and touched with a drop of diazo solution, in which case a color reaction indicates the presence of unreacted coupling compound. Alternatively, the drop on the paper may be treated with another coupling agent, for example, a solution of R-salt (2-naphthol-3,6-disulfonate). This produces a color reaction if excess diazo titer solution is present, that is, if the endpoint has been overstepped. For exact work, or in case the solution is quite dilute, it is desirable to add excess reagent, filter after salting out, and complete the titration with diazo or R-salt solution.

The diazo solution is standardized by the same procedure against a coupling compound, such as R-salt, which can easily be obtained in sufficiently pure state.

From the foregoing short description of these two titration methods it will be evident that no general rules based on the laws of physical chemistry can yet be formulated for them.[58] The most favorable working conditions for a given substance usually must be established empirically, to allow for the special circumstances that may be met.

5. Substitution Reactions.—Certain hydrogen atoms in saturated organic compounds may be replaced by halogens.[59] These substitution reactions, especially those in which the halogen is bromine or iodine, are of great value analytically. In contrast to addition processes, substitutions result in the formation of equivalent quantities of hydrogen halide. For analytical purposes brominations of aromatic hydroxyl and amino compounds are the most important:

$$C_6H_5NH_2 + 3Br_2 \rightarrow C_6H_2Br_3NH_2 + 3HBr.$$

[58] The first studies aiming to replace the usual spotting method by potentiometric indication, as well as to clarify the principles involved in diazotization and coupling processes, were undertaken by Erich Müller, *Z. Elektrochem.*, **31**, 662 (1925), and Friedrich Müller, *ibid.*, **34**, 63 (1928).

[59] For general considerations regarding substitution and for references to the earlier literature see L. F. Fieser, "The Directive Influence of Substituent Groups," pp. 140–149 in *Organic Chemistry, An Advanced Treatise*, edited by H. Gilman, Vol. I, John Wiley and Sons, New York 1938.

Under certain conditions the hydroxyl hydrogen of phenols may also be substituted by bromine, as in tribromophenol bromide, $C_6H_2Br_3OBr$, or according to Thiele:[60]

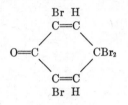

Addition of iodide to this compound restores the tribromophenol and liberates an equivalent amount of iodine. Similar considerations apply to aniline and its derivatives.

A valuable contribution to the theory of bromine substitution in aromatic compounds was made by Vaubel,[61] from whose work the following rules are quoted:

"Among benzene derivatives, those having hydroxyl groups or primary, alkylated, or acetylated amino groups directly on the nucleus possess the property of substituting bromine for hydrogen with great ease. The bromine always takes positions which are ortho or para to the NH_2 or OH groups. None of the ordinary substituents (CH_3, NO_2, Cl, Br, I, SO_3H, COOH, N=NR), when they are also in positions ortho and para to NH_2 or OH, hinder the entrance of bromine into other o- and p- positions. Hydroxyl and amino groups are exceptional, hindering bromination if they occupy locations o- or p- with respect to each other. On the other hand, resorcinol (m-dihydroxy benzene) behaves like phenol and forms a tribromoresorcinol.[62]

"Carboxyl and sulfonic groups situated o- or p- to amino or hydroxyl groups are replaceable by bromine; they do not lose this property even if other substituents like CH_3 or NO_2 are in the m-position with respect to them. Bromine does not replace SO_3H or COOH in the m- position with respect to OH or NH_2 groups.

"Thus, for example, salicylic acid (o-hydroxy benzoic acid) treated with an excess of bromine splits off the carboxyl groups and takes up three atoms of bromine to form tribromophenol; m-hydroxybenzoic

[60] J. Thiele and H. Eichwede, Ber., 33, 673 (1910); see also W. M. Lauer, J. Am. Chem. Soc., 48, 442 (1926).

[61] See the summary beginning on page 166 of Vaubel's text (ref. 45).

[62] Cf. H. Ditz and F. Cedivoda, Z. angew. Chem., 12, 873 (1899); F. Russig and G. Fortmann, ibid., 14, 157, 160 (1901).

acid likewise takes up three bromine atoms in positions 2, 4, 6 with respect to the hydroxyl group, but retains the carboxyl in position 3. The behavior of the aniline sulfonic acids is comparable with this. Two bromine atoms first enter o-aminobenzene sulfonic acid, while with further addition tribromoaniline is formed. Metanilic acid takes up three bromine atoms without loss of the sulfonic acid group. The para acid (sulfanilic) with careful work first gives a dibromo compound, then with excess bromine may form tribromoaniline. Toluidine sulfonic acids show analogous behavior.

"Alkylated or acetylated OH and NH₂ groups exert a small orienting influence on the bromine. The effect is scarcely noticeable with monoalkylated amines, but is evident for the dialkylated compounds. The latter cause the entrance of only two bromine atoms, apparently in o- and p- positions, while alkylated OH causes only one bromine to be taken up, in the p- position. Acetylated amino groups behave the same, allowing substitution in the o- position when the p- position is occupied, but otherwise giving only p- derivatives. Yet there are exceptions to this."

Illustrations: Monomethyl aniline and its homologues permit three atoms of bromine to enter; dimethyl aniline takes only two, but these enter quite rapidly, the first more so than the second. Acetanilide and acet-toluide each take one atom in the p- position.

The rules proposed by Vaubel do not have strict validity although they are useful for orienting one concerning the behavior of different aromatic compounds in bromine substitution. It might be expected, for example, that o- or p-cresol would take up two bromine atoms, while m-cresol would form a tribromo substitution product. On the other hand, many substances are capable of yielding more than one bromination product, and the particular product formed depends upon various conditions, such as temperature,[63] reac-

---

[63] For example, on treating 0.60 millimoles of p-phenol sulfonic acid with 5.0 milli-equivalents of bromine (bromate-bromide) in 100 ml. of 0.7 N sulfuric acid, and allowing to stand either in an ice bath or at 25°C., the following results were obtained by W. Kramer and V. A. Stenger (unpublished experiments):

Time of standing, minutes	Milli-equivalents of bromine taken up by one millimole of compound	
	Ice bath	25°C.
15	2.000	....
30	2.008	2.17
45	2.016	....
60	2.018	2.42
90	.....	2.53
120	2.046	....
180	.....	2.93
240	.....	3.14

tion time, excess of bromine, and perhaps also the acid concentration. Thus β-naphthol gives first, very smoothly, a monobromo derivative, with more bromine a di-substitution product, and finally a tetrabromo compound. Many other substances behave similarly (cf. Vaubel, loc. cit.). These properties are very useful in analytical practice.

In the determination of a compound by means of bromine substitution there are two general procedures:

(a) A strongly acidified solution of the substance to be determined is titrated with a standard potassium bromate-bromide reagent until free bromine just persists in the solution (as shown by the color or by a spot reaction upon starch-iodide paper). In this case the aim is to add exactly the required quantity of bromine.

(b) An excess of the standard bromate-bromide solution is added; after acidifying and allowing to stand, if necessary, the excess bromine is treated with potassium iodide and back-titrated with thiosulfate.

Since in the latter case the substance being titrated comes in contact with excess bromine, it is necessary (when more than one substitution product is possible) that the most favorable working conditions be found and adhered to exactly, in order that the reaction may proceed to a derivative of definite composition. Which of the methods (a) or (b) deserves preference cannot be foretold. In Vaubel's book is described the behavior towards bromine of various organic compounds, including dyes. Before employing for analysis the data given there, one should first establish the most favorable experimental conditions. Many materials, especially polyhydroxy phenols, are also oxidized by bromine so that these analytical procedures are not suitable for them.

Historically it is of interest that the bromination of phenols as a means for their determination was first proposed by Koppeschaar.[64] In general, bromine substitution reactions have more analytical significance than those of iodine.[65] Of especial practical importance, however, is the reaction between iodine and antipyrine, leading in

---

[64] W. F. Koppeschaar, Z. anal. Chem., 15, 233 (1876); E. Waller, Chem. News, 43, 152 (1881), titrated phenol with bromine water.

[65] Concerning the behavior of phenols and their derivatives toward iodine in alkaline medium, see Vaubel's text,[45] pp. 221 ff. See also J. Messinger and G. Vortmann, Ber., 23, 2753 (1890), (iodimetric determination of phenol, thymol, β-naphthol and salicylic acid); W. Fresenius and L. Grünhut, Z. anal. Chem., 38, 295 (1899); G. Frerichs, Apoth. Ztg., 1906, 415; W. M. Gardner and H. H. Hodgson, J. Chem. Soc., 95, 1825 (1909); W. O. Emery and H. C. Fuller, Ind. Eng. Chem. Anal. Ed., 7, 248 (1935).

neutral or very weakly alkaline solution to the formation of antipyrine iodide:

$$C_{11}H_{12}N_2O + I_2 \rightarrow C_{11}H_{11}N_2OI + HI.$$

An exact titration method for antipyrine is based on this reaction (*cf.* Vol. II).

Benzidine is also converted smoothly into a mono-iodo derivative:

$$C_{12}H_{12}N_2 + I_2 \rightarrow C_{12}H_{11}N_2I + HI.$$

Here again the solution should be very weakly alkaline.

D'Ans[66] studied the effect of p_H on the iodimetric determination of phenol and salicylic acid. He recommended that the solutions be buffered with disodium phosphate. Systematic investigations on the best conditions for the determination of phenol, salicylic acid and cresols with alkaline iodine have been made by Beukema-Goudsmit,[67] while Slotta and Neisser[68] have given procedures for the estimation of adrenaline, tyrosine and vitamin B_1.

The conversion of acetone into iodoform and acetic acid through the intermediate product tri-iodo acetone may also be regarded more or less as a substitution reaction:

$$CH_3COCH_3 + 3I_2 + H_2O \rightarrow CHI_3 + CH_3COOH + 3HI.$$

The mechanism of this complicated reaction, which proceeds at strong alkalinity, is not yet clear; nevertheless it permits a simple and accurate determination of acetone.

Metals are capable of substituting in certain compounds, although analytical applications of such reactions are scarce. In alkaline solution, mercuric chloride and phenol react to form *o*- and *p*-hydroxy phenyl mercuric chlorides:[69]

$$C_6H_5OH + NaOH + HgCl_2 \rightarrow C_6H_4(OH)HgCl + NaCl + H_2O.$$

[66] J. d'Ans, Z. anal. Chem., **96**, 1 (1934).

[67] M. Beukema-Goudsmit, *Pharm. Weekblad*, **71**, 380 (1934).

[68] K. H. Slotta and K. Neisser, *Ber.*, **71**, 1611, 1984 (1938).

[69] B. B. Grützner, *Arch. Pharm.*, **236**, 622 (1898). See also K. A. Kobe and T. F. Doumani, *Ind. Eng. Chem.*, **33**, 170 (1941).

Hydrogen on a carbon atom having an acetylenic linkage may be replaced by silver or cuprous copper[70] in ammoniacal solution, forming very unstable compounds of slight solubility; indirect determinations of the original acetylene derivatives may be based on these reactions.

6. Methods of Oxidation and Reduction.—Among the oxidation-reduction reactions of organic chemistry, several cases may be distinguished:

(a) *The reaction is reversible:* A well-known example of this rather rare case is the equilibrium between quinone and hydroquinone:

$$C_6H_4(OH)_2 \rightleftarrows C_6H_4O_2 + 2H^+ + 2e.$$
$$\text{hydroquinone} \qquad \text{quinone}$$

From the oxidation potential, which, as the equation shows, increases with rising hydrogen-ion concentration, one can calculate the conditions under which oxidation or reduction will take place. In approximately neutral solution, hydroquinone is quantitatively oxidized by iodine (*cf.* Chapter IV and also Volume II). Other quinones behave in a manner similar to the quinone-hydroquinone system; also similar, although more complicated, is the cystine-cysteine pair. The reversible oxidation or reduction of many dyes has been discussed in the chapter on indicators. Most of the other analytical oxidation-reduction processes of organic chemistry are irreversible.

(b) *The reaction is not reversible, but proceeds directly with the formation of a definite product:*[71] Individual reducible or oxidizable groups in an organic compound may under certain circumstances be oxidized or reduced without destroying the rest of the molecule. Such is true of the aldehyde group, which can be converted into carboxyl by careful oxidation:

$$\text{H—C—H} + \text{KOI} \rightarrow \text{HC—OH} + \text{KI.}$$
$$\quad \underset{\text{O}}{\|} \qquad\qquad\qquad \underset{\text{O}}{\|}$$

On this reaction is based Romijn's well-known formaldehyde determination.[72] Aldose sugars may be determined similarly through oxidation at mild alkalinity. Peculiarly, the carbonyl group of a

[70] J. W. Mellor, *Comprehensive Treatise on Inorganic and Theoretical Chemistry*, Vol. V, Longmans, Green and Co., London 1924, pp. 850–855.

[71] The theory has been discussed by J. B. Conant, *Chem. Rev.*, **3**, 1 (1926); J. B. Conant and M. F. Pratt, *J. Am. Chem. Soc.*, **48**, 3178, 3220 (1926).

[72] G. Romijn, *Z. anal. Chem.*, **36**, 349 (1897); J. Bougault, *J. pharm. chim.*, **16**, 97, 313 (1917).

ketose is not attacked under these conditions, so that one can determine glucose readily in the presence of fructose. It must be remembered, however, that many organic compounds are easily oxidized; when aldehydes are titrated with hypoiodite in the presence of other organic substances there is always the possibility of interference.

The carbonyl group of a simple aldehyde may be quantitatively oxidized by certain heavy metal salts in alkaline solution, as, for example, in the titration of formaldehyde with ammoniacal silver solution, or in the determination of furfural.[73]

It should be mentioned that many oxidants are capable of decomposing formic acid quantitatively into carbon dioxide and water:

$$HCOOH + O \rightarrow CO_2 + H_2O.$$

Mercuric salts in neutral solution bring about complete oxidation, thus making possible a convenient determination of formic acid in the presence of other acids.[74]

Especially interesting oxidimetric titrations are those of free organic radicals (compounds of trivalent carbon, divalent nitrogen, or monovalent oxygen) with solutions of permanganate, bromine, permonosulfuric acid, etc. These titrations were not proposed as analytical methods for determining the amounts of such compounds, but rather to demonstrate the presence of unsaturated atoms in them. Direct analysis for the elements would not be conclusive because of the difficulty of determining hydrogen accurately enough in substances of high molecular weight. If the molecular weight can be found by physical methods, the number of oxidizing equivalents required per mole may be determined by titration (the endpoint being recognizable by a color change, complete decolorization, or the disappearance of fluorescence). If one mole requires an odd number of oxygen equivalents, hydroxyl groups or bromine atoms, there must be present a compound with uneven valence number, such as one having a trivalent carbon atom.[75] While the finding of an

---

[73] W. Cormack, *J. Chem. Soc.*, **77**, 990 (1900).

[74] A. Leys, *Bull. soc. chim. biol.*, (3) **19**, 472 (1898); F. Auerbach and W. Plüddemann, *Arb. kaiserl. Gesundh.*, **1**, 209 (1911).

[75] The process may be schematically represented by an equation of one of the following types:

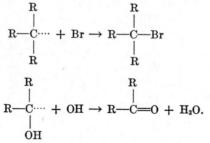

even number does not disprove the presence of these compounds, since in some cases peroxides or perhalides may be formed, yet an uneven number generally is conclusive evidence of their presence. Gomberg[76] treated triphenyl methyl, the classical example of a free radical, with iodine in this way; Scholl[77] employed titrations with permanganate, Caro's acid and bromine in nitrobenzene solution for the characterization of the oxanthronyl derivatives, a new class of radicals with trivalent carbon atoms. More recently he has studied radicals having monovalent oxygen[78] or divalent nitrogen[79] (the so-called azyls and azylium salts).

Among the reduction processes which are not strictly reversible, the determination of nitro compounds with titanous chloride or sulfate is capable of wide application. Titanous chloride was recommended as a volumetric reagent by Knecht.[80] Its reducing action increases with decreasing hydrogen-ion concentration, being in any case so great that the reagent must be kept and used in an inert atmosphere. Nitro groups of soluble compounds are readily reduced in slightly acid solution to amino groups:

$$\text{C}_6\text{H}_4(\text{OH})(\text{NO}_2) + 6\text{TiCl}_3 + 6\text{HCl} \rightarrow \text{C}_6\text{H}_4(\text{OH})(\text{NH}_2) + 6\text{TiCl}_4 + 2\text{H}_2\text{O}.$$

For compounds of slight solubility in water, methanol may be added. Ordinarily one uses an excess of titanous solution and back-titrates with ferric solution, after adding excess acid and thiocyanate indicator. It is necessary to carry through a blank determination on the reagents and solvents (see Vol. II).

(c) *An irreversible reaction leads to the formation of various products, depending upon the conditions:* In principle, reactions for which no simple stoichiometric relations prevail are of little account analytically. Yet insofar as all experimental conditions that influence the result may be established and controlled, such reactions can at times be employed with advantage. A case in point is the behavior of reducing sugars toward alkaline copper solutions. As is well-known, cupric salts in alkaline medium form with polyvalent alcohols or

[76] M. Gomberg, *Ber.*, **35**, 1826 (1902).

[77] R. Scholl, *Ber.*, **54**, 2376 (1921); **56**, 918, 1065, 1833 (1923).

[78] *Ann. Acad. Sci. Fennicae*, A, **29**, No. 13 (1927).

[79] *Ber.*, **60**, 1236, 1685 (1927); **61**, 968 (1928).

[80] E. Knecht, *Ber.*, **33**, 1550 (1903); see also E. Knecht and E. Hibbert, *New Reduction Methods in Volumetric Analysis*, 2nd Ed., Longmans, Green and Co., London 1925.

hydroxy acids blue complexes, from which hydrous cupric oxide is not precipitated by alkali. Solutions of this kind (Fehling's, Benedict's, Luff's) oxidize compounds containing the carbonyl group, whereupon cupric copper is reduced to red, insoluble cuprous oxide. For the determination of sugars with open carbonyl groups this reaction has found extensive application. It does not lead simply to the formation of the corresponding hydroxy acid; rather the molecules are generally split into lower organic acids.

The quantity of cuprous oxide precipitated depends upon various factors: the kind of sugar, its concentration and that of the copper solution, the alkalinity of the latter, the time and manner of heating, and occasionally also the presence of other substances. Determination of the yield of cuprous oxide or of the excess cupric solution gives an empirical measure of the amount of sugar.[81] Whatever copper reagent is used, specified conditions must be maintained and the procedure must be standardized with known amounts of the pure sugar. The quantity of cuprous oxide formed is not strictly proportional to the sugar content. It must also be considered that various copper reagents undergo a slight self-reduction upon boiling, for which correction should be made with a blank determination.

Strongly alkaline copper solutions have, as indicated above, a degrading as well as an oxidizing effect upon sugars. Therefore it is impossible to express in an equation the reaction that takes place. With decreasing alkalinity the degradation of the sugar molecules is less pronounced. At the same time monoses are oxidized much sooner than bioses, furnishing the basis for an important method of determining the former in the presence of the latter.[82] In spite of the aforementioned side and consecutive reactions, it should be emphasized that the oxidizing action of alkaline copper solution is essentially specific for the carbonyl group. From this fact it is clear why such a purely empirical procedure has been so widely adopted.

Another interesting oxidation reaction which appears to be quite specific is that of periodic acid with compounds containing hydroxyl groups on adjacent carbon atoms (α-glycols). This reaction, discovered by Malaprade[83] and improved as a volumetric procedure by

[81] *Cf.* C. A. Amick, *J. Phys. Chem.*, **31**, 144 (1927).

[82] C. Barfoed, *Z. anal. Chem.*, **12**, 27 (1873); F. C. Hinkel and H. C. Sherman, *J. Am. Chem. Soc.*, **29**, 1744 (1907).

[83] L. Malaprade, *Compt. rend.*, **186**, 382 (1928); *Bull. soc. chim.*, **43**, 683 (1928).

Fleury and coworkers,[84] takes place in slightly acid solution at ordinary temperature, according to an equation of the type:

$$R_1{-}\underset{\underset{\displaystyle OH}{|}}{\overset{\overset{\displaystyle H}{|}}{C}}{-}\underset{\underset{\displaystyle OH}{|}}{\overset{\overset{\displaystyle H}{|}}{C}}{-}R_2 \;+\; HIO_4 \;\longrightarrow$$

$$R_1{-}\overset{\overset{\displaystyle H}{|}}{C}{=}O \;+\; R_2{-}\overset{\overset{\displaystyle H}{|}}{C}{=}O \;+\; HIO_3 \;+\; H_2O,$$

$$H{-}\underset{\underset{\displaystyle OH}{|}}{\overset{\overset{\displaystyle H}{|}}{C}}{-}\underset{\underset{\displaystyle OH}{|}}{\overset{\overset{\displaystyle H}{|}}{C}}{-}\underset{\underset{\displaystyle OH}{|}}{\overset{\overset{\displaystyle H}{|}}{C}}{-}H \;+\; 2HIO_4 \;\longrightarrow$$

$$2H{-}\overset{\overset{\displaystyle H}{|}}{C}{=}O \;+\; H{-}\underset{\underset{\displaystyle O}{\|}}{C}{-}OH \;+\; 2HIO_3 \;+\; H_2O.$$

After completion of the oxidation, bicarbonate is added and the unused periodate is reduced with a slight excess of arsenite. The excess of the latter is determined by titration with standard iodine solution. Compounds such as glycolic, malic and citric acids and trimethylene glycol are not oxidized by periodate under these mild conditions, hence they do not interfere in determinations of α-glycols, sugars, and tartaric, gluconic, or saccharic acids.

(d) Oxidation proceeds more or less completely to the formation of carbon dioxide and water: Under suitable conditions most organic compounds can by strong oxidation be quantitatively decomposed to carbon dioxide and water. Apparently there are formed in the process other intermediate products, which are not of general analytical interest. As oxidizing agents, potassium permanganate, dichromate and iodate, and ceric sulfate are available.

Oxidations with permanganate may be carried out in acid, neutral or alkaline solution. In alkaline medium the product ordinarily is

[84] P. Fleury and J. Lange, Compt. rend., 195, 1395 (1932), J. pharm. chim., 17, 196, 313, 409 (1933) (studies of various acids and sugars); P. Fleury and R. Paris, ibid., 18, 470 (1933) (α-glycerophosphates); P. Fleury and M. Fatôme, ibid., 21, 247 (1935) (glycerine in the presence of sugars).

oxalic acid rather than carbonic,[85] but after acidifying, the oxidation proceeds with formation of carbon dioxide and water.[86] Frequently in these oxidations there arises a little acetic acid, which is not further attacked by the oxidant.[87]

The application of permanganate for the oxidation of various acids was described long ago by Péan de St. Gilles.[88] Since then, the method has been mentioned frequently in the literature. Usually the material is heated with excess permanganate long enough for complete oxidation to take place, after which the excess is titrated iodometrically or with oxalic acid. A general objection to this procedure is that permanganate on boiling undergoes an auto-decomposition, catalyzed by the manganese dioxide which is formed. Thus the method cannot give exact results without correction, nor can the correction be determined exactly in a blank experiment because the conditions are then different. An alternative procedure, more to be recommended although requiring a longer time, consists in allowing the oxidation to take place at room temperature. These methods will be discussed more fully in Volume III.

Potassium dichromate is a weaker oxidant than permanganate, yet it enjoys the preference as a reagent because it is more stable, especially upon boiling. Oxidations of organic compounds take place in acid solution. These reactions have been studied by Reischauer,[89] among others, and particularly by Heidenhain.[90] In general, the oxidizing action of dichromate increases with increasing acidity and with rising temperature. It is possible to devise purely empirical methods involving the partial oxidation of numerous compounds, such as alcohols, esters and acids. These procedures can be of good service in technical analysis, provided that the conditions are carefully specified and observed, and that interfering substances are absent.

[85] E. Donath and H. Ditz, *J. prakt. Chem.*, **60**, 566 (1899).

[86] Concerning the mechanism and reaction velocity of the oxidation of organic substances with permanganate and dichromate, see G. Lejeune, *Compt. rend.*, **182**, 194, 694 (1926).

[87] *Cf.* W. L. Evans and collaborators, *J. Am. Chem. Soc.*, **47**, 3085, 3098, 3102 (1925); regarding the oxidation of sugars and hexahydric alcohols, see R. Kuhn and F. W. Jauregg, *Ber.*, **58**, 1441 (1925).

[88] L. Péan de St. Gilles, *Ann. chim. phys.*, (3), **55**, 374 (1859).

[89] G. G. Reischauer, *Dinglers polytech. J.*, **165**, 457 (1862); C. F. Cross and E. J. Bevan, *Chem. News*, **5**, 2 (1887); R. Bourcat, *Z. anal. Chem.*, **29**, 609 (1890).

[90] H. Heidenhain, *Z. anal. Chem.*, **32**, 357 (1897).

The use of dichromate or chromic acid oxidation in a simplified procedure for organic elementary analysis has been proposed. In many cases the oxidation does not proceed completely to the formation of carbon dioxide and water, some of the irregularities being due to the escape of carbon monoxide. Simon[91] introduced a great improvement by applying the catalytic action of silver, added as silver sulfate or chromate. In a series of valuable investigations he studied the behavior of many organic compounds when treated with chromic acid-silver sulfate mixtures. The problem of completely oxidizing organic compounds has also been discussed by Williams.[92] He and his collaborators[93] developed a good procedure for determining the "organic oxidation equivalent" with potassium dichromate in about 30 N sulfuric acid, without the addition of a silver salt.

Concerning the complete oxidation of organic substances with potassium iodate in strongly acid medium, the investigations of Strebinger[94] and of Vortmann[95] are of interest. Williams, Rohrman and Christensen[96] studied and improved the method, which will be considered further in Volume II.

Willard and Young[97] investigated the oxidation of various organic acids with ceric sulfate. The latter is unique in that it does not appreciably attack formic acid in hot acid solutions. Therefore this acid (and also acetic) may be a product of the oxidation of higher

[91] L. J. Simon and coworkers, *Compt. rend.*, **170**, 514, 734 (1920); **174**, 1706 (1922); **175**, 167, 525, 768, 1070 (1922); **178**, 775, 1816 (1924); **179**, 975 (1924); **180**, 673, 833, 1405 (1925); see also H. Cordebard and V. Miehl, *Bull. soc. chim.*, **43**, 97 (1928); B. V. Tronov and A. A. Lukanin, *J. Russ. Phys. Chem. Soc.*, **59**, 1149, 1157, 1173 (1927), *Chem. Abstr.*, **22**, 3335 (1928). Concerning the catalysis of persulfate oxidations by silver, see D. H. Yost, *J. Am. Chem. Soc.*, **48**, 152 (1926).

[92] R. J. Williams, *J. Am. Chem. Soc.*, **59**, 288 (1937).

[93] B. E. Christensen, R. J. Williams and Anne E. King, *J. Am. Chem. Soc.*, **59**, 293 (1937).

[94] R. Strebinger, *Z. anal. Chem.*, **58**, 97 (1919).

[95] G. Vortmann, *Z. anal. Chem.*, **66**, 272 (1925). On the determination of organic acids with iodate, see L. Cluny, *J. pharm. chim.*, **3**, 112 (1926); *cf.* also V. Staněk and T. Nemes, *Z. anal. Chem.*, **95**, 244 (1933).

[96] R. J. Williams, E. Rohrman and B. E. Christensen, *J. Am. Chem. Soc.*, **59**, 291 (1937).

[97] H. H. Willard and Philena Young, *J. Am. Chem. Soc.*, **50**, 1322 (1928), **52**, 132 (1930); concerning the reaction velocities of ceric sulfate with several organic compounds see A. Benrath and K. Ruland, *Z. anorg. allgem. Chem.*, **114**, 267 (1920).

acids. Unfortunately the method requires the use of empirical factors, which may vary with the conditions.

In this chapter some of the more important volumetric methods of organic chemistry have been summarized on the basis of their physicochemical foundations. It will be evident to the reader that further fundamental studies are to be desired in many cases. No attempt has been made to include special procedures nor a complete survey of the literature, since both may be found in reference texts on organic analysis.

CHAPTER X

METHODS FOR THE DETERMINATION OF THE EQUIVALENCE-POINT

1. General Considerations.—As has been mentioned in Chapter I, any property of the solution which exhibits a definite change near the equivalence-point may furnish a means of recognizing this point. In volumetric analysis preference is generally given to indicator methods, that is, to methods in which the property undergoing change is that of light transmission. This is so because the change can be detected visually, without special apparatus. The indicator (whether it be one of the reactants, their product, or an added substance) reveals the endpoint by modifying the appearance of the mixture, producing a change in either its color or its turbidity.

If various indicators are available for a titration, the one most suitable for the purpose may be chosen on the basis of its properties and those of the system under examination, especially the equilibrium constant of the reaction and the dilution. The conditions necessary for good indicator action have been developed in the chapters on indicators (V) and Titration Error (VI).

Analytical methods may also be based on other physico-chemical properties which change only gradually during the course of a titration, but which shift abruptly at the endpoint. Of these, the electrometric titration procedures are best known; one may distinguish between *conductometric, potentiometric* and *amperometric (polarimetric)* methods. These and several less common procedures for locating the endpoint will be discussed briefly in succeeding sections.

2. Conductometric Titrations.—The use of conductometric determinations dates from the excellent pioneer work of Berthelot[1] and of Kohlrausch.[2] Küster and his collaborators[3] called attention to the

---

[1] D. Berthelot, *Ann. chim. phys.*, (6), **28**, 1 (1893).
[2] F. Kohlrausch, *Wied. Ann.*, **26**, 225 (1885).
[3] F. W. Küster, *Z. anorg. Chem.*, **35**, 454 (1902); **42**, 224 (1904).

analytical significance of the methods, while Dutoit and coworkers[4] developed procedures for quantitative neutralizations and precipitations.[5]

If one electrolyte is added to the solution of another without changing its volume appreciably, the conductivity increases, provided that the two electrolytes do not react with each other. However, if some of the ions can react to form a slightly dissociated or slightly soluble substance, or if the total ionic concentration can be changed by an oxidation-reduction process, the conductivity may either decrease, increase or remain unchanged. For example, a reaction leading to the formation of a slightly dissociated or insoluble product may be expressed as follows:

$$B^+ + A^- + C^+ + D^- \longrightarrow BD + A^- + C^+.$$

Ion being Ions of Product
determined reagent

While the A-ions remain unaffected in the solution, the B-ions are removed in the form of a slightly soluble or nearly undissociated compound BD, being replaced in solution by C-ions. Assuming that the total volume of solution is practically unaltered, one can predict from the mobilities of the individual ions what changes will occur in the conductivity of the mixture.

(a) If λ_B, the mobility of B-ions, is greater than λ_C, that of C-ions, the conductance of BA-solution decreases upon addition of CD. This occurs in the neutralization of a strong acid with a strong base. Hydrogen ions are about five times as mobile as the best-conducting of the other cations, hence as they react during titration with hydroxyl ions to form water, the conductance diminishes until the equivalence-point is reached. Here the solution contains neutral salt equivalent to the acid initially present. With further addition of alkali the conductance strongly increases, mainly on account of the hydroxyl ions introduced. If the specific conductance is measured after successive additions of reagent and the values obtained are plotted against the corresponding volumes of reagent added, one ob-

[4] P. Dutoit, *Bull. soc. chim.*, **7**, 1 (1910); *J. chim. phys.*, **8**, 12, 27 (1910).

[5] For further literature references and details of conductometric methods see I. M. Kolthoff, *Die konduktometrischen Titrationen*, Steinkopf, Dresden 1923; G. Jander and O. Pfundt, *Die visuelle Leitfähigkeitstitration*, 2nd Edition, Enke, Stuttgart 1932; H. T. S. Britton, *Conductometric Analysis*, D. Van Nostrand and Company, New York 1934.

tains two straight lines intersecting at the equivalence-point. The conductance has a minimum at this point.

In Figure 22 the course of the conductivity during titration of a strong acid with a strong base is shown by line I prior to the equivalence-point, and by line II thereafter.

(b) In case λ_B and λ_C are equal, the conductance remains unchanged up to the equivalence-point, and from there on it increases. Thus in the titration of silver nitrate with barium chloride, $\lambda_{\frac{1}{2}Ba} = 55$ and $\lambda_{Ag} = 54.3$, so that the replacement of silver by barium ions has very little effect on the conductance. Were sodium chloride used instead, the conductance would decrease slightly up to the equivalence-point,

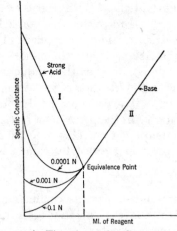

Fig. 22. Conductometric Titrations of a Strong Acid and of a Weak Acid at Various Concentrations

since λ_{Na} is only 43.5; with potassium chloride it would increase because λ_K is 64.6 (all at 18°C.). During a precipitation titration the conductance ordinarily changes but little before the equivalence-point and increases afterwards. Here again one obtains two straight lines intersecting at the equivalence-point. Generally, however, the conductance measured at this point is somewhat greater than that corresponding to the course of the lines. The solubility or dissociation of the product formed adds conducting ions whose effect should be considered. The greater the solubility or dissociation, the more does the experimental curve deviate from an extension of the two straight lines to their intersection, and the less accurate is the result. Errors due to this and to other causes are discussed in the texts that have been cited.[5]

(c) In the titration of a very weak acid with a strong base, or *vice versa*, the conductance increases throughout the titration. With intermediately strong acids, the conductance falls at first as the mobile hydrogen ions are used up, then slowly passes through a minimum of no analytical significance, and finally rises. The more dilute the solution and the stronger the acid, the nearer to the equivalence-point is this minimum found. After the equivalence-point the conductance increases more strongly, in that hydroxyl ions have a greater mobility than other anions.

For comparison there are given in Figure 22 several titration curves of a weak acid at different dilutions. With increasing strength of the acid or base being titrated, case (c) gradually approaches case (a).

In general, conductometric titrations are applied only when a satisfactory visual indicator is lacking, when the indicator method fails (as with highly colored liquids), or when the conductometric method is superior in accuracy (as in the titration of very weak acids or bases like boric acid, aniline, etc.). The principal disadvantage of the procedure is its lack of sensitivity in the presence of foreign electrolytes. A conductometric determination of one kind of ion in a solution containing large quantities of other electrolytes cannot lead to certain results.

3. Potentiometric Titrations.—Whereas conductometric methods give no direct measure of the concentration of a particular ionic species, potentiometric measurements show directly the course of an ionic concentration during titration. The electrode whose potential is determined plays the part of an indicator; the potential change at the equivalence-point is a function of the varying ion concentration, as has already been explained in earlier chapters. If the accuracy of potential measurement is known, the titration error may be calculated much as in the case of ordinary indicators. Böttger[6] first applied the hydrogen electrode to volumetric neutralizations, and interest in the use of the method increased following the appearance of an excellent paper by Hildebrand.[7] In order to apply potentiometric titrations for ion combination reactions (neutralizations, precipita-

[6] W. Böttger, *Z. physik. Chem.*, **24**, 253 (1897).
[7] J. H. Hildebrand, *J. Am. Chem. Soc.*, **35**, 869 (1913).

tions, or complex formations), it is necessary to have an electrode capable of indicating one of the ions in question.

When a metal is placed in a solution which contains ions of the particular metal, the potential difference (often called the potential of the electrode) between the metal and the solution is given by the expression:

$$\pi = \frac{-RT}{nF} \, ln \; aM + \text{constant,}$$

in which π is the potential difference between electrode and solution measured against a constant reference electrode, R is the gas constant, T the absolute temperature, and n the valence of the ion. F denotes the charge of a gram equivalent of an ion (one Faraday, equal to 96,500 coulombs); ln signifies the natural logarithm and aM the activity of the metal ions in the solution. Introducing the values of R and F and converting to Briggsian logarithms yields the equation:

$$\pi = \frac{-0.0001983}{n} \, T \, \log_{10} aM + \text{constant.}$$

Assuming for the sake of convenience that the activity coefficient of the metal ions is unity, one obtains at 25°C.:

$$\pi = \frac{-0.0591}{n} \, \log cM + \text{constant.}$$

When cM (actually aM) is equal to one,

$$\pi = \text{constant} = \pi_0.$$

This value of π at an ion concentration (activity) of unity is called the normal potential π_0 of the particular electrode. In standard texts of physical chemistry the normal potentials of various metals are given, referred to the normal hydrogen electrode as reference electrode. Quite generally then the potential of the metal electrode is given by:

$$\pi = \pi_0 - \frac{0.0591}{n} \, \log c_I = \pi_0 + \frac{0.0591}{n} \, p_I,$$

in which p_I is the ion exponent.

In potentiometric titrations one is interested mainly in the change of the potential during the titration. Since the ionic strength of the solution during the titration remains sensibly constant, the activity coefficient of the metal ions also remains constant. It is for this reason that the activity coefficient of the metal ions has not been considered in the above equations.

Various electrodes are used, according to the kind of ion being titrated; thus for the determination of hydrogen or hydroxyl ions one employs a hydrogen electrode (in which hydrogen gas adsorbed on a platinum surface acts electromotively as a metal), while for the determination of halogen or silver ions an electrode of silver is in order. The case is somewhat different for oxidation-reduction processes. An electrode of bright platinum or other noble metal dipped in the solution of an oxidizing or reducing agent shows a certain potential in the establishment of which the metal itself has no part. Here the metal serves only to indicate the oxidation potential of the system and is called the "indicator electrode."

If the relationship between the oxidized and reduced forms of a substance may be expressed by the equation:

$$Ox + ne \rightleftarrows Red,$$

then the potential of a noble metal electrode is:

$$\pi = \frac{RT}{nF} \, ln \, \frac{[Ox]}{[Red]} \, K,$$

or in simplified form:

$$\pi = \pi_0 + \frac{0.0591}{n} \log \frac{[Ox]}{[Red]}.$$

Here [Ox] and [Red] represent the concentrations of oxidized and reduced forms, respectively; n is the number of electrons taken up during reduction of one Ox atom (or radical) and π_0 is the normal potential, that of a solution in which [Ox] = [Red]. For a given system, therefore, the electrode potential is determined by the ratio of [Ox] to [Red].

Just as in ion combination reactions the change of ion concentration is sharpest at the equivalence-point, so also the potential (which is a measure of the ion concentration as derived previously) shows a sharp change there. The endpoint of a potentiometric titration is reached when the greatest relative change in potential is produced by a small addition of reagent, and the sharper is this change for a given addition, the more exactly may the endpoint be determined. The latter can be located readily by plotting the course of the potential against the volume of standard solution, whereupon the equivalence-point is revealed as an inflection of the curve. In Chapter III theoretical titration curves were calculated and plotted with p_H or p_I values as functions of the percentage of reaction or amount of solution used. Since in ion combination reactions the potentials vary in linear manner with p_I, the theoretical curves may by a suitable choice of coordinates be made to coincide completely with empirically established potential curves.

Likewise in oxidation-reduction reactions, the potential changes the most abruptly at the equivalence-point, since it is a function of the ratio [Ox]:[Red] and this quantity experiences the greatest change at that point.

In order to follow experimentally the potential change of a single electrode, it is connected with a reference electrode of constant potential and the electromotive force of the cell thus formed is measured after successive additions of reagent during the titration. This observed E.M.F. being the algebraic difference between the two electrode or half-cell potentials, one of which is constant, the variation in E.M.F. may be regarded as a direct measure of the potential change of the indicator or titration electrode. There is no need of determining the absolute values, since only the relative changes are of interest for titration purposes.

If the potential difference between the reference electrode and indicator electrode at the equivalence-point is known, one can titrate to this point, that is, to a definite "titration exponent," by opposing the E.M.F. in question with an equal potential and adding reagent until no current flows (compensation method). One way of doing this consists in using as reference half-cell an electrode identical with the titration electrode, but placed in a solution whose composition is the same as that expected at the equivalence-point. The endpoint is reached when the two electrodes show the same potential, so that the E.M.F. of the cell becomes zero. This procedure is analogous to titrating with the aid of an indicator and a reference solution.

Inasmuch as details concerning the practical performance and accuracy of potentiometric titrations are to be found in the various reference texts,[8] further discussion will be omitted here. It may be pointed out that potentiometric methods can be of great assistance in the development of titration procedures employing visual indicators, especially in cases for which the dissociation constants or solubility products are not known.

4. Amperometric (Polarimetric) Titrations.—In titrations of this type, application is made of electrolysis at a dropping mercury electrode[9] as developed by Heyrovsky and his coworkers,[10] or at a platinum wire micro-electrode. The principles underlying the use of these two electrodes are discussed briefly below.

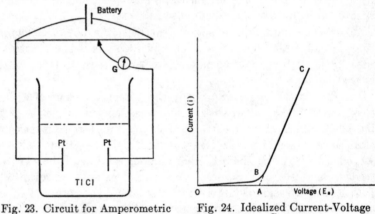

Fig. 23. Circuit for Amperometric Titrations   Fig. 24. Idealized Current-Voltage Curve

Figure 23 is a schematic diagram of an electrolysis cell, consisting of a very dilute solution of thallous chloride in an excess of potassium chloride between two platinum electrodes, and a battery and rheostat

[8] For example, I. M. Kolthoff and N. H. Furman, *Potentiometric Titrations*, 2nd Ed., John Wiley and Sons, Inc., New York 1931; Erich Müller, *Die elektrometrische Massanalyse*, 5th Ed., Th. Steinkopf, Dresden 1932; W. Böttger *et al.*, *Physikalische Methoden der analytischen Chemie*, Vol. III, Akad. Verlags., Leipzig 1939.

[9] G. Kucera, *Ann. Physik.*, **11**, 529, 698 (1903).

[10] For a review of the polarographic method and literature, see J. Heyrovsky, section on polarography in Vol. II, *Physikalische Methoden der Analytischen Chemie*, edited by W. Böttger, Akad. Verlags., Leipzig 1936; for a discussion of the theoretical fundamentals see I. M. Kolthoff and J. J. Lingane, *Chem. Rev.*, **24**, 1 (1939); *Polarography (Polarographic Analysis and Voltammetry; Amperometric Titrations)*, Interscience Publishers, Inc., New York 1941.

by means of which the E.M.F. applied to the cell can be varied at will.   The applied E.M.F. is gradually increased and the corresponding current through the cell is measured by means of an ammeter or a galvanometer (G).   The values of the applied potential are then plotted against corresponding values of the current.   The resulting current-voltage curve has the general shape shown in Fig. 24.   The current remains very small, practically zero (residual current) until point A, called the decomposition potential, is reached, after which it increases very rapidly as the applied E.M.F. is further increased (BC in Figure 24).   Under ideal conditions (vigorous stirring), BC is a straight line whose slope should be given by Ohm's law, $E_a - E_d = iR$, in which E_a is the total applied E.M.F., E_d is the decomposition voltage, i the current, and R the resistance of the cell. During electrolysis, however, the concentration of the discharging

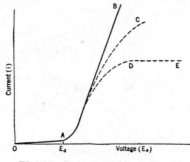

Fig. 25. Current-Voltage Curves

ions decreases in the immediate neighborhood of the electrodes, which results in more or less "concentration polarization."   The current voltage curve deviates under these conditions from a straight line, and its shape becomes as shown by the curve AC in Figure 25.

Now consider the case in which the anode consists of a large platinum electrode or, better, a large silver-silver chloride electrode, and the cathode is a small platinum wire.   When a thallous chloride solution is electrolyzed, the potential of the large silver-silver chloride electrode is fixed so long as the current is small, and it will remain constant, independent of the applied E.M.F. (depolarized electrode). With increasing applied potential the small platinum electrode remains polarized until the applied potential is equal to the decomposition voltage E_d, at which point the small electrode becomes depolarized and electrolysis starts.   From here on the current will increase according to AB in Figure 25. However, since the cathode is a small platinum wire there will be a depletion of thallium ions around the electrode, resulting in concentration polarization and an increase of the decomposition voltage (curves AC and ADE). After waiting for a few minutes, a steady state is set up and the current remains constant if the applied E.M.F. is not changed. With further increase of the E.M.F. the depletion of thallium ions around the electrode becomes greater and finally practically complete. From then on (point D on the curve ADE) the current will remain constant with increase of the applied E.M.F. (DE is horizontal). This constant current, called the *diffusion current*, i_d, is proportional to the concentration of thallium ions in the solution.[11]

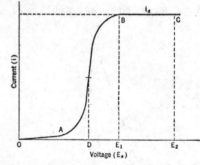

Fig. 26. Current-Voltage Curve Obtained at the Dropping
Mercury Electrode

When instead of the platinum micro electrode the dropping mercury electrode is used as a cathode, similar phenomena will be observed. The current varies during the growth of a drop, but this causes only slight fluctuations in the galvanometer deflection. The dropping electrode has this advantage over the platinum electrode, that the measurements are made without waiting until the final stationary state is reached. With the dropping electrode no true steady state is attained, but the average current measured corresponds to a perfectly reproducible state.

The shape of a current-voltage curve obtained at the dropping mercury electrode is given in Figure 26. OA is again the residual current curve; the electro-reduction starts at A, while at point B the current has become equal to the diffusion current i_d. The

[11] *Cf.* H. A. Laitinen and I. M. Kolthoff, *J. Am. Chem. Soc.*, **61**, 3344 (1939).

potential at point D, at which the current is equal to one half of the diffusion current, is characteristic of the particular electro-reduction process and is in general independent of the concentration.   Other conditions (rate of dropping, drop size, temperature, etc.) being constant, the magnitude of the diffusion current is determined by the amount of electro-reducible material which reaches the electrode. This amount is proportional to the concentration of such material in the bulk of the solution.   Hence, under these constant conditions, *the diffusion current is proportional to the concentration of electro-reducible material in the solution.*   This relation forms the basis for analytical application of the polarographic method.

We shall now consider a solution of a reducible substance A, whose concentration is being gradually diminished by the addition of small

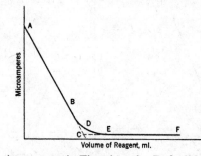

Fig. 27. Amperometric Titration of a Reducible Substance

portions of a reagent B, which forms a slightly soluble compound AB. We shall first assume that reagent B is not reduced at an applied E.M.F. between E_1 and E_2 (Figure 26), at which A yields a diffusion current.   The titration is started at an applied E.M.F. between E_1 and E_2 and the current is measured upon successive additions of reagent B.   Since the current is proportional to the concentration of A in the bulk of the solution, it will be found to decrease continuously during the titration.   When the current is plotted against the volume of reagent added and a correction is made for the dilution effect caused by the addition of reagent, a straight line is found (ABC in Figure 27).   The dilution correction is simply made by multiplying the values of the current measured by a factor $\dfrac{V + v}{V}$ in which V is the original volume and v the volume of reagent added. In order to keep this correction small the concentration of the reagent is taken 10 to 50 times greater than that of the solution titrated, the reagent being added from a microburet. If the solubility of precipitate AB is smaller than 10^{-5} to 10^{-6} molar, its contribution to the diffusion current is negligibly small. In such a case the current will decrease according to ABC in Figure 27, C corresponding to the endpoint. Upon further addition of reagent the current remains unchanged (CEF). If the solubility of AB is not negligibly small, its contribution to the diffusion current at the endpoint C is given by CD in Figure 27. From a practical point of view it is advantageous that even under such conditions the amperometric titration can yield excellent results. As a result of the suppression of the solubility by the common ion effect the solubility becomes negli-

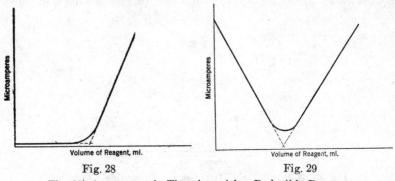

Fig. 28   Fig. 29

Fig. 28. Amperometric Titration with a Reducible Reagent
Fig. 29. Amperometric Titration of a Reducible Substance with a
Reducible Reagent

gible in the presence of a reasonable excess of A or of B. In such a case those points are determined which lie on the straight lines AB and EF. By determining three or four points on the precipitation line AB and a similar number of points on the reagent line EF, the endpoint C is found graphically with a satisfactory accuracy. It is of analytical interest to mention that such amperometric titrations yield accurate results even in highly dilute solutions.

When the substance titrated is not reduced at the applied E.M.F., but the reagent is, the titration lines are just the reverse of those given in the previous case (Figure 28). Thus it has been found possible[12] to titrate sulfate solutions with lead nitrate quite accurately at the potential at which lead yields a diffusion current.

[12] I. M. Kolthoff and Y.-D. Pan, *J. Am. Chem. Soc.*, **62**, 3332 (1940).

When both the substance titrated and the reagent yield a diffusion current at the applied E.M.F., the titration lines have the shape given in Figure 29. Such lines were obtained in the titration of dilute lead solutions with chromate[13] and in the titration of nickel with dimethylglyoxime.[14]

Fractional precipitation titrations can also be carried out amperometrically. Suppose that there are in the solution two ions A and B which yield insoluble salts with the reagent, and that B does not start to precipitate until practically all of A is precipitated. Assume further that A and the reagent yield a diffusion current at the applied E.M.F., while B is not reduced at this potential. It is easily seen, then, that the titration line will be of the shape given in Figure 30. Point A corresponds to complete precipitation of A, and point B to

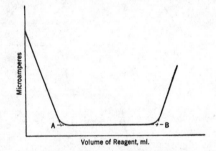

Fig. 30. Amperometric Fractional Precipitation Titration

that of B. Provided that A does not coprecipitate with B, the fractional precipitation titration should yield useful analytical results.

Amperometric titrations are not limited to precipitation reactions, but can also be applied to neutralization, complex formation, and oxidation-reduction reactions. For a more complete review the reader is referred to the literature.[15] From the historical viewpoint it may be mentioned that Heyrovsky[16] was the first to apply an amperometric titration to the determination of barium with sulfate. Heyrovsky suggested that the procedure be called a *polarographic titration*. Majer,[17] studying the determination of sulfate with lead,

[13] I. M. Kolthoff and Y.-D. Pan, *J. Am. Chem. Soc.*, **61**, 3402 (1939).

[14] I. M. Kolthoff and A. Langer, *J. Am. Chem. Soc.*, **62**, 211 (1940).

[15] See I. M. Kolthoff, *Trans. Electrochem. Soc.*, **78**, 191 (1941).

[16] J. Heyrovsky, *Bull. soc. chim.*, **41**, 1227 (1927); J. Heyrovsky and S. Berezicky, *Collection Czechoslov. Chem. Commun.*, **1**, 19 (1929).

[17] V. Majer, *Z. Elektrochem.*, **42**, 120 (1936).

proposed the name *polarometric* titration. As it is the change in current which indicates the endpoint, we prefer to use the term *amperometric* titration.

Amperometric titrations have certain limitations. Suppose that three reducible substances, A_1, A_2 and A_3, are present in the solution (Figure 31). A_1 is reduced at the potential E_1 giving a diffusion current i_1 proportional to its concentration, A_2 is reduced at the potential E_2 giving a current i_2, and A_3 is reduced at the potential E_3 giving a current i_3. Now suppose that a titration of (or with) A_1 is to be carried out in the presence of any desired amounts of A_2 and A_3. If the applied E.M.F. is kept between E_1 and E_2, only A_1 is reduced and the current is proportional to the concentration of A_1

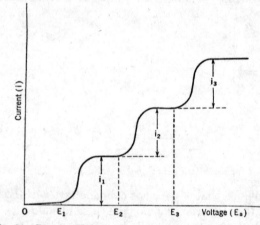

Fig. 31. Current-Voltage Curve with Three Reducible Substances

alone, A_2 and A_3 being without influence. However, if A_2 is titrated in the presence of A_1, the current is the sum of the diffusion current of A_1 (i_1) and the diffusion current i_2 of A_2 which decreases continuously during the titration. With increasing ratio of i_1/i_2 the accuracy in the measurement of i_2 becomes smaller. In the case in which the substance A_3 is titrated, analogous considerations apply. For example, it is not readily possible to carry out the amperometric titration of sulfate with barium (or the reverse) when there are present large amounts of metal ions more noble (more easily discharged) than barium, *e.g.* zinc, cadmium, nickel, cobalt, etc. In such a case, E_3 of Figure 31 would correspond to the discharge potential of barium and E_1 and E_2 to those of cadmium and zinc, for instance. In this case it would be better to use a lead solution instead of barium, since the discharge potential of lead is found at a potential more positive than E_1.

It is to be expected that many of the organic reagents which yield precipitates with metals will be found useful in amperometric titrations. The determination of nickel with dimethylglyoxime has been mentioned previously;[14] it is also possible to titrate cobalt, copper or palladium amperometrically with α-nitroso-β-naphthol.[18]

5. Less Common Methods.—Most of the physical properties of a solution that is being titrated will show variations (breaks) at the equivalence-point. In some cases the addition of an indicating substance is necessary, while in others the properties of the system itself may change sufficiently. Some of the methods which have been proposed are noted briefly in this section.

(a) *The Cryoscopic Method:* The freezing points of mixtures of acids and bases in various ratios were studied by Cornec,[19] who found that graphs of the values obtained showed distinct breaks at the equivalence-point. In contrast with conductometric titrations, in which the individual mobilities of the ions are concerned, cryoscopic titrations depend only upon changes in the total ionic concentration to reveal the break. Because the method is very time-consuming it offers little attraction in practical analysis, coming into question only for special physico-chemical investigations.

(b) *The Refractometric Method:* During titration, the refraction of light by a solution changes as the ionic concentrations are altered. Thus the refractive index reaches a minimum at the equivalence-point when an acid is titrated with a base or when a solution of chloride ions is titrated with silver nitrate. Cornec[19] applied the procedure for special purposes. The changes in refraction are too small to be measured with sufficient accuracy by means of an ordinary refractometer. However, Berl and Ranis[20] have shown that Löwe's liquid interferometer is suitable, so that the method may assume analytical importance. Berl and Ranis determined the refractions during some neutralization and precipitation reactions, finding that the values were joined by straight lines intersecting at the equivalence-point. Thus the data are similar to those obtained

---

[18] I. M. Kolthoff and A. Langer, *J. Am. Chem. Soc.*, **62**, 3172 (1940).

[19] E. Cornec, *Ann. chim. phys.*, (8), **29**, 491 (1913); **30**, 63 (1913).

[20] E. Berl and L. Ranis, *Ber.*, **61**, 92 (1928).

conductometrically, although the theoretical foundations of the two methods are obviously quite different.[21]

(c) *The Calorimetric or Thermometric Method:* By measuring with a thermometer or thermocouple the change in temperature of a solution during titration, one can approximate roughly the heat effect of a volumetric reaction. Up to the endpoint the temperature changes are proportional to the amount of heat used or liberated by the reaction; from then on the temperature remains nearly constant. This method, worked out by Dutoit and Grobet,[22] gives results of lower accuracy than potentiometric or conductometric titrations, but permits the recognition of small differences in constitution.

Dean and coworkers[23] applied a calorimetric procedure to the determination of sulfate with barium chloride and of chloride with silver nitrate. A thorough investigation of thermometric titration methods was made by Mayr and Fisch.[24] For chloride and sulfate determinations the method appears unsuitable, yet calcium, strontium, mono- or divalent mercury, and lead may be titrated with ammonium oxalate solution. Applications to oxidation-reduction procedures also appear serviceable: Mayr and Fisch titrated hypochlorite and hypobromite, as well as bromate at higher acidity, with arsenious acid. Oxalate, hydrogen peroxide, ferrous sulfate and potassium ferrocyanide could be titrated accurately with permanganate. For details the original publications should be consulted.[25]

Paris[26] studied the heat changes accompanying titrations of heavy metal salts with potassium ferrocyanide in aqueous solution. Breaks in the curves indicated the formation of $Pb_2FeC_6N_6$, $Ag_4FeC_6N_6$,

[21] E. Berl and L. Ranis, *Fortschritte Chem., Physik physik. Chem.*, **19**, 1 (1928); on the refractometric endpoint determination in the titration of oxalic, malonic and other organic acids with lead or mercuric acetates see Mme. G. Allard, *Bull. soc. chim.*, **51**, 372 (1932); *Compt. rend.*, **196**, 937, 1118 (1933).

[22] P. Dutoit and E. Grobet, *J. chim. phys.*, **19**, 324 (1922).

[23] P. M. Dean and O. O. Watts, *J. Am. Chem. Soc.*, **46**, 855 (1924), Dean and E. Newcomber, *ibid.*, **47**, 64 (1925).

[24] C. Mayr and J. Fisch, *Z. anal. Chem.*, **76**, 418 (1929).

[25] See also T. Somiya, *J. Soc. Chem. Ind. (Japan)*, **30**, 106 (1927), *ibid.*, (suppl.) **31**, 74 (1928); **32**, 153 (1929); **33**, 140, 174 (1930); *Proc. Imp. Acad. (Japan)*, **3**, 76, 79 (1927); **5**, 34 (1929); *Chem. News*, **137**, 14 (1928); *J. Soc. Chem. Ind.*, **51**, 135T (1932). Resumés of Somiya's papers are to be found in *Chem. Abst.*, **21**, 1425, 3030 (1927); **23**, 1840, 2907, 4907, 4908 (1929); **24**, 3389, 3915 (1930); **26**, 3200 (1932). *Cf.* R. H. Müller, Ind. Eng. Chem. Anal. Ed., **13**, 671 (1941).

[26] R. Paris, *Compt. rend.*, **199**, 863 (1934); see also P. Mondain-Monval and R. Paris, *ibid.*, **198**, 1154 (1934).

$Ag_3KFeC_6N_6$, $K_2Zn_3(FeC_6N_6)_2$, $Fe_4(FeC_6N_6)_3$, $FeKFeC_6N_6$, and a copper complex whose composition depended upon the order in which the reagents were combined.

(d) *The Viscosimetric Method:* The viscosity of various emulsoids is strongly dependent upon the hydrogen-ion concentration. With albuminous materials it reaches a maximum at the isoelectric point, which is characterized by a certain p_H. This point may therefore be located by viscosity measurements during titration with acid or alkali.[27] For analytical purposes the procedure is of little interest.

(e) *Physiological Methods:* Visual observation of the endpoint, the most generally useful procedure in volumetric analysis, may be classified as physiological in that it is subject to errors caused by defective vision, the personal element, etc. Practically no use is made of the other senses in ascertaining the equivalence-point. Merely for the sake of completeness it may be mentioned that a strong acid can be titrated with alkali until the taste is no longer sour.[28]

(f) *Spectrophotometric Methods; Photoelectric Titrations:* In case one is unable to recognize a color change visually because of an interfering color in the solution, determination of changes in the absorption spectrum can establish the endpoint quite sharply. This procedure has been investigated by Tingle.[29]

A valuable contribution was made by Partridge[30] in the application of photoelectric cells for determination of the endpoint in neutralization analysis. He recommended especially the so-called "photronic" cells,[31] which are commercially available. In reality their action is not electronic, but depends upon the photovoltaic E.M.F. developed, hence Partridge prefers to designate them as "photovoltaic" cells. They have the advantages over photoelectric cells of greater stability and lower resistance; their sensitivity is greatest in the yellow-green portion of the spectrum.

By passing light of controllable intensity through the titration container and thence to the cell, and opposing the output voltage of the latter with a fixed potential, variations in light intensity due to the

[27] *Cf.* J. Loeb, *Proteins and the Theory of Colloidal Behavior*, McGraw-Hill Book Company, New York 1922. For the volumetric application see also L. J. Simon, *Compt. rend.*, **178**, 1076 (1924); **181**, 862 (1925).

[28] T. W. Richards, *Am. Chem. J.*, **20**, 121 (1898).

[29] A. Tingle, *J. Am. Chem. Soc.*, **40**, 873 (1918); see also P. Bruère, *Ann. fals.*, **23**, 68 (1930).

[30] H. M. Partridge, *Electronics*, **1**, 166 (1930); *Ind. Eng. Chem. Anal. Ed.*, **2**, 207 (1930); R. H. Müller and H. M. Partridge, *Ind. Eng. Chem.*, **20**, 423 (1928).

[31] H. M. Partridge, *Ind. Eng. Chem. Anal. Ed.*, **4**, 315 (1932).

color change of the indicator may be measured by a compensation method. Light filters are employed to increase the relative changes in intensity; for example, with phenolphthalein as indicator a green filter is used. If the observed intensity is plotted against the volume of reagent added during titration, the resulting graph shows a nearly straight horizontal line until the indicator just begins to change, then it breaks sharply into a nearly vertical line. Partridge considers the endpoint to be reached at the intersection of these two lines, which is correct in the titration of a strong acid with a strong base with phenolphthalein as indicator. In this method the endpoint corresponds to the first change in the color of the indicator. In some cases this endpoint does not coincide with the equivalence-point, and the occurrence of a titration error should be considered.

Partridge and Smith[32] utilized photovoltaic indication with good results in micro-acidimetric titrations. For details of the apparatus and procedure, reference is made to the original articles.[31,32] Photo-electric titrations with relatively simple and inexpensive apparatus have also been described by Müller[33] and by Russell and Latham.[34]

(g) *The Stalagmometric Method* (*Measurement of Surface Tension*): Solutions of surface-active agents (substances which strongly lower the surface tension of water) are inclined to produce a foam upon shaking. This phenomenon rests upon a marked adsorption of the active agent at the water-air interface. As early as 1841, Clark made an analytical application of it to the determination of the hardness of water; he titrated with a soap solution which yields an insoluble salt with calcium and magnesium. So long as these ions are in excess, any foam produced by shaking breaks up again very quickly; but as soon as excess soap has been added the foam remains. Unfortunately the method is not exact; Schoorl has shown that alkali salts seriously affect the results. Working with a given calcium chloride solution, he obtained the following values expressed in degrees of hardness:

Addition	Hardness found
None	10.4
0.1 per cent KCl	10.0
1 per cent KCl	7.7
1 per cent NaCl	6.0
1 per cent NH$_4$Cl	5.8

[32] H. M. Partridge and R. A. Smith, *Mikrochemie*, **11**, 311 (1932).
[33] F. Müller, *Z. Elektrochem.*, **40**, 46 (1934).
[34] W. W. Russell and D. S. Latham, *Ind. Eng. Chem. Anal. Ed.*, **6**, 463 (1934).

These interesting phenomena have not been explained from the viewpoint of colloid chemistry. Larger amounts of magnesium salts render the method useless. Winkler[35] brought about a distinct improvement by titrating with potassium oleate solution in the presence of considerable Rochelle salt, until on shaking a stable, fine-bubbled foam is produced. Since the titration requires preliminary experience and since simpler and better methods are available, the procedure is now of limited practical importance.

For titration purposes Dubrisay[36] measured the interfacial tension between water and petroleum hydrocarbons. According to Donnan this is greatly diminished by a trace of alkali, if some fatty acid (stearic or oleic) is dissolved in the hydrocarbon. Traube and Somogyi[37] simplified the method and measured the tension at the air-water interface. The principle involved may be illustrated briefly as follows:

Suppose that one has in solution the salt of a weak acid, which in the free state is capillary-active. Upon the addition of a stronger but capillary-inactive acid, some weak acid is liberated and the surface tension is lowered, this diminution proceeding until all of the weak acid has been set free. Conversely, one may use the inactive salt of an active weak base (*e.g.*, quinine hydrochloride). Upon introduction of a stronger base, the surface-active base is displaced with consequent lowering of the surface tension. Thus capillary-active solutions of weak acids or bases can serve as indicators for hydrogen or hydroxyl ions. The great change in surface tension takes place in the p_H region in which the major portion of the active agent is liberated. One may speak of the *transition interval of a capillary-active indicator* just as one does concerning a color indicator.

Traube and Somogyi employed sodium isovalerate as indicator. According to Traube's rule,[38] the effect of organic acids in lowering the surface tension of an aqueous solution increases strongly and regularly with ascent of a homologous series. The rule has been confirmed by Forch[39] for the lower fatty acids between formic and nonylic.

Windisch and Dietrich[40] sought for suitable indicators and recom-

[35] L. W. Winkler, *Z. anal. Chem.*, **53**, 414 (1914).
[36] R. Dubrisay, *Compt. rend.*, **156**, 894, 1902 (1913).
[37] I. Traube and R. Somogyi, *Intern. Z. physik. chem. Biol.*, **1**, 479 (1914).
[38] I. Traube, *Ann.*, **265**, 27 (1891).
[39] C. Forch, *Ann. Physik.*, (4), **17**, 744 (1905).
[40] W. Windisch and W. Dietrich, *Biochem. Z.*, **97**, 135 (1919).

mended sodium undecylate. The indicator solution was prepared by neutralizing 0.0744 g. of undecylic acid with 4 ml. of 0.1 N alkali and diluting to 200 ml. with water. Addition of acid lowered the surface tension sharply. With a visco-stagonometer Windisch and Dietrich determined relative values at 18–20°C., the water value being 114.5 scale divisions per drop. A solution containing 5 ml. of the prepared indicator per 50 ml. of water was treated with 0.1 N hydrochloric acid, drop by drop, and tested with the following results:

Drops of 0.1 N HCl added...........	0	1	2	3
Scale divisions per drop of solution..	113.3	91.2	60.3	51.0

The surface tension, therefore, falls greatly upon addition of a trace of acid. At the third drop there ensues a turbidity of free undecylic acid, which is nearly insoluble (saturated solution about 0.00011 N; visco-stagonometer reading = 64.6 scale divisions per drop). By a series of measurements in phosphate buffer solutions, Windisch and Dietrich demonstrated that the indicator has a definite transition interval.

As the salt of a capillary active base, quinine hydrochloride had been selected for an indicator by Traube and Somogyi.[37] Salts of other bases were investigated by Windisch and Dietrich,[41] who found a sensitive indicator in the dihydrochloride of eucipine (isoamyl hydrocupreine). Yet they observed that it is less pleasant to work with this compound than with the fatty acids. Variable surface tension values are shown and after each addition of reagent one must wait five minutes before the reading can be taken. This precaution is necessary only in the vicinity of the endpoint.

Lottermoser and Schladitz[42] described various acidimetric titrations with sodium oleate as indicator.

Taubmann[43] employed a "capillary-manometric" method for the titration of surface-active acids and bases, applying it especially to the determination of the solubilities of such compounds in water. The theory underlying these titrations is not so simple as Taubmann

---

[41] W. Windisch and W. Dietrich, *Biochem. Z.*, **100**, 130 (1919). The same workers also applied other surface tension indicators in the chemistry of brewing: *Biochem. Z.*, **101**, 82 (1919); **102**, 141 (1920); **103**, 142 (1920); **105**, 96 (1920); **106**, 92 (1920); **107**, 172 (1920). See also Windisch and P. Osswald, *Z. physik. Chem.*, **90**, 172 (1921).

[42] A. Lottermoser and E. Schladitz, *Kolloid-Z.*, **64**, 44 (1933).

[43] A. B. Taubmann, *Z. physik. Chem.*, **A161**, 141 (1932).

and others have assumed. For example, if a capillary-active weak base, whose cation is inactive, is titrated with an acid, then at the equivalence-point some free base will be present as a result of hydrolysis (see page 20). If titration is continued until the surface tension rises to a constant value (that is, until the concentration of free active base is negligibly small), the equivalence-point will have been passed.

It should be remarked also that our knowledge of the analytical characteristics of capillary-active substances is limited. It would be desirable to have a series of indicators with various transition intervals. For this purpose the ionization constants of a number of capillary-active acids and bases should be determined. The most satisfactory concentration of indicator in the solution should also be found.

As yet the relation between surface tension and concentration is not expressed by any formula that is well founded theoretically. As an approximation the equation of Freundlich may be applied:

$$\Delta = \frac{\sigma_0 - \sigma_s}{\sigma_0} = \alpha c^{\frac{1}{n}},$$

in which σ_0 and σ_s are surface tensions of the solvent and of the solution, respectively, α and n are constants for the particular system, and c represents the concentration. The variation of the relative surface tension lowering (Δ) with concentration is therefore greatest in very dilute solutions. It stands to reason that the "sensitivity" of an indicator for hydrogen ions may be shifted by suitable changes in the indicator concentration. For practical purposes it would be necessary to ascertain under what conditions a maximum change in Δ (for a given addition of reagent) corresponds to the equivalence-point.

On the experimental side one must take into account the fact that the surface tension of a capillary-active solution does not at once become constant, but drops gradually and in some cases passes through a minimum.[44] There may also be difficulties caused by the interference of surface-active impurities, in physiological fluids for example. At best, capillarity procedures are tedious due to the lack

[44] Concerning nonylic acid see W. D. Harkins and H. H. King, *Kansas State Agr. Coll. Publ.*, **1920**; sodium palmitate, R. E. Wilson and E. D. Ries, *Colloid Symposium Monograph*, **1**, 163 (1923); S. L. Bigelow and E. R. Washburn, *J. Phys. Chem.*, **32**, 321 (1928).

of simple and rapid methods for measuring surface tension during the course of a titration. Hence they are not likely to be adopted except for certain special purposes.

It is the hope of the authors that the foregoing considerations have made clear the more important theoretical principles of volumetric analysis. Upon these principles will be based the second volume of this text (to which frequent reference has already been made), dealing with the practical performance of titration methods. Various details of the procedures, which here could be mentioned only briefly or not at all, will there be discussed more extensively.

APPENDIX

TABLE I
ACTIVITY PRODUCT OF WATER AT VARIOUS TEMPERATURES
$$K_{a_w} = (aH^+)(aOH^-)$$

°C.	K_{a_w}	$p_{K_{a_w}}$	°C.	K_{a_w}	$p_{K_{a_w}}$
10	3.0×10^{-15}	14.52	50	8.0×10^{-14}	13.10
15	4.7×10^{-15}	14.33	70	2.12×10^{-13}	12.67
20	7.2×10^{-15}	14.14	80	3.5×10^{-13}	12.46
25	1.05×10^{-14}	13.98	90	5.3×10^{-13}	12.28
30	1.55×10^{-14}	13.81	100	7.3×10^{-13}	12.14

ACTIVITY CONSTANTS AND CONCENTRATION CONSTANTS

Equilibrium constants are true constants only if the concentrations of reactants and reaction products are expressed as activities. For an uncharged acid HA one has:

$$\frac{(aH^+)(aA^-)}{(aHA)} = K_a, \tag{1}$$

in which "a" denotes the activity of the particular ionic or molecular component. Between the activity and the concentration of a component A there exists the relation $a_A = c_A f_A$, in which f_A is the activity coefficient. The latter is taken to be unity at an ionic strength of zero (infinitely dilute solution). With increasing ionic strength the activity coefficient of an ion decreases, in many cases reaching a minimum at a certain strength. For practical purposes one may assume that the activity coefficient of an uncharged compound remains unity up to an ionic strength of 0.1. The ionic strength μ as defined by G. N. Lewis is calculated from the following expression:

$$\mu = \frac{c_1 z_1^2 + c_2 z_2^2 + \cdots c_n z_n^2}{2} = \sum \frac{cz^2}{2}. \tag{2}$$

Here c represents the concentration and z the valence of each kind of ion in the solution.

Equation (1) can also be written in the form:

$$K_a = \frac{[H^+][A^-]}{[HA]} \times \frac{f_{H^+} f_{A^-}}{f_{HA}} = K_c \frac{f_{H^+} f_{A^-}}{f_{HA}}. \tag{3}$$

Similarly for the second ionization constant of an uncharged dibasic acid:

$$K_{2a} = \frac{(aH^+)(aA^=)}{(aHA^-)} = \frac{[H^+][A^=]}{[HA^-]} \times \frac{f_{H^+}f_{A^=}}{f_{HA^-}} = K_{2c}\frac{f_{H^+}f_{A^=}}{f_{HA^-}}. \tag{4}$$

In these equations K_c and K_{2c} represent the "concentration constants." These are not truly constant, but change with the ionic strength:

$$K_c = K_a \frac{f_{HA}}{f_{H^+}f_{A^-}}. \tag{5}$$

As the activity coefficients of ions decrease upon going from an ionic strength of zero to, say, 0.1, it is evident that K_c increases. The change in ionic strength is greatly dependent upon the valence of the ion. For practical calculations one may use the following approximate values of the activity coefficient for ions of various valence, when the ionic strength is 0.1 or less:

Valence of ion	Activity coefficient of ion at the indicated ionic strength				
	0	0.005	0.01	0.05	0.1
1	1	0.95	0.93	0.85	0.80
2	1	0.80	0.74	0.56	0.46
3	1	0.62	0.52	0.28	0.20
4	1	0.43	0.32	0.11	0.06

Hence, for the concentration constant of an uncharged monobasic acid (or for the first concentration constant of an uncharged polybasic acid) at an ionic strength of 0.1, one finds:

$$K_c = K_a \frac{1}{0.80^2} = 1.56\ K_a.$$

Similarly for the second constant:

$$K_{2c} = K_{2a} \frac{0.80}{0.80 \times 0.46} = 2.17\ K_{2a}.$$

Illustration: Find $[H^+]$, p_H, (aH^+) and p_{aH} in 0.1 M potassium biphthalate. The ionic strength of this solution is 0.1, so that the constants have the same ratios as shown above. From equation (45), page 27, $[H^+] = \sqrt{K_1 K_2}$, in which K_1 and K_2 represent concentration constants. Therefore:

$$[H^+] = \sqrt{K_{1a}K_{2a} \times 1.56 \times 2.17}.$$

According to Table II, $K_{1a} = 1.3 \times 10^{-3}$ and $K_{2a} = 3.9 \times 10^{-6}$:

$$[H^+] = 1.31 \times 10^{-4},$$

$$p_H = 3.88.$$

(Had the p_H been calculated from activity constants without correction for the effect of ionic strength, the value found would have been 4.15 instead of 3.88.)

$$(aH^+) = [H] \times f_{H^+} = 1.31 \times 10^{-4} \times 0.80 = 1.05 \times 10^{-4},$$

$$p_{aH} = 3.98.$$

Measurements with the hydrogen electrode, which yield values of p_{aH} rather than p_H, indicate that the p_{aH} is 3.96. This example shows that the approximate values for activity coefficients listed above can be of good service for the calculation of (aH^+) and $[H^+]$ at ionic strengths up to 0.1. At higher strengths the differences between individual ions become too great to allow the use of average values; in fact, a value of 0.86 is better than 0.80 for the activity coefficient of ions in 0.1 M potassium biphthalate solution.

TABLE II

IONIZATION CONSTANTS OF SOME ACIDS AND BASES AT 25°C.

Figures in italics are activity constants (ionic strength of zero)

$$p_{K_a} = -\log K_a$$

Acid			K_a	p_{K_a}
INORGANIC ACIDS				
Arsenic acid		K_1	5 × 10⁻³	2.30
		K_2	8.3 × 10⁻⁸	7.08
Arsenious acid		K_1	6.0 × 10⁻¹⁰	9.22
Boric acid		K_1	*5.8 × 10⁻¹⁰*	*9.24*
Carbonic acid		K_1	*4.3 × 10⁻⁷*	*6.37*
		K_2	*5.6 × 10⁻¹¹*	*10.25*
Chromic acid[1]		K_2	*3.2 × 10⁻⁷*	*6.49*
Hydrazoic acid			2.6 × 10⁻⁵	4.59
Hydrofluoric acid			*7.2 × 10⁻⁴*	*3.14*
Hydrogen sulfide		K_1	5.7 × 10⁻⁸	7.24
		K_2	1.2 × 10⁻¹⁵	14.92
Hypochlorous acid			3.5 × 10⁻⁸	7.46
Iodic acid			*1.67 × 10⁻¹*	*0.78*
Nitrous acid			4 × 10⁻⁴	3.40
Periodic acid			2.3 × 10⁻²	1.64
Phosphoric acid		K_1	*7.5 × 10⁻³*	*2.13*
		K_2	*6.2 × 10⁻⁸*	*7.21*
		K_3	*4.8 × 10⁻¹³*	*12.32*
Phosphorous acid		K_1	1.6 × 10⁻²	1.80
		K_2	7 × 10⁻⁷	6.15
Pyrophosphoric acid		K_1	1.4 × 10⁻¹	0.85
		K_2	1.1 × 10⁻²	1.96
		K_3	*2.1 × 10⁻⁷*	*6.68*
		K_4	*4.06 × 10⁻¹⁰*	*9.39*
Selenious acid		K_1	3 × 10⁻³	2.52
		K_2	5 × 10⁻⁸	7.30
Silicic acid		K_1	2 × 10⁻¹⁰	9.7 (approx.)
Sulfuric acid		K_2	*1.2 × 10⁻²*	*1.92*
Sulfurous acid		K_1	*1.72 × 10⁻²*	*1.76*
		K_2	*6.24 × 10⁻⁸*	*7.21*
ORGANIC ACIDS				
Aliphatic				
Acetic acid			1.75 × 10⁻⁵	4.76
Alanine			1.9 × 10⁻¹⁰	9.72

[1] According to J. D. Neuss and W. Rieman, *J. Am. Chem. Soc.*, **56**, 2238 (1934), the constant $\dfrac{[HCrO_4^-]^2}{[Cr_2O_7^-]}$ is equal to 0.023.

TABLE II—*Continued*

Acid		K_a	p_{K_a}
		ORGANIC ACIDS	
		Aliphatic	
Citric acid..................	K_1	8.7×10^{-4}	3.06
	K_2	1.8×10^{-5}	4.74
	K_3	4.0×10^{-6}	5.40
Dichloroacetic acid...........		5×10^{-2}	1.30
Formic acid..................		1.77×10^{-4}	3.75
Fumaric acid................	K_1	9.3×10^{-4}	3.03
	K_2	3.4×10^{-5}	4.47
Glycerophosphoric acid......	K_1	3.4×10^{-2}	1.47
	K_2	6.4×10^{-7}	6.19
Glycine......................		1.67×10^{-10}	9.78
Glycolic acid.................		1.52×10^{-4}	3.82
Hydrocyanic acid.............		7.2×10^{-10}	9.14
Lactic acid...................		1.4×10^{-4}	3.85
Maleic acid..................	K_1	1.0×10^{-2}	2.00
	K_2	5.5×10^{-7}	6.26
Malic acid...................	K_1	4×10^{-4}	3.40
	K_2	9×10^{-6}	5.05
Malonic acid.................	K_1	1.6×10^{-3}	2.80
	K_2	8.0×10^{-7}	6.10
Monochloroacetic acid........		1.5×10^{-3}	2.82
Oxalic acid..................	K_1	6.5×10^{-2}	1.19
	K_2	6.1×10^{-5}	4.21
Succinic acid................	K_1	6.4×10^{-5}	4.19
	K_2	2.7×10^{-6}	5.57
Tartaric acid................	K_1	9.6×10^{-4}	3.02
	K_2	2.9×10^{-5}	4.54
Trichloroacetic acid..........		1.3×10^{-1}	0.89
		Aromatic and Cyclic	
Benzoic acid.................		6.3×10^{-5}	4.20
Camphoric acid..............	K_1	2.7×10^{-5}	4.57
	K_2	8×10^{-6}	5.10
Cinnamic acid................		3.7×10^{-5}	4.43
Diethylbarbituric acid........		3.7×10^{-8}	7.43
Dinitro-*o*-cresol..............		4.5×10^{-5}	4.35
Gallic acid...................		4×10^{-5}	4.4
Hippuric acid................		2.3×10^{-4}	3.64
p-Hydroxybenzoic acid.......	K_1	3.3×10^{-5}	4.48
	K_2	4.0×10^{-10}	9.40
Phenol......................		1.3×10^{-10}	9.89

TABLE II—*Continued*

Acid		K_a	p_{K_a}
Aromatic and Cyclic			
o-Phthalic acid............	K_1	1.3×10^{-3}	2.89
	K_2	3.9×10^{-6}	5.41
Picric acid..................		4.2×10^{-1}	0.38
Saccharin..................	K_1	2.5×10^{-2}	1.40
Salicylic acid.............	K_1	1.06×10^{-3}	2.98
	K_2	3.6×10^{-14}	13.44
Sulfanilic acid..		6.5×10^{-4}	3.19
Uric acid..................		1.3×10^{-4}	3.89

Base		K_b	p_{K_b}
INORGANIC BASES			
Ammonium hydroxide..........		1.75×10^{-5}	4.76
Lead hydroxide...............		9.6×10^{-4}	3.02
Hydrazine....................		3×10^{-6}	5.52
Hydroxylamine...............		1.07×10^{-8}	7.97
Zinc hydroxide................	K_2	4.4×10^{-5}	4.36
ORGANIC BASES			
Aliphatic			
Butylamine (normal)..........		4.1×10^{-4}	3.39
Diethylamine.................		1.26×10^{-3}	2.90
Dimethylamine...............		5.12×10^{-4}	3.29
Ethylamine..................		5.6×10^{-4}	3.25
Ethylenediamine.............		8.5×10^{-5}	4.07
Glycine.....................		2.26×10^{-12}	11.65
Methylamine.................		4.38×10^{-4}	3.36
Monoethanolamine............		2.77×10^{-5}	4.56
Triethylamine................		5.65×10^{-4}	3.25
Trimethylamine..............		5.27×10^{-5}	4.28
Urea........................		1.5×10^{-14}	13.82
Aromatic			
Aniline.....................		3.82×10^{-10}	9.42
Benzidine...................	K_1	9.3×10^{-10}	9.03
	K_2	5.6×10^{-11}	10.25
Naphthylamine (α)..........		8.36×10^{-11}	10.08
Naphthylamine (β)...........		1.29×10^{-10}	9.89
Novocain....................		7×10^{-6}	5.15
p-Phenetidine...............		2.2×10^{-9}	8.66
p-Phenylenediamine..........	K_1	1.1×10^{-8}	7.96
	K_2	3.5×10^{-12}	11.46

TABLE II—*Concluded*

Base			K_b	p_{K_b}
Heterocyclic[2]				
Aconitine....................			1.3×10^{-6}	5.89
Apomorphine.................			1.0×10^{-7}	7.00
Brucine....................	K_1		9×10^{-7}	6.05
	K_2		2×10^{-12}	11.7
Cinchonidine...............	K_1		1.6×10^{-6}	5.80
	K_2		8.4×10^{-11}	10.08
Cinchonine.................	K_1		1.4×10^{-6}	5.85
	K_2		1.1×10^{-10}	9.96
Cocaine....................			2.6×10^{-6}	5.6
Codeine....................			9×10^{-7}	6.05
Colchicine.................			4.5×10^{-13}	12.35
Coniine....................			1×10^{-3}	3.0
Dimethylaminoantipyrine......			6.9×10^{-10}	9.16
Emetine....................	K_1		1.7×10^{-6}	5.77
	K_2		2.3×10^{-7}	6.64
Hydrastine.................			1.7×10^{-8}	7.77
Hydroquinine...............			4.7×10^{-6}	5.33
Morphine...................			7.4×10^{-7}	6.13
Narceine...................			2×10^{-11}	10.7
Narcotine..................			1.5×10^{-8}	7.82
Nicotine...................	K_1		7×10^{-7}	6.15
	K_2		1.4×10^{-11}	10.85
Papaverine.................			8×10^{-9}	8.1
Physostigmine..............	K_1		7.6×10^{-7}	6.12
	K_2		5.7×10^{-13}	12.24
Pilocarpine................	K_1		7×10^{-8}	7.15
	K_2		2×10^{-13}	12.7
Piperazine.................	K_1		6.4×10^{-5}	4.19
	K_2		3.7×10^{-9}	8.43
Piperidine.................			1.6×10^{-3}	2.80
Piperine...................			1.0×10^{-14}	14.0
Pyridine...................			1.4×10^{-9}	8.85
Quinidine..................	K_1		3.5×10^{-6}	5.46
	K_2		1×10^{-10}	10.0
Quinine....................	K_1		1×10^{-6}	6.0
	K_2		1.3×10^{-10}	9.89
Quinoline..................			6.3×10^{-10}	9.20
Solanine...................			2.2×10^{-7}	6.66
Sparteine..................	K_1		5.7×10^{-3}	2.24
	K_2		1×10^{-6}	6.0
Strychnine.................	K_1		1×10^{-6}	6.0
	K_2		2×10^{-12}	11.7
Thebaine...................			9×10^{-7}	6.05
Veratrine..................			7×10^{-6}	5.15

[2] Constants for a number of less common alkaloids are given by N. Schoorl, *Pharm. Weekblad.*, **76**, 1497, 1513 (1939); see *Chem. Abstr.*, **34**, 1900, 2136 (1940).

TABLE III

SOLUBILITY PRODUCTS, S, OF VARIOUS SALTS AT ABOUT 25°C.

Salt	S	$p_S = -\log S$
Barium carbonate	4.9×10^{-9}	8.31
Barium chromate	2×10^{-10}	9.7
Barium fluoride	1.7×10^{-6}	5.77
Barium iodate	1.25×10^{-9}	8.90
Barium manganate	2.5×10^{-10}	9.60
Barium oxalate	1.7×10^{-7}	6.77
Barium sulfate	1×10^{-10}	10.0
Cadmium carbonate	2.5×10^{-14}	13.6
Cadmium oxalate	2.8×10^{-8}	7.55
Cadmium sulfide	1.4×10^{-28}	27.85
Calcium carbonate	4.8×10^{-9}	8.32
Calcium fluoride	3.9×10^{-11}	10.41
Calcium iodate	1.9×10^{-6}	5.72
Calcium oxalate	2.3×10^{-9}	8.64
Calcium sulfate	6.1×10^{-5}	4.22
Calcium tartrate	7.7×10^{-7}	6.11
Cerous iodate	3.5×10^{-10}	9.46
Cerous oxalate	2.6×10^{-29}	28.39
Cerous tartrate	9.7×10^{-20}	19.01
Cupric iodate	1.4×10^{-7}	6.85
Cupric oxalate	2.9×10^{-8}	7.54
Cupric sulfide	8.5×10^{-45}	44.07
Cuprous bromide	5.3×10^{-9}	8.28
Cuprous chloride	1.8×10^{-7}	6.74
Cuprous iodide	1.1×10^{-12}	11.96
Cuprous sulfide	2.5×10^{-50}	49.6
Cuprous thiocyanate	4×10^{-14}	13.4
Ferric hydroxide	3.8×10^{-38}	37.42
Ferrous hydroxide	4.8×10^{-16}	15.32
Ferrous sulfide	4×10^{-19}	18.4
Lanthanum iodate	5.9×10^{-10}	9.23
Lanthanum oxalate	2×10^{-28}	27.7
Lanthanum tartrate	2×10^{-19}	18.7
Lead carbonate	1.5×10^{-13}	12.82
Lead chromate	1.8×10^{-14}	13.74
Lead fluoride	3.7×10^{-8}	7.43

TABLE III —*Continued*

Salt	S		$p = -\log S$
Lead iodate............................	3	$\times 10^{-13}$	12.5
Lead iodide............................	8.7	$\times 10^{-9}$	8.06
Lead oxalate...........................	3.4	$\times 10^{-11}$	10.47
Lead sulfate...........................	2.25	$\times 10^{-8}$	7.65
Lead sulfide...........................	1	$\times 10^{-29}$	29.0
Magnesium ammonium phosphate...........	2.5	$\times 10^{-13}$	12.6
Magnesium carbonate....................	1	$\times 10^{-5}$	5.0
Magnesium fluoride.....................	7	$\times 10^{-9}$	8.16
Magnesium hydroxide....................	1.2	$\times 10^{-11}$	10.92
Magnesium oxalate......................	8.6	$\times 10^{-5}$	4.07
Mercuric hydroxide.....................	1.4	$\times 10^{-26}$	25.85
Mercuric sulfide.......................	4	$\times 10^{-53}$	52.4
Mercurous bromide......................	5.2	$\times 10^{-23}$	22.28
Mercurous chloride.....................	1.1	$\times 10^{-18}$	17.96
Mercurous iodate.......................	3	$\times 10^{-20}$	19.5
Mercurous iodide.......................	4.5	$\times 10^{-29}$	28.35
Mercurous oxalate......................	1	$\times 10^{-13}$	13.0
Potassium bitartrate....................	3	$\times 10^{-4}$	3.5
Potassium perchlorate...................	1.07	$\times 10^{-2}$	1.97
Potassium chloroplatinate...............	1.1	$\times 10^{-5}$	4.96
Silver benzoate........................	9.3	$\times 10^{-5}$	4.03
Silver bromate.........................	5	$\times 10^{-5}$	4.3
Silver bromide.........................	3.3	$\times 10^{-13}$	12.48
Silver carbonate.......................	8.2	$\times 10^{-12}$	11.09
Silver chloride........................	1.7	$\times 10^{-10}$	9.77
Silver chromate........................	1.1	$\times 10^{-12}$	11.96
Silver cyanide.........................	2	$\times 10^{-12}$	11.7
Silver dichromate......................	2	$\times 10^{-7}$	6.7
Silver ferrocyanide....................	1.5	$\times 10^{-41}$	40.8
Silver hydroxide.......................	2	$\times 10^{-8}$	7.7
Silver iodate..........................	5.3	$\times 10^{-8}$	7.28
Silver iodide..........................	1	$\times 10^{-16}$	16.0
Silver nitroprusside...................	7.8	$\times 10^{-13}$	12.11
Silver oxalate.........................	1.1	$\times 10^{-11}$	10.96
Silver salicylate......................	1.4	$\times 10^{-5}$	4.85
Silver sulfide.........................	1.6	$\times 10^{-49}$	48.8
Silver thiocyanate.....................	3	$\times 10^{-12}$	11.5
Silver valerate........................	8	$\times 10^{-5}$	4.1

TABLE III—*Concluded*

Salt	S	$p_S = -\log S$
Strontium carbonate	1.6×10^{-9}	8.80
Strontium fluoride	3×10^{-9}	8.5
Strontium oxalate	5×10^{-8}	7.3
Strontium sulfate	2.8×10^{-7}	6.55
Thallous bromate	3.9×10^{-4}	3.41
Thallous bromide	3.6×10^{-6}	5.44
Thallous chloride	1.5×10^{-4}	3.82
Thallous iodate	4.5×10^{-6}	5.35
Thallous iodide	5.8×10^{-8}	7.24
Thallous sulfide	4.5×10^{-23}	22.35
Zinc hydroxide	1×10^{-17}	17.0
Zinc oxalate	7.5×10^{-9}	8.12
Zinc sulfide	4.5×10^{-24}	23.35

TABLE IV

SOLUBILITY PRODUCTS OF VARIOUS ALKALOIDS
(From Biochem. Z. **162**, 289 (1925)).

Compound	S	p_S
Aconitine	5×10^{-10}	9.3
Apomorphine	4×10^{-11}	10.4
Atropine	2.5×10^{-7}	6.6
Brucine	1.2×10^{-9}	8.92
Cocaine	1×10^{-8}	8.0
Cinchonidine	1.4×10^{-9}	8.85
Cinchonine	6×10^{-11}	10.22
Emetine	3.75×10^{-9}	8.43
Hydrastine	1.4×10^{-11}	10.85
Hydroquinine	5×10^{-9}	8.3
Morphine	3.1×10^{-10}	9.51
Narceine	2.6×10^{-14}	13.49
Narcotine	6×10^{-13}	12.22
Quinidine	2.5×10^{-9}	8.6
Quinine	4.5×10^{-9}	8.35
Solanine	6.4×10^{-12}	11.19
Strychnine	4×10^{-10}	9.4
Thebaine	2×10^{-9}	8.7
Tropacocaine	8×10^{-8}	7.1
Veratrine	6×10^{-8}	7.22

TABLE V
Dissociation Constants of Several Complex Ions

$$\frac{[Ag^+][NH_3]^2}{[Ag(NH_3)_2^+]} = 6.8 \times 10^{-8}$$

$$\frac{[Ag^+][NO_2^-]^2}{[Ag(NO_2)_2^-]} = 1.5 \times 10^{-3}$$

$$\frac{[Ag^+][S_2O_3^-]}{[AgS_2O_3^-]} = 1 \times 10^{-13}$$

$$\frac{[Ag^+][CN^-]^2}{[Ag(CN)_2^-]} = 1 \times 10^{-21}$$

$$\frac{[Cd^{++}][NH_3]^4}{[Cd(NH_3)_4^{++}]} = 2.5 \times 10^{-7}$$

$$\frac{[Cd^{++}][CN^-]^4}{[Cd(CN)_4^-]} = 1.4 \times 10^{-17}$$

$$\frac{[Co^{+++}][NH_3]^6}{[Co(NH_3)_6^{+++}]} = 2.2 \times 10^{-34}$$

$$\frac{[Cu^{++}][NH_3]^4}{[Cu(NH_3)_4^{++}]} = 4.6 \times 10^{-14}$$

$$\frac{[Cu^{++}][CN^-]^4}{[Cu(CN)_4^-]} = 5 \times 10^{-28}$$

$$\frac{[Hg^{++}][Br^-]^4}{[HgBr_4^-]} = 2.2 \times 10^{-22}$$

$$\frac{[Hg^{++}][Cl^-]^4}{[HgCl_4^-]} = 6 \times 10^{-17}$$

$$\frac{[HgCl_2][Cl^-]^2}{[HgCl_4^-]} = 1 \times 10^{-2}$$

$$\frac{[Hg^{++}][I^-]^4}{[HgI_4^-]} = 5 \times 10^{-31}$$

$$\frac{[Hg^{++}][CN^-]^4}{[Hg(CN)_4^-]} = 4 \times 10^{-41}$$

$$\frac{[Hg^{++}][SCN^-]^4}{[Hg(SCN)_4^-]} = 1 \times 10^{-22}$$

$$\frac{[Zn^{++}][NH_3]^4}{[Zn(NH_3)_4^{++}]} = 1 \times 10^{-9}$$

$$\frac{[Zn^{++}][CN^-]^4}{[Zn(CN)_4^-]} = 2 \times 10^{-17}$$

TABLE VI

OXIDATION POTENTIALS (REFERRED TO THE NORMAL HYDROGEN ELECTRODE)
OF SOME SYSTEMS WHICH ARE OF INTEREST IN VOLUMETRIC ANALYSIS

Reaction	π in Volts
$Mg \rightleftarrows Mg^{++} + 2e$	-2.4
$Al \rightleftarrows Al^{+++} + 3e$	-1.7
$Zn \rightleftarrows Zn^{++} + 2e$	-0.76
$S^- + Hg \rightleftarrows HgS + 2e$	-0.70
$Cr \rightleftarrows Cr^{++} + 2e$	-0.6
$2CN^- + Au \rightleftarrows Au(CN)_2^- + e$	-0.60
$Fe \rightleftarrows Fe^{++} + 2e$	-0.43
$Eu^{++} \rightleftarrows Eu^{+++} + e$	-0.43
$Cr^{++} \rightleftarrows Cr^{+++} + e$	-0.41
$Cd \rightleftarrows Cd^{++} + 2e$	-0.40
$Cb^{III} \rightleftarrows Cb^V + 2e$ (in 3M H_2SO_4)	-0.37
$H_2Se \rightleftarrows Se + 2H^+ + 2e$	-0.36
$2Cu + 2OH^- \rightleftarrows Cu_2O + H_2O + 2e$	-0.35
$Tl \rightleftarrows Tl^+ + e$	-0.34
$Ag + 2CN^- \rightleftarrows Ag(CN)_2^- + e$	-0.29
$Co \rightleftarrows Co^{++} + 2e$	-0.28
$Ni \rightleftarrows Ni^{++} + 2e$	-0.25
$V^{++} \rightleftarrows V^{+++} + e$	-0.2
$Cu + I^- \rightleftarrows CuI + e$	-0.19
$Ag + I^- \rightleftarrows AgI + e$	-0.15
$Sn \rightleftarrows Sn^{++} + 2e$	-0.14
$Pb \rightleftarrows Pb^{++} + 2e$	-0.13
$H_2 \rightleftarrows 2H^+ + 2e$	0.00
$Ti^{+++} + H_2O \rightleftarrows TiO^{++} + 2H^+ + e$	$+0.10$
$2S_2O_3^- \rightleftarrows S_4O_6^- + 2e$	$+0.1$
$Sn^{++} \rightleftarrows Sn^{++++} + 2e$	$+0.15$
$Re + 4H_2O \rightleftarrows ReO_4^- + 8H^+ + 7e$	$+0.15$
$Cu^+ \rightleftarrows Cu^{++} + e$	$+0.17$
$2Hg + 2Cl^- \rightleftarrows Hg_2Cl_2 + 2e$	$+0.27$
$V^{+++} + H_2O \rightleftarrows VO^{++} + 2H^+ + e$	$+0.31$
$2Ag + 2OH^- \rightleftarrows Ag_2O + H_2O + 2e$	$+0.35$
$Fe(CN)_6^{----} \rightleftarrows Fe(CN)_6^{---} + e$	$+0.36$
$4OH^- \rightleftarrows O_2 + 2H_2O + 4e$	$+0.41$
$AsO_3^{---} + H_2O \rightleftarrows AsO_4^{---} + 2H^+ + 2e$	$+0.49$
$Cu \rightleftarrows Cu^+ + e$	$+0.52$
$2I^- \rightleftarrows I_2 + 2e$	$+0.53$
$MnO_4^- \rightleftarrows MnO_4^- + e$	$+0.54$
$2SbO^+ + 3H_2O \rightleftarrows Sb_2O_5 + 6H^+ + 4e$	$+0.64$
$H_2O_2 \rightleftarrows O_2 + 2H^+ + 2e$	$+0.68$
$Mo(CN)_6^{----} \rightleftarrows Mo(CN)_6^{---} + e$	$+0.73$
$Se + 3H_2O \rightleftarrows H_2SeO_3 + 4H^+ + 4e$	$+0.74$

TABLE VI—*Concluded*

Reaction	π in Volts
$Fe^{++} \rightleftarrows Fe^{+++} + e$	+0.76
$2Hg \rightleftarrows Hg_2^{++} + 2e$	+0.80
$Ag \rightleftarrows Ag^+ + e$	+0.80
$Os + 4H_2O \rightleftarrows OsO_4 + 8H^+ + 8e$	+0.85
$Hg \rightleftarrows Hg^{++} + 2e$	+0.85
$3OH^- \rightleftarrows HO_2^- + H_2O + 2e$	+0.87
$Hg_2^{++} \rightleftarrows 2Hg^{++} + 2e$	+0.91
$NO + 2H_2O \rightleftarrows NO_3^- + 4H^+ + 3e$	+0.99
$VO^{++} + 3H_2O \rightleftarrows V(OH)_4^+ + 2H^+ + e$	+1.00
$TeO_2 + 4H_2O \rightleftarrows H_6TeO_6 + 2H^+ + 2e$	+1.02
$2Br^- \rightleftarrows Br_2 + 2e$	+1.09
$\frac{1}{2}I_2 + 3H_2O \rightleftarrows IO_3^- + 6H^+ + 5e$	+1.20
$Pt \rightleftarrows Pt^{++} + 2e$	+1.2
$2H_2O \rightleftarrows O_2 + 4H^+ + 4e$	+1.23
$Mn^{++} + 2H_2O \rightleftarrows MnO_2 + 4H^+ + 2e$	+1.24
$Tl^+ \rightleftarrows Tl^{+++} + 2e$	+1.25
$Au^+ \rightleftarrows Au^{+++} + 2e$	+1.29
$PdCl_4^- + 2Cl^- \rightleftarrows PdCl_6^- + 2e$	+1.29
$2Cr^{+++} + 7H_2O \rightleftarrows Cr_2O_7^- + 14H^+ + 6e$	+1.36
$2Cl^- \rightleftarrows Cl_2 + 2e$	+1.36
$Cl^- + 3H_2O \rightleftarrows ClO_3^- + 6H^+ + 6e$	+1.44
$Pb^{++} + 2H_2O \rightleftarrows PbO_2 + 4H^+ + 2e$	+1.46
$Mn^{++} \rightleftarrows Mn^{+++} + e$	+1.51
$IO_3^- + H_2O \rightleftarrows IO_4^- + 2H^+ + 2e$	+1.51
$Mn^{++} + 4H_2O \rightleftarrows MnO_4^- + 8H^+ + 5e$	+1.52
$\frac{1}{2}Br_2 + 3H_2O \rightleftarrows BrO_3^- + 6H^+ + 5e$	+1.52
$MnO_2 + 2H_2O \rightleftarrows MnO_4^- + 4H^+ + 3e$	+1.59
$Ce^{+++} \rightleftarrows Ce^{++++} + e$	+1.60
$Pb^{++} \rightleftarrows Pb^{++++} + 2e$	+1.69
$Co^{++} \rightleftarrows Co^{+++} + e$	+1.84
$Ag^+ \rightleftarrows Ag^{+++} + 2e$	+1.98

TABLE VII
Properties of Certain Solvents

Compound	Molecular Weight	Dielectric Constant[1] (approx. 20°C.)	Refractive Index (approx. 20°C.)	Density (g. per ml., 20°C.)	$\frac{\Delta V}{\Delta t} \times \frac{1000}{V}$ [2]
Water	18.02	80.	1.333	0.997	0.23
Sulfuric acid	98.08	>84.	1.429	1.834	0.6
Acetic acid	60.05	9.5	1.372	1.049	1.1
Methanol	32.04	32.3	1.329	0.792	1.2
Ethanol	46.07	25.0	1.362	0.789	1.1
i-Propanol	60.09	18.6	1.377	0.785	1.1
n-Butanol	74.12	7.8	1.399	0.810	0.9
Ethylene glycol	62.07	38.6	1.427	1.115	0.6
Cyclohexanol	100.16	10.	1.465	0.962	0.8
Benzyl alcohol	108.13	11.	1.539	1.045	0.7
Acetone	58.08	21.4	1.359	0.791	1.5
Ethyl ether	74.12	4.3	1.354	0.714	1.6
Ethyl acetate	88.10	6.4	1.372	0.901	1.3
1,4-Dioxane	88.10	2.3	1.422	1.033	1.1
Furfural	96.08	39.	1.526	1.160	0.9
Monoethanolamine	61.08		1.454	1.018	
n-Butylamine	73.14	5.4	1.401	0.740	1.2
Aniline	93.12	7.2	1.586	1.022	0.9
Pyridine	79.10	12.5	1.509	0.982	1.1
n-Hexane	86.17	1.9	1.375	0.660	1.3
Carbon tetrachloride	153.84	2.2	1.461	1.595	1.2
Chloroform[3]	119.39	5.1	1.446	1.489	1.3
Ethylene dichloride	98.97	10.5	1.444	1.257	1.1
Benzene	78.11	2.3	1.501	0.879	1.1
Toluene	92.13	2.4	1.497	0.866	1.1
Monochlorobenzene	112.56	5.7	1.525	1.106	0.9
o-Dichlorobenzene	147.01	7.5	1.552	1.305	0.9
Nitrobenzene	123.11	35.7	1.553	1.203	0.8

[1] In general, these dielectric constants refer to measurements at high wave-lengths.

[2] These "expansion coefficients" represent the relative volume change, in parts per thousand, produced by a variation of one degree Centigrade in the region near room temperature.

[3] Chloroform generally contains 0.5 per cent ethanol as a stabilizer.

TABLE VII—*Concluded*

Compound	Freezing Point (°C.)	Boiling Point (°C.)	Vapor Pressure (cm. Hg)	Viscosity (centipoises, 20°C.)	Surface Tension (dynes per cm.)	Solubility in water, (g. per 100 ml.)
Water..............	0.0	100.0	2.37^{25}	1.008	72.0^{25}	....
Sulfuric acid......	10.5	(330.)	$<0.0001^{25}$	23.	$(55.)^{20}$	∞
Acetic acid........	16.6	118.1	1.5^{25}	1.2	27.2^{25}	∞
Methanol..........	−97.8	64.6	12.2^{25}	0.59	22.1^{25}	∞
Ethanol...........	−117.3	78.3	5.9^{25}	1.20	21.9^{25}	∞
i-Propanol........	−88.5	82.3		2.3	21.7^{20}	∞
n-Butanol.........	−89.5	117.7	0.64^{25}	2.9	24.6^{20}	7.9^{20}
Ethylene glycol...	−17.4	197.2		16.	47.7^{20}	∞
Cyclohexanol......	24.	161.5		49.	34.2^{15}	5.7^{15}
Benzyl alcohol....	−15.3	203.9	0.1^{60}	5.6	39.0^{20}	$4.^{17}$
Acetone...........	−95.	56.1	22.9^{25}	0.33	23.7^{20}	· ∞
Ethyl ether.......	−116.	34.6	53.7^{25}	0.24	17.0^{20}	7.5^{20}
Ethyl acetate.....	−83.6	77.1	7.3^{20}	0.45	23.1^{25}	8.6^{20}
1,4-Dioxane.......	11.7	100.3	2.7^{20}	1.25	35.4^{20}	∞
Furfural..........	−36.5	161.7	2.5^{72}	1.7	43.5^{20}	8.3^{20}
Monoethanol-amine..........	10.5	172.2				∞
n-Butylamine.....	−50.5	77.8		0.7	21.6^{20}	∞
Aniline...........	−6.2	184.4	0.24^{50}	4.5	42.9^{20}	3.4^{20}
Pyridine..........	−42.	115.3		0.9	38.0^{20}	∞
n-Hexane..........	−94.	69.0	15.1^{25}	0.32	18.4^{20}	0.014^{16}
Carbon tetrachloride..............	−22.8	76.7	11.5^{25}	0.90	26.8^{20}	0.08^{20}
Chloroform[3].......	−63.5	61.2	19.9^{25}	0.55	27.1^{20}	1.0^{15}
Ethylene dichloride..............	−35.3	83.5	7.7^{25}	0.84	32.2^{20}	0.87^{20}
Benzene..........	5.5	80.2	9.4^{25}	0.65	28.9^{20}	0.082^{22}
Toluene..........	−95.	110.8	2.8^{25}	0.59	28.4^{20}	0.047^{16}
Monochlorobenzene..............	−55.	131.6	0.88^{20}	0.80	33.2^{20}	0.049^{30}
o-Dichlorobenzene	−17.5	180.2	0.13^{25}	1.0		0.008^{25}
Nitrobenzene......	5.4	210.	0.75^{80}	1.98	43.9^{20}	0.19^{20}

AUTHOR INDEX

A

Allard, G., 272
Allen, C. T. H., 226
Almenrader, K., 136
Alyea, H. N., 4, 164
Amick, C. A., 251
André, E., 228
d'Ans, J., 247
Ardagh, E. R., 234
Arrhenius, S., 2, 41, 163, 164
Auerbach, F., 154, 249

B

Bäckström, H. L. J., 164, 172
Bancroft, W. D., 172
Bandrowski, E. von, 130
Barfoed, C., 251
Bartlett, P. D., 238
Bauer, E., 215, 216
Bauer, K. H., 224
Beckerath, K. von, 103, 184, 185, 186
Beckurts, H., 98
Beekley, J. S., 192
Benedetti-Pichler, A. A., 159
Benedict, S. R., 251
Benrath, A., 254
Berezicky, S., 269
Berl, E., 271, 272
Bernthsen, A., 127
Berthelot, D., 257
Berthollet, C. L., 168
Beukema-Goudsmit, M., 247
Bevan, E. J., 253
Beythien, A., 210
Bigelow, S. L., 277
Biilmann, E., 223, 224
Bjerrum, N., 2, 94, 143
Blatt, A. H., 226
Blau, F., 137
Bliss, H. H., 141
Bodforss, S., 235
Bodländer, G., 46
Böeseken, J., 164, 229, 230
Böttger, W., 69, 103, 260, 264
Born, M., 184
Bougault, J., 248
Bourcat, R., 253
Boyd, G. R. Jr., 139
Bray, W. C., 166, 172, 174, 177
Brecher, C., 212
Br eest, F., 222

B (continued - right column)

Britton, H. T. S., 258
Brode, J., 178
Brönsted, J. N., 3, 4, 8, 238
Brügelmann, G., 98
Bruère, P., 273
Bruner, L., 211
Bruun, B., 201, 205
Bryant, W. M. D., 211
Bucherer, H. T., 98, 240, 242
Buckwalter, H. M., 231

C

Cannan, B. K., 110
Caponetto, A., 235
Caro, H., 250
Carr, C. W., 205
Cedivoda, F., 244
Chapman, R. P., 137
Charlot, G., 131
Chen, T.-T., 119
Chervet, D., 194, 195
Christensen, B. E., 254
Christiansen, J. A., 164, 165
Clark, R. H., 179
Clark, T., 274
Clark, W. M., 107, 109, 110, 111, 112, 113, 114, 115, 119, 121, 123, 128
Cluny, L., 254
Cohen, B., 107, 109, 110, 111, 114, 115, 128
Cohen, S., 135
Conant, J. B., 8, 238, 248
Connor, R., 224
Cordebard, H., 254
Cormack, W., 249
Cornec, E., 271
Cross, C. F., 253
Czerwinski, J., 64

D

Davis, R. O. E., 210
Dean, P. M., 272
Debye, P., 2
Deisz, E., 175
Denigès, G., 156, 222
Dietrich, W., 275, 276
Dietz, N. Jr., 8
Dillon, R. T., 230
Ditz, H., 244, 253
Doerner, H. A., 200, 201, 203, 204
Donath, E., 253

295

SUBJECT INDEX

Compounds marked (A) are adsorption indicators.
Compounds marked (R) are reversible oxidation-reduction indicators.

A

Acceptor, 169
Acetaldehyde, 215, 220
Acetone, 215, 220, 247
p-Acetylaminodiphenylamine, (R), 136
Acetylation, 211
Acetylene derivatives, 248
Acid, definition of, 3
Acid, acetic, formation in oxidations, 253, 254
  neutralization in presence of boric, 57, 58
  neutralization with alkali, 52, 53, 90
  neutralization with ammonia, 55, 94
  titration error, 148, 150, 151
  boric, 57, 58
  carbonic, formation in oxidations, 252–254
  neutralization of, 57
  titration error, 151, 152
  citric, 57
  elaidic, 225
  formic, 249, 254
  fumaric, 57
  gluconic, 252
  hydrochloric, induced oxidation, 174–176
  neutralization with alkali, 49–51
  titration error, 146, 147
  malic, 57
  malonic, 57
  oleic, 225
  oxalic, 57, 253
  reaction with permanganate, 173–175
  reaction with persulfate, 180
  phosphoric, 57, 153
  phosphorous, induced oxidation, 176
  phthalic, 57, 280, 281
  saccharic, 252
  salicylic, 247
  sulfurous, 57, 221, 222
  tartaric, 57, 252
  induced oxidation, 169
Acid-base indicators, 87–96

Acid-base reactions, see Neutralization.
Acid exponent, 18
Acid reaction, 16, 17
Acid salts, $[H^+]$ of, 28
Acids, amino, 239
  dibasic, 57
  influence on solubility of salts, 41–43
  ionization constants of, 18
  table of, 282–284
  mixtures of, neutralization of, 56
  titration error in, 151–154
  oxidation by ceric salts, 254
  oxidation by dichromate, 253
  oxidation by periodate, 252
  oxidation by permanganate, 253
  polybasic, 19
  neutralization of, 56, 151–154
  weak, $[H^+]$ of mixtures of, 26
  at first equivalence-point, 29
  $[H^+]$ of mixtures with salts, 25
  neutralization with alkali, 53, 54, 147
  neutralization with weak bases, 55, 150
Active concentrations, 2
Active molecules, 163
Activity coefficients, 2, 147, 279–281
Activity constants, 279, 282
Activity product of water, 279
Actor, 169
Addition products, formation of, 212–232
  dissociation constants of, 214, 223
Addition reactions, reversible, 213–224
  bisulfite-carbonyl, 213–222
  titration error in, 218–221
  with halogens, 224–232
  with mercury, 222–224
Adrenaline, 247
Adsorption, 60, 183–194
  by silver iodide, 185–188, 190, 191
  by silver thiocyanate, 188
  during flocculation of colloids, 191, 192
  during growth of crystals, 196, 197
  equivalent, 191, 192

300

Date Due
